UNDERSTANDING ACOL

the Good Bidding Guide

UNDERSTANDING ACOL

the Good Bidding Guide

Eric Crowhurst

AND

Andrew Kambites

LONDON
VICTOR GOLLANCZ LTD
in association with
PETER CRAWLEY
1990

First published in Great Britain 1990
in association with Peter Crawley
by Victor Gollancz Ltd
14 Henrietta Street, London WC2E 8QJ

British Library Cataloguing in Publication Data
Crowhurst, Eric
    Understanding Acol: the good bidding guide. –
    (Master bridge series).
    1. Contract bridge. Acol bidding
    I. Title   II. Kambites, Andrew   III. Series
    795.41'52

    ISBN 0 575 04719 4

Photoset in Great Britain by
Rowland Phototypesetting Ltd, Bury St Edmunds, Suffolk
and printed by St Edmundsbury Press Ltd
Bury St Edmunds, Suffolk

Contents

Introduction

This book is not for beginners. Neither is it an encyclopedia for grand masters! It is meant for the large number of bridge players in clubs and evening classes who have mastered the material found in beginners books and would like to see a further improvement in their bidding. Our system is Acol, based on the weak no trump (although most of these principles apply equally well for strong no trumpers) and we aim to present it in a sympathetic and logical fashion. We are aiming for understanding rather than great feats of memory, and we are not afraid to ignore rare and exotic sequences that only serve to clutter the mind.

Of course Acol is an evolving system, and ideas that would have been considered heretical 20 years ago are now universally accepted. We have sought to present modern Acol without taking on the most avant garde ideas, thus such revolutionary concepts as transfer bidding and Sputnik doubles do not form part of the system, although they are included in two appendices at the end. In particular we seek to develop your judgement in the all too frequent auctions where there does not appear to be an ideal bid, just a choice between evils.

The main part of the book is divided into two sections. Chapters 1–9 deal with the uncontested auction. Before considering opener's strategic plan in chapters 2 and 3 we make sure you understand the reverse, for without that solid foundation you are building upon sand. Chapters 4 and 5 deal with responder's strategy and the remainder of section 1 deals with the developing auction, hand evaluation, and slam bidding. Section 2 consists of chapters 10–13 and deals with competitive bidding, where unfamiliar sequences abound, and good judgement is imperative.

Finally if you and your partner want to take modern Acol on board you will, no doubt, wish to embellish it with modern conventions. In order to avoid making our book formidably large we have ignored these (apart from the appendices on the Sputnik double and transfer bidding), but don't imagine that we do not consider them worthwhile. Good luck, and sound bidding!

Part One—The Uncontested Auction

1. Simple Preference and the Reverse

SIMPLE PREFERENCE
What do you bid if your partner opens 1♡ and fate has been unkind enough to deal you:

    ♠ 9 8 7 5 3   ♡ –   ♢ 7 5 3 2   ♣ 8 7 5 3?

'Simple', you say, 'pass'. 1♡ is probably not your best contract but if you shortsightedly try to improve matters by bidding 1♠ your partner will assume you have six points and the bidding may well soar into the stratosphere. The reason that you need six points to reply is that partner is unlikely to have more than nineteen, hence game is unlikely if you cannot contribute six to the combined assets. It is usual to bring the auction to a close when it becomes evident that the values for game are not present but there are a number of important exceptions: for example the weakness take out of your partner's 1NT opening. This is an example of preference. Partner has shown at least two cards in each suit and 12–14 points. Suppose you have:

    ♠ J 9 8 6 5 3   ♡ 3   ♢ 10 9 8   ♣ 9 7 6

Your side is so badly outgunned in high cards that you are unlikely to make any contract. However, the carnage will be less severe if you play in 2♠. You can, of course, bid 2♠ only because you know that partner will pass. He has announced his values, you are simply declaring that you prefer 2♠ to 1NT. SIMPLE PREFERENCE.

Now suppose you, as East, face this problem:

♠ Q 9 7 5 3		West	East
♡ 8 4 2		1♡	1♠
♢ 7 4		2♢	?
♣ K 6 3			

West's failure to rebid 3♢ (19–20 points and game-forcing) makes game improbable. You want this auction to end as quickly as possible but you certainly cannot pass 2♢. West has bid two suits. You are not wildly keen on either of them but you certainly prefer hearts to diamonds. Give simple preference to his first suit by bidding 2♡. You are not showing any extra values and your hearts may be poor. Replace the ♡2 by the ♣2 and you would still have to bid this way. By considering the alternatives you can systematically exclude them all. To pass 2♢ would probably leave West playing in a 4-2 fit when a 5-2 fit is available in hearts. You would need six sturdy spades to repeat your suit and both 2NT and 3♣ show far stronger hands than you possess. The theme of preference is developed in later chapters.

THE REVERSE

The idea of a REVERSE is closely linked with preference. A reverse occurs when a player bids two suits in such an order that if his partner wishes to give simple preference to the first suit he cannot do so below the three level. If opener starts with 1♡ and rebids 2♢ over your 1♠ response you can retreat to 2♡. He is not reversing. However, if he opens 1♢ and rebids 2♡ over your 1♠ response you cannot go back to 2♢. If you want to give preference you can only do so at the three level—with 3♢. This time he is reversing. If he chooses to bid his hand in a manner that is likely to push the bidding unnecessarily high when you may have a very poor, misfitting hand he must adhere to strict requirements.

a) 1♣ P 1♡ P   b) 1♡ P 2♣ P   c) 1♠ P 2♡ P   d) 1♢ P 1♠ P
   2♢ P (3♣)   2♠ P (3♡)   3♢ P (3♠)   3♣

Sequences a), b) and c) are all reverses, with the reversing bid underlined and the three level 'preference' bid in brackets. If opener reverses he promises at least five cards in his first suit and at least 16 high card points (unless he has exceptional shape, including some fit with responder's suit.)

In auctions a) and b) the reversing bid is made at the two level in a higher suit. These sequences are often called 'low reverses'. They *guarantee* more cards in the first suit than the second suit; 5-4, 6-4 or 6-5. Many players would open 1♡, with the intention of reversing into 2♠ with:

♠ A J 6 4 3   ♡ A J 7 5 3   ◇ A Q   ♣ 7

This is wrong because partner will always believe that you have more hearts than spades. Even if you subsequently bid spades twice to show that you have five, he will think you are showing six hearts also. You must open 1♠ and make a simple rebid of 2♡. Although not absolutely forcing this bid is rarely passed, and if partner cannot make a further move you are probably quite high enough. Replace the ♡J by the ♡K and you are strong enough for the game-forcing jump rebid of 3♡. The idea that after a 1♠ opening there are hands that are too strong for a 2♡ rebid but not strong enough for a 3♡ rebid is erroneous. You certainly cannot show 'intermediate' hands with a reversing sequence unless you have the correct shape.

In sequence c) the reversing bid is actually made at the three level, frequently called a 'high reverse'. Now the hand shape can on occasions be 5-5. Suppose you are dealt:

♠ A J 6 4 3   ♡ A Q   ◇ A J 7 5 3   ♣ 7

You should open 1♠, intending to rebid 3◇ over a 2♡ response.

Sequence d) is a game-forcing JUMP SHIFT, not a reverse. A jump bid is never a reverse.

There always seems to be utter confusion about whether or not a reverse is forcing. You don't need long lists of sequences. Common sense makes sequences b) and c) game-forcing. Opener has shown 16 high card points and responder has at least a well fitting 8 for his change of suit at the two level (see chapter 4). How often do you want to play in a part score with such combined assets? In sequence a) responder may only have six points for his change of suit at the one level so if opener has just 16 it is logical that the partnership should be able to opt out below game level.

Summing up, only two different categories are needed. A reverse following a response at the one level is forcing for one round. A reverse following a change of suit at the two level is game-forcing.

BIDDING AFTER A REVERSE

a) ♠ A 9 8 5 3   ♡ 9 8   ◇ 8   ♣ Q 10 9 5 3
b) ♠ A 9 8 6 4   ♡ J 8   ◇ Q 5   ♣ K J 10 9
c) ♠ A Q 8   ♡ J 8   ◇ Q 8   ♣ A J 10 8 6 5

Holding hand a), you respond 1♠ to your partner's 1♡ opening bid. When he rebids 2◇ you can only give preference to 2♡. The superficially attractive bid of 2NT is out of the question because it shows 10-12 points. 2NT would be correct if you held b).

Now consider the same hands if he opens 1◇ and reverses into 2♡ over your 1♠ response. This time he is showing 16+ points and forcing another bid from you. You are now justified in bidding 2NT with a), showing a minimum response. With b) you must show your considerable extra values by bidding 3NT.

With c) you would have responded 2♣ to partner's 1◇ opening bid. If his rebid is 2♡ a game-forcing situation has been established, therefore 2NT will suffice, leaving him room to describe his assets further.

Frequently the best method of proceeding over partner's reverse is to bid the 'fourth suit' to request more information. This theme is expanded in chapter 6.

OPENER'S FIRST BID

a) ♠ A 8 6 2   ♡ A K Q 6   ◇ 9 7   ♣ 9 8 2
b) ♠ A 8 7 5   ♡ 7 6 4   ◇ A K Q 8   ♣ 9 4
c) ♠ A 7   ♡ Q 7   ◇ A 8 7 6   ♣ J 9 7 6 4

It must constantly be stressed that, before deciding upon your opening bid, you should have considered your rebid over partner's most inconvenient response. If you are playing a weak no trump you cannot open hand a) with 1♡, however attractive the suit appears. This is because you have no acceptable rebid if partner responds 2◇. A 2♡ rebid guarantees a five-card suit, a 2♠ rebid is a reverse, and a 2NT rebid shows 15-16 points. You could open 1♠, intending to rebid 2♡, but not if that sequence guarantees five spades as you will see later. You are left with no sensible alternative to 1NT. You have a similar problem with hand b) if you open 1◇ because a 2♣ response will leave you fixed.

A critical examination of hand c) may lead you to the conclusion that the best course of action is to pass. A 1♣ opening would force a revolting 2♣ rebid because a 1NT rebid shows 15-16 points and a 2◇ rebid is a reverse. A 1◇ opening would allow a 2♣ rebid, but then partner may well give preference to 2◇ with a small doubleton in each minor suit. There are many similar awkward decisions to be made. *The important thing is to make these decisions before your first bid and not to make a superficially attractive start only to find that partner's response has left you without recourse.* So often a vaguely considered rebid turns out to be a reverse which cannot be justified.

CAN I BE FORCED TO REVERSE BY INTERVENTION?
The answer is, simply, 'No'. Consider this problem, as West:

	South	West	North	East
♠ K J 4				
♡ Q 7 6 3		1♣	1♠	2◇
◇ 5	No	?		
♣ A Q 10 7 5				

You carefully considered the consequences before opening 1♣. If East had responded 1◇ you intended to rebid 1♡. If instead he ventured 1♠ you would have raised to 2♠. However North's overcall and your partner's forcing 2◇ have caught you unprepared. Any bid you now make sounds strong when you want to sound as weak as possible. Should you have considered this? Before your first bid you need only consider your rebid over partner's change of suit *at the lowest possible level*. You will be expected to have a rebid available over a response of 1◇ but not 2◇. You are not expected to consider intervention. Thus you can bid 2♡ which is *not* a reverse. Partner will realise that the interference followed by his forcing bid may well have obliged you to make a rebid at a higher level than you intended.

As a contrast, suppose you are West, facing this auction:

♠ 5	South	West	North	East
♡ K J 4		1♣	1♡	1♠
◇ Q 7 6 3	No	?		
♣ A Q 10 7 5				

You must not imagine that you can use the intervention as an excuse to bid 2◇. You are expected to have a rebid thought out over a 1♠ response, and there is no reason to alter your rebid. The crucial difference is that this time the intervention has not raised the level of East's response.

Quiz on Chapter 1

1) What is your opening bid, and your planned rebid over a 1♠ response, with these hands?

a)	♠ 9 8	♡ A Q 7 5	◇ A Q J 5 3	♣ 6 2
b)	♠ A 8	♡ A Q 7 5	◇ A Q J 5 3	♣ 6 2
c)	♠ Q 8	♡ A 9 7 5 2	◇ A Q 6 5 3	♣ 6
d)	♠ K 8	♡ A Q 7 5 2	◇ A Q 10 5 3	♣ 6
e)	♠ K 8	♡ A K J 8 7	◇ A Q J 5 3	♣ 6
f)	♠ A	♡ A Q 8 7 5	◇ A Q 8 7 5 3	♣ 8

2) Your partner opens 1♡ and rebids 2◇ over your 1♠ response. What do you call with these hands?

a)	♠ Q 8 6 4 3	♡ Q 6	◇ 5 3	♣ Q J 8 6
b)	♠ Q 8 7 6 3	♡ 6 4	◇ K 10 8	♣ A Q 6
c)	♠ A 8 7 5	♡ K 8 6	◇ Q 8	♣ Q 10 9 3
d)	♠ K Q 10 9 8 6	♡ 9	◇ 9 8	♣ 8 7 5 2
e)	♠ K 9 8 6 5	♡ 8	◇ 9 8 6	♣ Q 5 3 2

3) How would your second bid change for the hands in question 2) if partner had opened 1◇ and reversed into 2♡ over your 1♠ response?

Answers to Quiz

1) a) Open 1◇ and rebid 2◇. You have the shape to reverse into 2♡, but not the strength.

b) Open 1◇ and rebid 2♡, a one round force showing 16+ high card points and longer diamonds than hearts.

c) Open 1♡ and rebid 2◇. If partner gives preference to 2♡ you must pass. Remember that he may have a small doubleton in each of your suits.

d) Open 1♡ and rebid 2◇. You have plenty to spare and if partner gives preference to 2♡ you will make a game try with 3◇, showing at least 5-5 shape. The alternative rebid of 3◇ commits you to game opposite a misfitting six points and thus cannot be justified.

e) Open 1♡ and rebid 3◇. This time you are delighted to force to game.

f) Open 1◇ and rebid 2♡, forcing for one round. Your next bid will be 3♡, showing five hearts and therefore six diamonds.

2) a) 2♡. Simple preference. You are far too weak for anything else.

b) 2NT. 10-12 points.

c) 3♡. Jump preference, not forcing and showing exactly three hearts.

d) 2♠. Weak hand, good suit.

e) Pass. There really is nowhere else to go.

3) a) 2NT. Minimum and not forcing.

b) 3NT. The obvious contract with such good club guards. Don't risk partner passing 2NT.

c) 3NT. Same as b). 3♡ would show four-card support as this is your first chance to support hearts.

d) 2♠. No change.

e) 3◇. Not forcing. Settle for the 5-3 fit rather than 2NT with such a precarious club guard.

15

2. Opener has a Balanced Hand

THE WEAK NO TRUMP

'Weak or strong no trump, partner?' Some pairs play a variable no trump, weak if not vulnerable and strong if vulnerable. The trouble with this is that they are playing two entirely different systems. You cannot change your no trump strength without major repercussions elsewhere. First master one system before you try to play two! Many of the principles described in this book apply equally if you play the strong no trump, but we are assuming that you are playing the 1NT opening bid as showing 12-14 points. Before proceeding further it is worth listing the merits and demerits of the weak no trump.

The obvious disadvantage is seen when partner has nothing and the opponents are able to make a penalty double. This can be embarrassing and expensive, indeed many expert partnerships play the strong no trump with this in mind. However, most partnerships who play the strong no trump end up using artificial bids to cater for weak, balanced hands and these require a great deal of experience and exhaustive partnership discussion. The fear of a large penalty should not dominate your thinking. A certain amount of caution is obviously a necessary attribute in any player but if you are dominated by fear at the bridge table you will never be a winner.

To counter this, there are three worthwhile advantages of the weak no trump.

Firstly, balanced hands in the range 12-14 points are far more frequent than balanced hands with 16-18 points. Bidding tends to be straightforward after a 1NT opening because it is a limit bid, thus responder can usually select the correct contract quickly and without risk of partnership misunderstanding. Short bidding sequences also have the hidden advantage of not telling the opposition what to lead. It makes sense to use this highly descriptive, and user-friendly, bid as often as possible.

Secondly, if you play the weak no trump you never need to open 1♣ with a three-card suit. Many stupid contracts start with a 'phoney club'.

Thirdly the 1NT opening bid has excellent pre-emptive value. If each of your opponents has thirteen points you will probably be left to play in 1NT undoubled, drifting peacefully three off when they could have made game.

Note that you don't have to open every twelve point hand!

| ♠ K Q | ♡ Q 6 5 3 | ◇ J 7 6 3 | ♣ A 8 4 |

The above collection simply isn't an opening bid at any vulnerability (see chapter 7). If you choose to open this rubbish with 1NT and suffer a large penalty that is attributable to bad judgement, not the weak no trump. However, once you have decided to open a balanced hand in the 12-14 range, 1NT is usually correct and frequently imperative, even if your hand contains a small doubleton. There are strong reasons behind this which will be explained in the next section. If you are used to opening 1NT only if you have an honour card in each suit, the following hand demonstrates the counterbalancing argument. Consider what contract you would like to declare with these cards:

West	East
♠ A Q 6 2	♠ K 4
♡ K 5 3	♡ A 7 6 2
◇ A 5 3 2	◇ K Q J 8
♣ 7 4	♣ 9 6 2

The answer is, of course, that it depends on the bidding.

a) West	East	b) West	East	c) West	East
1◇	1♡	1♠	2◇	1NT	3NT
1♠	3NT	3◇	3♡		
		4◇	5◇		

After sequence a) a club lead is pinpointed to the defenders. 3NT will then only succeed if the missing clubs break 4-4, about one third of the time. The 'super science' of b) is even more counter productive! By the time East bids 3♡ each player has a splendid picture of his partner's assets. Neither of them is prepared to bid

3NT with the club suit unguarded so they proceed to the hopeless minor suit game. On the other hand after c) North has a blind lead. If he has five clubs no doubt he will find the successful lead but what if he only has three clubs? Any other lead and West wraps up nine tricks before drawing breath. His *practical* chances have risen to about two thirds. Remember that bridge has an element of bluff in it and that most experts regularly bid and make dubious game contracts that would terrify lesser players. Inexperienced players worry too much about bidding no trumps with a weak suit. Much of the time your partner will have cover in the suit. Even if he hasn't, provided you haven't given the game away by your bidding, you may get away with murder. The time to worry about a weak suit is when the lead of that suit is pinpointed to defenders, either because they have bid it, or because you have bid two or three of the other suits.

OPENER REBIDS NO TRUMPS

We must now deal with some essential theory. If you open 1♡ and partner responds at the one level (1♠) you have three available no trump rebids. 1NT shows 15-16 points, 2NT shows 17-18 points and 3NT shows 19-20 points. If he responds at the two level (2♣ or 2◇) you only have two available no trump rebids. 2NT shows 15-16 points and 3NT shows 17+. This last figure is quite logical since responder will have at least eight high card points for a change of suit at the two level. The no trump rebids exactly cover the range of values between the 1NT and 2NT openings. A consequence of this is that there isn't a no trump rebid to show a hand in the range 12-14. If you are dealt such a hand you have the choice of opening 1NT or bidding two suits. You must dismiss the illusion that you can open with an attractive four-card suit and rebid no trumps later.

Finally, before leaving this subject, it is worth mentioning that it is possible to play a 1NT rebid to show 12-16 points. Such an agreement sometimes gives you an attractive alternative to opening 1NT with a small doubleton, or rebidding a poor quality five-card major, but it does mean that responder has to investigate game with 10 points which can lead to an uncomfortably high contract if opener has just 12. The continuations are similar to those described in chapter 12 (the protective 1NT overcall) with the modification that after responder's 2♣ enquiry rebid opener has three features he can show:

   i)   A fifth card in his opening major suit.

   ii) An undisclosed four-card major.

   iii) Delayed three-card support for responder's major suit.

If in doubt he shows his cheapest feature.

Although very popular, with good reason, it does not form part of our basic system as it is a convention, requiring specific agreement with partner, rather than an accepted part of Acol.

THE DEFINITION OF A BALANCED HAND

Probably the most fundamental decision you have to take about a hand is whether you want to convey an 'unbalanced' or 'balanced' message to partner. An unbalanced hand will be shown by bidding two suits or rebidding your first suit. A balanced hand has shape 4-3-3-3, 4-4-3-2 or sometimes 5-3-3-2, particularly if the five-card suit is a minor. It should be announced with a no trump opening bid or no trump rebid. In particular, if you hold a hand with 4-4-3-2 shape you should not try to bid both suits. (A possible exception to this is if you can be sure of bidding them both at the one level.) If you accept this there is one invaluable bonus. If you open with a suit bid and rebid a second suit at the two level you are *unbalanced*. This means that unless your shape is 4-4-4-1 and partner has responded in your singleton suit, you have at least five cards in your first suit! More of that anon. The consequential gains reverberate throughout the system.

OPENER HAS 4-3-3-3 SHAPE

There is no problem here. If you have 12-14 points you open 1NT. If you have a stronger hand you open with your four-card suit and rebid no trumps at an appropriate level.

OPENER HAS 4-4-3-2 SHAPE

a)	♠ A Q 6 2	♡ 7 4	◇ K 5 4	♣ A 5 3 2
b)	♠ 7 4	♡ K J 9 4	◇ 9 5 2	♣ A K Q 7
c)	♠ K J 9 4	♡ A K Q 7	◇ 9 5 2	♣ 7 4
d)	♠ K J 9 4	♡ A K Q 7	◇ A 5 2	♣ 7 4
e)	♠ K 10	♡ A K Q 10	◇ 7 4 3 2	♣ K J 7
f)	♠ 7 4	♡ K J 9 4	◇ A 5 2	♣ A K Q 7

With rare exceptions, any 12-14 point hand should be opened 1NT. Hand a) is an exception in that you have a reasonable alternative. There is a lot to be said for opening 1NT but it can be opened 1♣ with a guaranteed 1♠ rebid over the likely red suit response. Bidding both suits at the one level does not promise 5-4 shape. However hand b) is full of traps. A 1♣ opening leaves you without a rebid over an all-too-likely 1♠ response. Remember 1NT now shows 15-16 points and 2♡ would be a reverse. A 1♡ opening leaves you equally stuck over 1♠, since a 2♣ rebid guarantees five hearts. You have no alternative to opening 1NT.

With hand c) there is a strong temptation to bid your two good major suits, but to open with 1♠ and rebid 2♡ promises five spades. Again you must bid 1NT. Don't worry too much about this one. If partner has a reasonable hand with a four-card major he will use Stayman to find the fit. Really, the most efficient tactic is to open all these hands 1NT with a minimum of thought. If you spend valuable energy agonising over each hand, worrying whether you can treat each one as an exception, you will make errors from sheer exhaustion.

Hands d), e) and f) come into the category of a no trump rebid. You can therefore bid only one of your suits and you should choose the one that gives partner the best chance of bringing the other into play. This means opening 1♡ with d), the *lower* of the two touching suits. You will see later that responder will plan his bidding strategy so that the spade suit will not be lost if he has four, therefore there is no danger of missing a major suit fit. If he responds 1♠ your rebid is 3♠. If he bids 2♣ or 2♢ you must rebid 3NT. If instead you were to open 1♠ he cannot respond 2♡ without a five-card suit. The practice of bidding the lower of touching four-card suits is regarded as controversial by those who learned their bridge from elementary books which seem to suggest the opposite tactic. Really there is no contradiction. If you intend to bid both suits you must open the higher to avoid reversing. You don't need to bid both with hand d) as there are more efficient methods of bringing both suits into play.

We must, of course, avoid being too dogmatic. Hand e) contains an excellent four-card major and a very poor four-card minor. Common sense suggests opening 1♡ and forgetting the diamonds. You have a natural 1NT or 2NT rebid.

Finally we consider hand f) where the four-card suits are not touching. If you want a simple rule then open with the major suit: after all you are more concerned with finding a 4-4 major fit than a similar minor fit. However, it really isn't necessary to give rules here. You really won't come to much harm if you open 1♣. You can rebid 1♡ over 1◇ or 2NT over 1♠. This will become clearer when you investigate responder's first bid in chapters 4 and 5.

OPENER HAS 5-3-3-2 SHAPE

a) ♠ K 8 5   ♡ 9 3   ◇ J 6 4   ♣ A K Q 5 4
b) ♠ K 8 4   ♡ K 8   ◇ A Q 6   ♣ J 8 7 5 4
c) ♠ 9 3   ♡ A K Q 5 4   ◇ J 6 4   ♣ K 8 5
d) ♠ K 8   ♡ J 8 7 5 4   ◇ K 8 4   ♣ A Q 6
e) ♠ 9 3   ♡ A K Q 5 4   ◇ K 6 4   ♣ K 8 5
f) ♠ K 8   ♡ J 8 7 5 4   ◇ K Q 5   ♣ A Q 6

Hands a), b), c) and d) are in the range 12-14 and give you two options. You can open and rebid your five-card suit or you can open 1NT. The two parameters are the quality of the suit and whether it is a major or minor. Hands a) and c) have suits of excellent quality and you have every reason to stress your suit. However, to bid your miserable club suit twice with b) is truly revolting. An opening bid of 1NT is clearly superior. Hand d) is more difficult. One little voice tells you that it is a crime to open 1NT with a five-card major, however poor. Nevertheless your conscience also points out the distorted picture you are presenting to partner by opening 1♡ and rebidding 2♡ over 1♠. This is a close decision. We marginally prefer the 1NT opening as the lesser of evils.

Hands e) and f) fall into the range of 1NT rebids so you can, to some extent, have your cake and eat it. In each case open 1♡, intending to rebid 1NT over 1♠ or 2NT over 2♣ or 2◇. You might feel uneasy about rebidding no trumps with e) when your hearts are so good but no other bid fits this hand. It is too strong for a 2♡ rebid (which you would make without the ♣K) and lacks the sixth heart necessary for a jump rebid in hearts.

Quiz on Chapter 2

1) As dealer, what do you bid with these hands? If you open with a suit bid what is your rebid?

a)	♠ K Q J	♡ Q 7 6	♢ Q 8 6	♣ Q 7 5 3
b)	♠ K J 5 4	♡ A Q 5 3	♢ K 5 3	♣ 4 3
c)	♠ K J 5 4	♡ A Q 5 3	♢ K 5 3	♣ K 3
d)	♠ A 8 3 2	♡ K 4 3 2	♢ A 7	♣ K Q 3
e)	♠ K J 5 4	♡ A Q 5 3	♢ A Q 4	♣ K 3
f)	♠ 5 4	♡ A K 3 2	♢ 9 7 4	♣ A K 4 2
g)	♠ A K 3 2	♡ 5 4	♢ 9 7 4	♣ A K 4 2
h)	♠ K 4	♡ K Q J 10	♢ Q 7 6 4	♣ A 10 4
i)	♠ K Q J 10	♡ Q 7 6 4	♢ K 4	♣ A J 4
j)	♠ A Q 2	♡ K J 3	♢ K 10	♣ 10 6 5 4 3
k)	♠ 10 6 5 4 3	♡ K J 3	♢ K 10	♣ A Q 2
l)	♠ 7 6 4	♡ K 7 5	♢ 9 3	♣ A K Q J 3
m)	♠ K J 6 5 4	♡ K 9	♢ K 6 4	♣ K 7 5

2) With each of these hands you open 1♡ and hear a 1♠ response? What is your rebid?

a)	♠ 8 7 5	♡ A Q 8 6	♢ K J 4	♣ A Q 10
b)	♠ 8 7 5	♡ A Q 8 6	♢ A Q 4	♣ A Q 10
c)	♠ K 3	♡ A Q 4 3 2	♢ K Q 4	♣ J 7 6

3) How would you rebid for the hands in question 2) if the response was 2♣?

Answers to Quiz

1) a) Pass. No tens or nines and your spade holding is not worth six points.

b) 1NT. Not 1♠ which would compel a 2♡ rebid. That would show 5-4 shape.

c) 1♡. The lower of two touching four-card suits. Rebid 3♠ over 1♠ or 2NT over 2♣ or 2♢.

d) 1♡. As above, even though the hearts are weaker.

e) 1♡. Rebid 4♠ over 1♠ or 3NT over 2♣ or 2♢.

f) 1NT. 1♣ or 1♡ would leave you with no rebid over a 1♠ response.

g) 1♣. With a guaranteed 1♠ rebid this is slightly superior to 1NT with two unguarded suits.

h) 1♡. Forget the diamonds. If your opponents buy the contract you want a heart lead. Rebid 1NT over 1♠, 2NT over 2♣, or 3♢ over 2♢.

i) 1♡. This hand, when compared to h), illustrates the priority of a major suit over a minor. You are prepared to forget a diamond suit of queen and three small, but not a major. Rebid 3♠ over 1♠ or 2NT over 2♣ or 2♢.

j) 1NT. To open 1♣ and rebid 2♣ is not a pleasant option.

k) 1NT. Ditto, even though your suit is a major this time.

l) 1♣. A good suit, well worth rebidding. Also the club lead is worth pinpointing if your opponents buy the contract and partner makes the opening lead. Rebid 2♣.

m) 1♠. Don't carry the idea of opening 1NT with a five-card major too far. Later you will see that responder will not force you to rebid these spades unless it will lead to a reasonable contract.

2) a) 1NT. Balanced 15-16.

b) 2NT. Balanced 17-18.

c) 1NT. Better than a space consuming 2♡ with 5-3-3-2 shape.

3) a) 2NT. 15-16 points.

b) 3NT. 17-20 points.

c) 2NT. A bit too strong for 2♡.

3. Opener has an Unbalanced Hand

OPENER HAS 5-4-2-2 OR 5-4-3-1 SHAPE

It is always correct to open with the five-card suit. It is desirable to rebid the four-card suit whenever possible. This is always possible if you have as many as sixteen high card points but if you have fewer you cannot bid your second suit if that bid would be a reverse. In that case you can always rebid your five-card suit.

Sometimes there is a better alternative available. With each of these hands you open 1♡ and partner responds 1♠:

a)	♠ K 5	♡ A 7 5 4 2	◇ Q 5 4 3	♣ K 8
b)	♠ K 5	♡ A 7 5 4 2	◇ Q 5 4 3	♣ A Q
c)	♠ Q	♡ A 7 5 4 3	◇ Q 5 4 3	♣ A K J
d)	♠ A Q 3	♡ K J 5 4 3	◇ Q J 4 3	♣ 6
e)	♠ A Q 3	♡ K J 5 4 3	◇ A Q 5 3	♣ 6

Holding a) you have no sensible alternative to a 2◇ rebid. However b) comes within the range of a 1NT rebid and with so much strength concentrated in clubs a no trump rebid is more descriptive than introducing your tepid diamond suit.

You can make quite a strong case for a 1NT rebid with c) although the bid would offend the purists. Most of your strength is concentrated outside your long suits and if partner does revert to spades your singleton queen may fill a vital hole.

If you rebid 2◇ with d) you will probably never have an opportunity to show your excellent three-card support for responder's spades. If he gives preference to hearts (possibly with a two-card suit) you are too weak to make the constructive continuation of 2♠. You are only worth two bids with this minimum opening and should therefore choose the most practical rebid, a raise to 2♠. If responder has a five-card suit you will be in the right strain and even if he only has four it should be possible to cross ruff your way to eight tricks. A strong 4-3 fit can be very effective, particularly at the two level.

Hand e) is similar to d), but stronger. You are too strong to bid 2♠ and a jump to 3♠ guarantees four-card support. Even with a partial spade fit you are not strong enough for a game-forcing bid of 3◇, hence you must rebid 2◇. This bid is not forcing but it is rarely passed (see the section on false preference later in this chapter). If responder gives preference to 2♡ you will continue with 2♠, pinpointing your 3-5-4-1 shape as well as your strength. With 17 points opener is usually worth a third bid after simple preference.

Hands d) and e) examined together demonstrate that you should consider whether your hand is worth a third bid before deciding upon your second bid. If the bidding is likely to die quickly you should aim for a sensible contract, rather than indulge in delicate scientific probing.

OPENER HAS TWO FIVE-CARD SUITS

Unless you have clubs and spades it is correct to open the higher suit. If the suits are touching you will always be able to rebid the lower one. If they are not touching and partner's response is inconvenient you may have to rebid the first suit, leaving the lower suit unbid. Consider these hands:

a) ♠ Q 6 5 4 2   ♡ 7   ◇ A Q 5 4 3   ♣ A 5
b) ♠ A J 6 3 2   ♡ A J   ◇ A Q 5 4 3   ♣ 6

With a) you must open 1♠. If partner responds 2♣ or 1NT your rebid is 2◇ but if he responds 2♡ you must rebid 2♠ as you are far too weak to reverse into 3◇. It would not have helped to start with 1◇ since a 2♣ response would leave you unable to show the spades. Suppressing a five-card minor suit is unfortunate but ignoring a five-card major suit is almost criminal, hence the 1♠ opening.

There are no such problems with hand b) because you are strong enough to reverse, if necessary. Open 1♠ and rebid 2◇ (not a reverse) over 2♣. You have plenty in hand for this minimum rebid but with a potential misfit you are not worth a game-forcing jump to 3◇. If responder then gives preference to 2♠ you can make a further game try with 3◇. If, on the other hand, partner's initial response is 2♡ you can reverse into 3◇.

Remember that a reverse at the three level can be made with 5-5 shape.

With five clubs and five spades you must use judgement.

c) ♠ A Q J 8 7   ♡ 7   ◇ A 5   ♣ 9 8 6 4 3
d) ♠ 9 8 6 4 3   ♡ 7   ◇ A 5   ♣ A Q J 8 7

With either of these weak hands you can expect to make an opening bid and a rebid. You are simply not strong enough to make a third bid unless partner forces you to do so. If you open 1♣ and rebid 1♠ you will never show your fifth spade. If you open and rebid spades, the clubs will be completely lost. Hand c) has such outstanding spades that your priority is surely to stress them, so open 1♠. To bid such a poor spade suit twice without mentioning your excellent clubs feels unnatural with d), so open 1♣.

OPENER HAS 4-4-4-1 SHAPE

Tradition states that you should open with the suit below the singleton. We have already dropped hints that we are aiming for a system where to bid two suits suggests at least five cards in the first suit unless both are bid at the one level. This is nearly attainable but not quite, the exceptions being 4-4-4-1 hands. However, if we pick our bids carefully we can come very close to this ideal in auctions where the first suit bid is a major. Automatically bidding the suit below the singleton may be easy to remember but it subverts too many other good things to be efficient. Here is a more efficient method.

With a singleton club open 1♡ and rebid 2◇ over 2♣.

With a singleton diamond open 1♣ and rebid 1♡ over 1◇. If you have game-going values and a 4-4 spade fit it should still prove possible to reach the correct contract (see chapter 6).

With a singleton heart open 1♣ or 1◇ and rebid 1♠ over 1♡.

With a singleton spade open 1◇, aiming to rebid 2♣. You can rely on partner introducing the hearts if he has four, although there might be a problem if he has five spades and four hearts. (See chapter 4). Of course, if he does respond 1♡ you forget the clubs and raise hearts.

If you want a new 'aide memoire' to replace the suit below the singleton try this! With a red singleton open 1♣ and with a black singleton open the middle of your three suits. There are good reasons for avoiding opening these hands with a major suit unless absolutely necessary.

You sometimes have another option with a spade singleton if you are not too squeamish about rebidding 1NT with a singleton in responder's suit.

a) ♠ 3   ♡ A K J 4   ◇ A 5 4 3   ♣ K 7 6 5
b) ♠ 3   ♡ A K J 4   ◇ A 5 4 3   ♣ J 7 6 5
c) ♠ 3   ♡ A K J 4   ◇ A 5 4 3   ♣ A Q J 2
d) ♠ 3   ♡ A K Q J   ◇ 6 5 3 2   ♣ K 7 4 2

Holding a) you can open 1♡ and rebid 1NT over 1♠. This option is obviously not available with b) because your point count is below any no trump rebid. It is also highly dangerous to rebid 3NT with c) because responder, without room to explore, will automatically correct to 4♠ with a poor six-card spade suit. Here you *must* open 1◇, intending to make a *game-forcing* rebid of 3♣.

With d) you may decide to open 1♡ even though your rebid will suggest you have five hearts. With a trump suit of this strength a 4-3 fit, or even a 4-2 fit at a low level, should be playable. The advantages of this slightly 'anti-system' bid are, firstly, lead-directing (if your left hand opponent buys the contract) and, secondly, the possibility that if you open 1◇ partner, holding hand e), may respond 1♠ and the heart suit will get lost.

e) ♠ A K 7 5 4   ♡ 9 7 5 3   ◇ 8   ♣ 8 6 3

SUMMARY
It is helpful to look for some conclusions. Suppose your partner opens with a suit bid and rebids a second suit at the two level: e.g.,

a) 1♠ No 2♣ No
   2♡

b) 1♠ No 2♣ No
   2◇

c) 1♡ No 1♠ No
   2◇

d) 1♡ No 1♠ No
   2♣

e) 1♡ No 2♣ No
   2◇

f) 1◇ No 1♠ No
   2♣

Could he have two four-card suits? With 4-4-3-2 shape he would have opened or rebid no trumps. This only leaves 4-4-4-1 hands. No such hand is ever opened 1♠, therefore a) and b) *guarantee* a five-card suit, which must be spades since a five-card suit is always opened ahead of a four-card suit. Similarly c) and d) guarantee five hearts. This is because 4-4-4-1 hands are only opened with 1♡ if the singleton is in clubs. This cannot be the case as opener would then have had an obvious raise in spades.

Auctions e) and f) could occur with opener having three four-card suits, but only if responder's bid hit the singleton suit. Generally it pays to assume that opener has five cards in his first suit.

You can, in fact, make inferences about opener's shape as soon as you hear his first bid. If he opens 1♠ he either has a five-card suit or a balanced hand too strong to open 1NT. The same is largely true of 1◇ and 1♡ opening bids, the 4-4-4-1 hands described above being the exception. This has major significance later on when we discuss the possibility of responder raising opener's major suit with only three-card support.

RESPONDER GIVES FALSE PREFERENCE
We now come to a traditional problem in Acol which has partially acquired a solution. You are East, considering how best to continue this auction:

♠ A Q 10 3	West	East
♡ Q 4	1♡	1♠
◇ 8 6 4	2◇	?
♣ 9 7 3 2.		

West has not made a limit bid, indeed he could have as many as eighteen points even though his bid is not forcing. You cannot bid 2NT which shows 10-12 high card points, neither can you repeat your four-card spade suit. Equally a raise to 3◇ is not acceptable without four-card support. Unless you feel confident that he has five hearts, preference to 2♡ may take you from a playable 4-3 fit into a ludicrous 4-2 fit. You seem to be left with little alternative but to pass, yet game may be laydown. Now, of course, there is an alternative. West *has* got at least five hearts so you give FALSE PREFERENCE to 2♡. If this is passed the 5-2 heart fit will no doubt play at least as well as the 4-3 diamond fit. If, on the other hand, West has a strong hand, he can make a further game try. This you would willingly accept since you would have bid the same way without one of your queens. Hearts may not even be the final denomination. If West continues with 2NT, you raise to 3NT. If he continues with 3♦ (at least 5-5 shape now) you can show your preference for hearts was false by raising to 4♦.

In chapter 1, and earlier in this chapter, we tried to reassure you that you could open 1♡ and rebid 2♦ over a 1♠ response with quite a strong hand since, although not forcing, this sequence is rarely passed. It is possible to construct hands that would merit a pass of the 2♦ rebid; for example, replace the ♡4 by the ♣4. In this case the hands fit badly and even a combined 26 points by no means guarantee game.

Finally, although SIMPLE PREFERENCE may be 'false', JUMP PREFERENCE (also not forcing) to a major suit guarantees three-card support and to a minor often suggests four-card support. Because jump preference shows 10-12 points there are usually other alternatives (like 2NT), hence it is unlikely that you are forced to make the bid with an unsuitable hand.

Quiz on Chapter 3

1) What is your opening bid with these hands? What is your rebid over each of the stated responses (shown in brackets)?

a) ♠ A 6 5 3   ♡ Q 10 4 3 2   ♦ Q 2   ♣ A 2
   (1♠) (2♦)

b) ♠ A K 5 3   ♡ K 10 4 3 2   ♦ Q 2   ♣ A 2
   (1♠) (2♦)

c) ♠ 6 5   ♡ Q 9 7 4 3   ♦ A 4 3 2   ♣ A K
   (1♠) (2♣)

d) ♠ Q 8   ♡ K 9 7 4 3   ♦ K 8 7 5   ♣ A K
   (1♠) (2♣)

e) ♠ K J 3   ♡ 5   ♦ K 8 7 6 4   ♣ A J 8 6
   (1♠)

f) ♠ K J 3   ♡ 5   ♦ A K 7 6 5   ♣ A J 8 6
   (1♠)

g) ♠ K 9 7 5   ♡ A Q 2   ♦ A 8 7 5 4   ♣ 3
   (1♡) (2♣)

h) ♠ A Q 2   ♡ K 9 7 5   ◇ A 8 7 5 4   ♣ 3
                                                          (1♠) (2♣)

i) ♠ A 8 6 5 3   ♡ A K J 6 4   ◇ 7 5   ♣ 3
                                                           (2♣)

j) ♠ 3   ♡ J 10 7 6 4   ◇ A K   ♣ A J 7 6 5
                                                        (1♠) (2◇)

k) ♠ 3   ♡ A J 8 6 4   ◇ A K   ♣ A J 7 6 5
                                                        (1♠) (2◇)

l) ♠ K Q J 8 4   ♡ 5   ◇ K 7   ♣ Q 8 6 4 3
                     (minimum heart response)

m) ♠ Q 8 6 4 3   ♡ 5   ◇ K 7   ♣ K Q J 8 4
                     (minimum heart response)

n) ♠ A Q 5 3   ♡ J 7 5 3   ◇ K Q J 5   ♣ 6
                                                           (2♣)

o) ♠ Q 8 6 5   ♡ K J 3 2   ◇ 5   ♣ A Q 7 5
                   (minimum diamond response)

p) ♠ 3   ♡ A Q 6 5   ◇ A 8 7 5   ♣ K 5 3 2
                                                           (1♠)

2) Over your partner's 1♡ opening bid you respond 1♠. If he rebids 2◇ how do you continue with these hands?

a) ♠ K J 7 6   ♡ 6 4   ◇ 6 5 4   ♣ K J 7 6
b) ♠ K 8 7 6 2   ♡ 6   ◇ J 5 4   ♣ K J 7 6
c) ♠ A Q J 5   ♡ 7 5   ◇ 6 5 4   ♣ K J 7 6
d) ♠ A Q 7 6   ♡ Q 8 7   ◇ K 7 6   ♣ 9 7 5
e) ♠ A Q 7 5   ♡ Q 8 6   ◇ K 7 6   ♣ K 8 6
f) ♠ A Q J 7   ♡ 5 3   ◇ 7 6 4 3   ♣ A Q 4

3) You open 1♡ and rebid 2◇ over partner's 1♠ response. He then gives preference to 2♡. How do you continue with these hands?

a) ♠ 3   ♡ A J 6 5 3   ◇ A Q 8 6   ♣ A Q 7
b) ♠ 3   ♡ A J 7 6 5 3   ◇ A Q 6 4   ♣ A 3
c) ♠ 5   ♡ A K J 8 7   ◇ A Q J 8 7   ♣ 8 5
d) ♠ 5   ♡ A J 8 7 6   ◇ A Q J 8 7   ♣ 8 5
e) ♠ A J 5   ♡ A Q 8 7 6   ◇ A Q 7 6   ♣ 2
f) ♠ 8 7 6   ♡ A Q 8 7 6   ◇ A Q 7 6   ♣ 2

30

Answers to Quiz

1) a) Open 1♡. Raise 1♠ to 2♠ or rebid 2♡ over 2◇.

b) Open 1♡. Raise 1♠ to 3♠ or rebid 2♠ (game-forcing) over 2◇. This time you are strong enough to reverse.

c) Open 1♡. Rebid 2◇ over either response.

d) Open 1♡. Rebid 1NT over 1♠. The limit bid is most descriptive here with your doubleton club providing two guards. After a 2♣ response make the natural rebid of 2◇.

e) Open 1◇. Raise 1♠ to 2♠.

f) Open 1◇. Rebid 2♣ over 1♠, aiming to complete your hand description with a spade bid on the third round.

g) Open 1◇. Rebid 1♠ over 1♡ or 2◇ over 2♣.

h) Open 1◇. Raise 1♠ to 2♠. With g) you rightly introduced your second suit at the one level in preference to raising hearts with only three-card support. This time you cannot bring your second suit into play. Raising spades with such excellent three-card support is certainly preferable to rebidding your insipid diamonds. Over a 2♣ response you have no alternative to a 2◇ rebid.

i) Open 1♠ (higher of touching five-card suits) and rebid 2♡.

j) Open 1♡ (again the higher of two five-card suits). Rebid 2♣ over 1♠ or 2♡ over 2◇.

k) Open 1♡. Rebid 2♣ over 1♠ or 3♣ (a game-forcing reverse) over 2◇.

l) Open 1♠, and rebid 2♠. Stress the excellent spade suit.

m) Open 1♣, and rebid 1♠. The normal way to bid 5-5 in the black suits unless the spades are much stronger.

n) Open 1♡ and rebid 2◇. This is the only sequence when an opening 1♡ bid followed by a rebid of a new suit does not guarantee five hearts.

o) Open 1♣ and rebid 1♡ over 1◇.

p) Open 1◇ and rebid 2♣ over 1♠.

2) a) 2♡. False preference. You know partner has at least five hearts.

b) Pass. Nowhere to go. Your spades are not good enough for 2♠. Even if partner has eighteen points game may be difficult with a misfit.

31

c) 2NT. No need for false preference this time.

d) 3♡. Jump preference showing three hearts and 10-12 points.

e) 4♡. Play in the known 5-3 fit. Incidentally, this is not a delayed game raise which would guarantee four hearts. You have been deflected from your planned 3NT rebid by partner's rebid which promises five hearts.

f) 3NT. Forget your four-card diamond support and bid the nine trick game.

3) a) 2NT. Game try. Give partner a choice of games since he may have only two small hearts. If he converts to 3♡ you must pass.

b) 3♡. Game try, showing a sixth heart.

c) 3♢. Game try, showing 5-5 shape. Partner can decline your invitation by converting to 3♡, or indeed by passing if he gave false preference to 2♡ with three diamonds and only two hearts.

d) Pass. Too weak to show your 5-5 shape.

e) 2♠. Game try, showing three spades. Partner now knows you have at most one club.

f) Pass. Now that you have chosen to rebid 2♢ rather than 2♠ your three-card spade support will have to remain hidden.

4. The First Response

RESPONDER SUPPORTS OPENER'S MAJOR SUIT

If you have four-card support for partner's major it is usually correct to support him immediately rather than introduce another suit. The exception to this rule is if you have a hand strong enough for a delayed game raise or jump shift (see chapter 9).

 ♠ A K 7 6 ♡ 8 7 6 4 ◇ J 8 ♣ 8 7 5

With this hand it might be tempting to respond 1♠ to 1♡ but you will run into serious problems if partner rebids 3NT. If you now try to correct this to 4♡ partner will reason that you would not have run from 3NT into a 4-3 fit, and therefore you must have four hearts. If he makes the justifiable inference that you have a hand *too strong* for an immediate leap to 4♡, you will end up in a foolish slam. As mentioned in chapter three, belated preference or jump preference for a major suit tends to deny four-card support, whereas such preference for a minor suit frequently contains four-card support. This is because the discovery of an eight-card major fit virtually seals the denomination, but such a minor fit is frequently ignored if an alternative contract in no trumps, or a major suit, might be available.

Now suppose that your partner has opened 1♠ and you have to respond with:

 ♠ Q 6 4 ♡ K 6 ◇ 7 5 4 2 ♣ Q 9 6 2

By considering his intended rebid you can deduce a surprising amount. If he intends to introduce a second suit or rebid spades he must have five spades. Therefore the *only* time he will open 1♠ with a four-card suit is when he is planning a no trump rebid, in other words when he has a balanced hand too strong to open 1NT. If you consider the implications of this it is fairly safe to raise him to 2♠ with three-card support. If he has a five-card suit you will be in the right denomination, and if he has a balanced hand with only four spades he should not abandon the idea of rebidding no trumps just because you give a single raise in his suit. By raising to 2♠ you may have temporarily agreed a 4-3 fit but if opener has the values to make a game try you will be able to escape into no trumps. The only time you will be left in a 4-3 fit is if opener has a balanced hand with 15-16 points, enough to rebid 2NT if you had changed suit at the two level but not enough to make a game try over your single raise. Even then the 4-3 fit with the possibility of using one of dummy's trumps for ruffing could prove quite successful. It is always correct to raise 1♠ to 2♠ (in preference to a 1NT response) if you have three-card support and some ruffing value (such as a doubleton in a side suit). However, do not make a double raise with only three. Holding 10-12 points you are strong enough to make two bids, thus you can bid 3♠ on the second round pinpointing that you have only three.

If your hand is a completely balanced 4-3-3-3 shape it is probably best to respond 1NT unless your spades are particularly strong. Suppose you must respond to a 1♠ opening with these hands:

a) ♠ 7 6 4   ♡ K 8 6   ◇ Q 8 7 5   ♣ K 6 3
b) ♠ K J 7   ♡ 7 6 4   ◇ A 8 7 6   ♣ 4 3 2

With a) 1NT is obvious. You will learn that opener will not now look for a spade fit if he has a strong hand with 5-3-3-2 shape, but missing the 5-3 major fit may not be fatal. With two balanced hands and no prospect of ruffing anything in the short hand, 3NT may prove easier than trying to find the tenth trick in a contract of 4♠. Hand b), with so much of your strength in the spade suit and two weak side suits, deserves a raise to 2♠.

Holding the following hand, suppose partner opens 1♡:

♠ K 6   ♡ Q 6 4   ◇ 7 5 4 2   ♣ Q 9 6 2

The same arguments apply, except that there is the possibility that he intends a 2◇ rebid with a 4-4-4-1 shape (singleton club). It is still best to raise to 2♡. We are virtually saying that a 1NT response to 1♡ or 1♠ denies three-card support unless the hand has 4-3-3-3 shape. When the 1NT response is examined in detail

34

later in this chapter you will see that it could, in extreme circumstances, be made with a void in opener's suit. This bid must not be overloaded. If it can conceal anything from respectable three-card support to a total misfit, how can opener sensibly judge whether or not to rebid his suit?

There is one crucial exception after a 1♡ opening. With four spades as well as three hearts you must respond 1♠. This is because with four cards in each major suit partner will open 1♡, intending to rebid no trumps. If you raise him to 2♡, you may discover that hearts provide only a 4-3 fit but be too late to investigate a 4-4 spade fit: e.g.,

West	East	West	East
♠ A K Q 7	♠ J 6 3 2	1♡	2♡??
♡ A K J 2	♡ Q 6 4	3NT	No
◇ Q 7	◇ K 5 4 2		
♣ 8 6 2	♣ 10 7		

Clearly here 4♠ is far superior to 3NT, but you will never find the spade fit unless *you* bid them.

It must be stressed that if opener hears his major suit raised to the two level he should, if continuing the auction, be as descriptive as possible with his second bid. Suppose your 1♡ opening is raised to 2♡ and you hold these hands:

c)	♠ K J 6	♡ A Q 3 2	◇ K Q 5	♣ Q 7 5
d)	♠ K J 8 6	♡ A Q 3 2	◇ K Q 5	♣ Q 7
e)	♠ 5	♡ A Q 10 9 6	◇ Q 9 8 5	♣ A Q J
f)	♠ 5	♡ A Q 10 9 6 2	◇ Q 9 8	♣ A Q 10

With c) and d) your correct game try is 2NT (showing 17-18 points). This gives the message that you started with only four hearts and intended a no trump rebid. Partner will retreat to hearts if he has four, either at the three or four level depending on his strength.

Holding e) or f) your correct continuation is 3◇, a TRIAL BID. This is a game try, virtually guaranteeing five hearts (by your failure to rebid 2NT or 3NT) and showing at least three cards in the suit bid. The message to partner is that he should accept or reject your invitation to game with the particular knowledge that any high cards he holds in your second suit will be gold-plated. Conversely only aces, and to a lesser extent kings, in the other two side suits will be useful. A queen opposite a singleton is usually waste paper.

g) ♠ 7 6 3   ♡ K J 8 7   ◇ K J 6   ♣ 6 5 3
h) ♠ K J 6   ♡ K J 8 7   ◇ 7 6 3   ♣ 6 5 3

With either g) or h) responder will raise 1♡ to 2♡. If opener makes a game try he doesn't know whether to consider his hand maximum or minimum unless he is given some guidance. If that invitation is a 3◇ trial bid he will happily jump to 4♡ with g) but sign off in 3♡ with h), suspecting that his spade values may be wasted. Just consider each of these hands as dummy to e) or f) and you will see how sound this judgement is.

RESPONDER CHANGES SUIT AT THE TWO LEVEL

West	East	West	East
♠ K J 8 4 3	♠ 2	1♠	2♡
♡ 8	♡ A Q 6 5 2	2♠	No
◇ K Q 6	◇ 9 4 3 2		
♣ A 8 4 3	♣ Q 5 2		

The final contract of 2♠ reached in the above auction has little chance of success, yet it is an auction that would be reproduced by many inexperienced partnerships. Who should shoulder the blame? You cannot fault West for opening a respectable five-card spade suit. It was East's 2♡ bid that caused the problem. With eight high card points and five hearts his hand met the criteria laid down by some books for a change of suit at the two level but with a badly fitting, minimum hand it was ill-judged. If he had responded 1NT that would have ended the auction and he would have achieved a plus score. To avoid this type of embarrassment many experts today demand ten points for a two-level response. This gives them sufficient values to make a second bid (often 2NT) if they dislike partner's rebid. We suggest that you can respond at the two level with eight or nine high card points, but only if you would feel happy about passing opener's rebid. Consider these hands if you are facing a 1♠ opening bid:

a) ♠ 8 6 5 ♡ A Q 6 5 2 ◇ K 4 3 ♣ 9 8
b) ♠ K 2 ♡ A Q 6 5 2 ◇ 9 4 3 ♣ 5 3 2
c) ♠ 6 ♡ A Q 6 5 2 ◇ K 4 3 2 ♣ Q 5 2

Holding any of them you can happily respond 2♡. With a) you could have raised to 2♠, except that this course would give you little chance of discovering a 5-3 heart fit if opener rebid 2NT. If partner rebids 2♠ that should prove an excellent contract. You can equally pass a 2♠ rebid with b). Hand c) is a misfit but you can truthfully bid 2NT over a 2♠ rebid, showing 10-12 points. Incidentally, note that a bid of 2♡ over 1♠ guarantees a five-card suit. Other two-level responses can be made with four-card suits on occasion.

At this point it is worth recalling the statement in chapter 1 that a reverse by opener following a change of suit at the two level is game-forcing. If you keep your responses at the two level up to scratch it is clear that if such a hand is facing reversing values you can never want to play in a part score.

Finally, consider the implications of the above theory on sequence i) below:

i) West	East	ii) West	East	iii) West	East
1♡	2♣	1♡	1♠	1♡	2♣
2◇	?	2◇		3◇	

East has either appropriate values for a second constructive bid, or a weaker hand on which he has sufficient tolerance for West's hearts to happily give preference. It thus makes sense to play that if responder changes suit at the two level, a third suit by opener is forcing. Therefore 2◇ is forcing in i) but not in ii). This leaves sequence iii) unused, therefore it makes sense to give it a precise meaning. A popular use for a jump shift after a two-level response is to show game values with at least 5-5 shape in opener's two suits.

RESPONDER JUMPS IN NO TRUMPS
Elementary bridge books rightly stress that a no trump bid on the first round of bidding guarantees at least a doubleton in each suit.

Beginners tend to respond to 1♡ with 3NT when holding either of these hands.

a) ♠ K J 3   ♡ 8 7 4   ♢ K Q 6 3   ♣ A 5 2
b) ♠ K J 3 2   ♡ 4   ♢ K Q 6 3   ♣ A 5 4 2

They are correct in believing that with b) the final contract may well be 3NT, but if the 3NT bid covers such a wide variety of holdings how is opener to judge what to do with:

c) ♠ A Q 6 4   ♡ K Q 10 6 5   ♢ J 8 7   ♣ 8?

Facing either a) or b) 3NT is most unlikely to succeed after a club lead. The correct contracts are 4♡ and 4♠ respectively. Any bid which uses up so much space must convey a precise message. The 3NT response should deny four spades and guarantee exactly 4-3-3-3 shape, hence opener can confidently sign off in 4♡ if he has c).

d) ♠ K J 3   ♡ 8 7   ♢ K Q 6 3   ♣ A 5 4 3

If responder, holding d), hears an opening bid of 1♡ he marks time with a response of 2♣ which, as was implied in the previous section, can be made with a four-card suit. He can then bid 3NT at his next turn.

It is not quite so necessary to demand the perfect 4-3-3-3 shape for a 2NT response, since if opener decides a game contract is appropriate he has more space to investigate. A doubleton in partner's suit is acceptable.

Suppose you open 1♡ with:

♠ K 7 6   ♡ A J 7 6 4   ♢ A K 5   ♣ 9 6

If partner responds 2NT you cannot ask him whether he has three hearts by bidding 3♡ because a repeat of your own suit after a no trump bid is a sign-off. However, you can tell a little lie with 3♢. In an uncontested auction a new suit at the three level is always forcing. Partner will certainly bid 3♡ if he has three, else he will retreat to 3NT which you will pass. In such an auction responder must realise that opener is far more likely to be looking for the 5-3 major fit than hoping to hear his minor raised. If responder has strong enough diamonds to raise to 4♢ he should probably have responded 2♦ rather than 2NT. Once again the search for a major suit contract takes priority.

THE 1NT RESPONSE
This breaks all the rules that we normally associate with no trump bidding. Just about the only thing you can say is that it denies a four-card major biddable at the one level and denies three-card support for partner's major suit except in a 4-3-3-3 hand. Because a response at the two level requires a 'fitting' eight points, there are many hands where responder simply hasn't got another bid available.

For example, how do you respond to 1♠ with:

♠ –   ♡ Q 6 4 3 2   ♦ A 7 5 4   ♣ 10 6 3 2 ?

If you pass you could go down in 1♠ with 4♡ laydown. You have to respond 1NT, a bid which simply says 'I can't think of anything else to bid.' You might even be forced to bid 1NT with a singleton in an unbid suit! Before you recoil in horror just try to find an alternative response to 1♠ if you hold:

♠ 8   ♡ 3   ♦ K 8 7 6 4   ♣ K 8 7 6 3 2

It really is much better to bid 1NT with these awkward hands than to respond at the two level. If you have a bad hand you must try to construct an auction which can die as quickly as possible. Partner can pass a 1NT bid and he will do so rather than rebid a five-card suit. He cannot pass a change of suit at the two level. Why force him to rebid a mediocre five-card suit if you know that will leave you in a stupid contract?

Traditional theory states that over 1♣ or 1♦ a 1NT response shows a balanced 8-10 high card points. This makes sense over 1♣ but you won't find an intelligent alternative to 1NT over 1♦ if you hold:

♠ Q 6 2   ♡ A 5 3   ♦ 8   ♣ 9 8 7 5 4 2

It is sufficient to say that 1NT over 1♦ *usually* shows at least a doubleton in each suit. Of course it also denies a four-card major. The higher the suit of the opening bid, the fewer options are available for weak hands so the likelihood of a 1NT response being 'offbeat' increases. A 1NT response to 1◇, 1♡ or 1♠ shows 6-9 points. It certainly cannot show 6-8 or you are left with nine-point hands that are unbiddable.

Opener must, of course, make his second bid with the knowledge that partner may well dislike his suit intensely. Suppose you open 1♠ and hear a 1NT response.

a) ♠ A K 7 6 5 ♡ Q 8 6 ◇ A 8 6 ♣ 7 5
b) ♠ 9 6 5 4 3 2 ♡ K 8 ◇ A 7 ♣ K Q 5
c) ♠ K J 10 8 7 6 ♡ Q 8 7 ◇ A 7 ♣ K 5
d) ♠ A K 8 7 6 ♡ A 8 ◇ 9 8 6 2 ♣ Q 10
e) ♠ A K 8 7 6 ♡ 8 7 ◇ 8 6 ♣ A Q 8 6

a) is an obvious pass. Remember that if partner has three spades he is completely balanced. You can construct hands with such a spade fit where 2♠ is better but you can also construct hands where 1NT is superior. If, on the other hand, partner has no spades you will bitterly regret any decision to bid again. With b) we would also advise a pass; after all, your tepid spade suit will hardly play well opposite a singleton. However, hand c) might play quite well in spades opposite a singleton because your intermediate cards are better, so sign off in 2♠.

If you rebid 2◇ with d) you may stumble into a super fit, but on the other hand you may not. A pass is safer. Hand e) is much more suitable for a rebid of 2♣. Firstly, your clubs are stronger (with the consequence of more weaknesses elsewhere) and secondly, your partner can introduce either red suit at the two level. That would show a weak hand with a long suit and you would pass quickly.

RESPONDER HAS TWO SUITS BIDDABLE AT THE ONE LEVEL

With two four-card suits it is usually correct to 'bid upwards', leaving partner to introduce the higher if he has it. Note the parallel with the principle of opening the lower of touching four-card suits if you have a balanced hand too strong to open 1NT. Suppose partner opens 1♣ and you hold these hands:

a)	♠ A K 6 4	♡ K J 7 5	◇ 9 8 6	♣ 7 4
b)	♠ A K 6 4	♡ Q 6 5 3	◇ 9 8 6	♣ 7 4
c)	♠ 9 8 6	♡ A K 6 4	◇ K J 7 5	♣ 7 4
d)	♠ 9 8 6	♡ A K 6 4	◇ Q 6 5 3	♣ 7 4

With a) or b) you must respond 1♡, allowing partner to introduce the spade suit cheaply if he has four. You cannot afford to miss *any* 4-4 major suit fit. With c) 1◇ is best but with d) you have no wish to play in diamonds unless partner bids the suit, so respond 1♡.

With 5-4 shape it is usually correct to bid the five-card suit. However, if partner opens with a minor suit and you have five spades and four hearts you may face an awkward decision.

e)	♠ A J 8 7 6	♡ K J 7 6	◇ 6	♣ Q 8 5
f)	♠ 8 7 6 5 4	♡ A K 7 4	◇ 6	♣ 8 7 5
g)	♠ K Q 7 6 5	♡ 7 6 5 4	◇ 6	♣ 8 7 5
h)	♠ K 7 6 5 4	♡ K 7 6 4	◇ 6	♣ 8 7 5

With e) it is clearly right to respond 1♠ to 1◇ because you are strong enough to continue with 2♡ over a 2◇ rebid. However, with f), g) or h) whatever you decide could be wrong because you may be only strong enough for one bid. If you respond 1♠ you will be able to bid 2♡ after a 1NT rebid but not after a 2♣ or 2◇ rebid. Hence you risk losing a 4-4 heart fit. Alternatively, if you respond 1♡ you will find a 5-4 spade fit, but not a 5-3 fit. The quality of the respective suits should push you towards 1♡ with f) and 1♠ with g). The decision is close with h) but on the whole 1♡ seems marginally best, if only because you may not find a 5-3 fit even if you do respond 1♠.

With 5-5 shape you should usually respond with the higher suit, although with a weak major two-suiter you face the same dilemma as with five spades and four hearts. As an example of the general principle you have to respond to 1♣ with:

♠ Q 8 7 5 4   ♡ 5 3   ◇ A 9 8 6 5   ♣ 7

1◇ may seem tempting but if partner responds 2♣ you will never have a chance to show your spades. Facing the choice of losing a major or losing a minor you must protect your major.

Quiz on Chapter 4

1) What do you respond to your partner's 1♡ opening bid with these hands?

	♠	♡	◇	♣
a)	K 7 5	Q 8 7	8 6	J 8 7 6 3
b)	K 7 5	Q 8 7	A 6	Q 8 7 6 3
c)	K 7 6	9 8 7	J 10 6 5	Q 7 5
d)	9 8 7	A Q 9	J 10 8 5	8 5 2
e)	K 8 7 5	Q 8 7	9 8 5	Q 7 5
f)	K Q 8 7	8 7 5	A Q 8	Q 9 7
g)	Q 9 7	8 7 5	A Q 3	K Q 8 7
h)	K J 7	8 7	K Q 3 2	K Q 8 7
i)	Q 8 7	8 7	A 9 7 6	K Q 8 7
j)	A Q 3	6	10 9 7 5	6 5 4 3 2
k)	A Q 3	6	10 9 7 5	K 5 4 3 2
l)	A Q 3	6	10 9 8 5	K Q 4 3 2
m)	Q 8 7	A 6	10 9 8	K 9 8 7 5
n)	4	4	A 8 7 5 3	K 8 7 5 4 2

2) What do you respond to a 1♣ opening with these hands?

	♠	♡	◇	♣
a)	A 7 6	Q 9 8	9 8 6 2	8 7 6
b)	A Q 8 6	9 6 5 3	K 7	8 7 6
c)	A Q 8 6	K 7	A Q 8 6	8 7 6
d)	A Q 8 6	K 7	9 6 5 3	8 7 6
e)	A K 8 6	5 4	J 8 6 4 2	9 8
f)	J 7 6 4 2	A J 10 4	8 6	8 3
g)	A Q 6 4 2	K Q 6 4	7 5	7 3
h)	9 7	A 8 7 5 4	A 6 5 4 2	5

3) Your partner responds 1NT to your 1♡ opening bid. What do you rebid with these hands?

	♠	♡	◇	♣
a)	9 8	A K 9 8 3	K 8 6	K 8 6
b)	A K J 6	A J 10 8 7	9 8 6	7
c)	6	K Q 10 8 7 4	A Q 7	J 7 5
d)	A Q	K 9 7 6 3	J 8 7 3	A 7
e)	10 4 2	K Q 9 8 7	7	A K 7 6

4) You open 1♡ and your partner raises to 2♡. How do you continue with these hands?

a) ♠ A Q 8 6   ♡ A Q 8 6   ◇ A J 8   ♣ 10 8
b) ♠ A 8 6   ♡ A Q 8 6   ◇ K 9 8   ♣ Q 10 8
c) ♠ A Q 7 5   ♡ A Q 8 6 4   ◇ A 8   ♣ 7 4
d) ♠ A Q J 6   ♡ A Q 8 6   ◇ K J 7 6   ♣ 3
e) ♠ A K   ♡ A 10 9 8 6 3   ◇ A 8 6   ♣ 7 5

5) You raise your partner's 1♠ opening to 2♠. What do you call if he continues with the bids shown in brackets?

a) ♠ A 9 8 6   ♡ 7 4   ◇ A 8 6 4   ♣ 9 6 4 (2NT)
(3♣)

b) ♠ K 9 8 5   ♡ 8 6   ◇ Q J 6 5   ♣ 9 8 4 (2NT)
(3♣) (3◇)

c) ♠ K 10 7   ♡ 9 7   ◇ Q 4 3 2   ♣ 8 5 3 2
(2NT) (3◇)

d) ♠ 8 7 3   ♡ K Q 4 2   ◇ Q J 3 2   ♣ 8 5 (2NT)
(3♣) (3♡)

Answers to Quiz
1) a) 2♡. Unless he has a 4-4-4-1 shape with a singleton club, opener either has five hearts or a no trump rebid. If he continues with 2NT or 3NT (showing his heart suit is only four cards) you will pass.
   b) 2♣. Don't jump to 3♡ with only three-card support. Your next bid will be 3♡.
   c) 1NT. 4-3-3-3 shape with three poor hearts and scattered values outside.
   d) 2♡. Still 4-3-3-3 shape but your hearts are so good!
   e) 1♠. Don't raise hearts with only three-card support if you have four spades because opener may be 4-4 in the major suits.
   f) 1♠. Not 3NT which denies four spades.
   g) 3NT. Guarantees 4-3-3-3 shape. Partner can thus confidently retreat to 4♡ with a five-card suit.
   h) 2♣. Then 3NT next time.
   i) 2NT. Unlike 3NT this bid doesn't guarantee three hearts.
   j) 1NT. What else? Not so much a balanced hand, more an inability to bid anything else.

k) 1NT. Not 2♣ which would probably leave you in a silly contract after a 2♡ rebid.

l) 2♣. Followed by 2NT showing 10-12 points.

m) 2♣. OK because you can pass a 2♡ rebid or give preference to 2♡ over 2♢. 1NT is an acceptable alternative.

n) 1NT. No sensible alternative.

2) a) 1♢. You can usually do better than raise a minor with only three-card support in an uncontested auction and you do not have the 8-10 points required for 1NT.

b) 1♡. The lower of two four-card suits biddable at the one level.

c) 1♢. As above.

d) 1♠. 1♢ wouldn't be wrong, but with the major suit so much stronger 1♠ describes your assets better.

e) 1♢. Bid a five-card suit before a four-card suit. Opener is likely to rebid 1♠ if he has four.

f) 1♡. You are only worth one bid. The hearts are much stronger than the spades and at least you will find the fit if opener has four cards in either major.

g) 1♠. This time you are strong enough to follow up with 2♡ if opener rebids 2♢.

h) 1♡. With 5-5 shape it is usually correct to bid the higher suit. There are many continuations which will allow you to show your diamonds, e.g., if opener rebids 1NT.

3) a) Pass. Do you want to play in 2♡ opposite a singleton or void heart?

b) Pass. Responder has denied four spades. He could just have three hearts but more often than not he will have at least eight cards in the minor suits.

c) 2♡. Not only are your hearts more sturdy but you have reason to fear spades. Your opponents have at least nine between them.

d) Pass. 2♢ may turn out well, but not if responder has 3-1-3-6 shape. Admittedly your side cannot have more than five spades but with ten of your fourteen points concentrated in your two doubleton suits, 1NT should be reasonable.

e) 2♣. If responder now bids 2♦ you must pass.

4) a) 2NT. Not a 2♠ trial bid which would convince partner that you had five hearts.

b) Pass. You had intended to rebid 1NT over 1♠ or 2NT over a two-level change of suit. Over 2♡ you are not worth a game try. If you are in a 4-3 fit partner should have ruffing values.

c) 2♠. Trial bid showing five hearts. All spade honours are welcome. Small honours in the minor suits are less so.

d) 3♦. You must make a game try and 2NT is hardly honest with a singleton club. No doubt partner will assume you have five hearts but you have no better option. Diamond honours would certainly be welcome.

e) 3♦. You haven't got four diamonds, but small honours are probably more useful in diamonds than in clubs or spades.

5) a) 4♠ over 2NT. Near maximum with four spades.

4♠ over 3♣. You can't help with the clubs but two aces, a doubleton, and four trumps are not to be sneered at.

b) 3♠ over 2NT. Minimum with four spades.

3♠ over 3♣. Your ♦Q and ♦J are probably worthless.

4♠ over 3♦. The hands obviously fit well.

c) Pass over 2NT. Minimum values and only three spades.

3♠ over 3♦. Your cards seem useful but you have so little!

d) 3NT over 2NT. Only three spades but your combined hands have at least 25 points.

3♠ over 3♣. Few, if any, of your points seem to be working!

4♡ over 3♡, showing you have more hearts than spades. 4♠ isn't wrong but why not show partner your excellent four-card support? After all he may have five cards in each major.

5. The 4-4 Major Suit Fit

RESPONDER SEEKS A 4-4 MAJOR SUIT FIT
AFTER A 1NT OPENING

It is usually desirable to uncover an eight-card fit in a major suit and make it the trump suit. It tends to be less important to play in such a minor suit fit because of the difficulties of making eleven tricks for game. Such hands are usually played in 3NT.

If your partner opens 1NT and you have a five-card major, you can ask for three card support by jumping in that suit to the three level. The STAYMAN convention is available for the purpose of locating a 4-4 major suit fit. After a 1NT opening responder bids an artificial 2♣ which demands that opener bids his lower four-card major (or 2◇ if he hasn't got one). Responder guarantees that he himself holds a four-card major and he must feel that he can see a satisfactory resting place whatever opener rebids. This usually, though not always, means eleven or more points because if he fails to locate his required fit he will have to retreat to 2NT (which shows the same 11-12 points as a direct raise of 1NT to 2NT). It is superficially attractive to bid a Stayman 2♣ with:

    ♠ Q 7 6 4   ♡ K 8 6 5   ◇ 7   ♣ Q 5 4 2

However if opener rebids 2◇ you have fixed yourself.

Here are some Stayman sequences:

	West	East	West	East
a)	♠ A Q 4 2	♠ K 8	1NT	2♣
	♡ K 10	♡ A Q 6 5	2♠ (1)	2NT (2)
	◇ Q 7 4 3	◇ K 10 8 2	3NT (3)	No
	♣ K 7 3	♣ 9 4 2		

(1) Four spades, not four hearts.
(2) Enough to raise to 2NT. With an extra point East should bid 3NT.
(3) Maximum no trump opening.

	West	East	West	East
b)	♠ A Q 4 2	♠ K 7 5 3	1NT	2♣
	♡ Q 7 6 4	♡ K 8	2♡ (1)	2NT (2)
	◇ K 10	◇ A Q 6 2	4♠ (3)	No
	♣ K 7 3	♣ 9 4 2		

(1) Four hearts, possibly four spades also.
(2) Only enough to raise to 2NT. Not interested in hearts.
(3) West knows East must have a four-card major to bid Stayman. Since he doesn't like hearts he must have spades. If West had a minimum 1NT opening he would sign off in 3♠ but with a maximum fourteen points he accepts East's game try and jumps to 4♠.

	West	East	West	East
c)	♠ K 6 3	♠ Q 9 7 4 2	1NT	2♣ (1)
	♡ A 5 4	♡ K 6 3 2	2◇ (2)	2♠ (3)
	◇ A Q 7	◇ 10 4	No	
	♣ 9 8 3 2	♣ 7 4		

(1) A rare occasion when it is safe to bid Stayman with a weak hand. East has *thought out all the consequences*. If West rebids 2♡ or 2♠ he will pass. If West rebids 2◇, denying a four-card major, he will sign off in 2♠.
(2) No major.
(3) A sign off. This will be either a 5-3 or 5-2 fit.

Suppose your partner opens 1NT and you hold:

    ♠ Q 7 6 3   ♡ A Q 8   ◇ Q 10 9   ♣ K 9 7

Should you use Stayman to investigate a 4-4 major fit or settle for an immediate 3NT? There is no clearcut answer to this. If he also has 4-3-3-3 shape the nine trick game may be easier. However, if he is less balanced the combined hands may well provide an extra trick in spades and the security of your chosen trump suit may help you to keep control and develop your tricks. We would recommend that you make a habit of always looking for the 4-4 major fit because opener will so often have to open 1NT with slightly 'offbeat' hands. If partner has opened 1NT with four sturdy spades and a small doubleton diamond 4♠ looks far more promising than 3NT. The more your partnership opens 1NT with slightly unbalanced hands, the greater the need for Stayman. Look at it this way. You are virtually obliged to open 1NT with:

♠ K J 9 4   ♡ K 5 4   ◇ A K 8 7   ♣ 8 5

Don't you have a little more peace of mind if you know that partner, with sufficient values to invite game, will investigate a spade fit rather than just blast 3NT? Stayman ensures that you always find such a fit at game level, though not necessarily at part score level.

RESPONDER SEEKS A MAJOR SUIT FIT OVER A SUIT OPENING BID

It is, of course, just as important to find a 4-4 major fit if the opening bid is not 1NT. If such a fit is missed responder is usually to blame. If you, as responder, can bid a four-card major at the one level your priority is to bid this suit rather than respond no trumps or change suit at the two level. If you choose to first bid a five-card minor at the two level it will be because you intend to bid your major suit on the second round. You can only do that if you have a hand suitable for a RESPONDER'S REVERSE. A responder's reverse at the two level shows at least eleven high card points and is forcing for one round. Remember that with two touching four-card suits and a hand too strong to open 1NT opener bids the *lower* suit. He is relying on you to introduce the other if you have it. He may have a splendid holding like ♠ A K Q J and you can only contribute a miserable ♠ 5 4 3 2. Together you have a royal trump suit, provided *you* have the courage to introduce spades. *There is no such thing as an unbiddable four-card major suit.*

Suppose partner opens 1◇ and you hold one of these hands.

a)	♠ J 7 3 2	♡ K 6 4	◇ 10 7	♣ K J 6 4
b)	♠ K J 3 2	♡ Q 4 3 2	◇ 6 5	♣ J 6 4
c)	♠ K 8 5 2	♡ 7 5	◇ 8 5	♣ A J 7 6 4
d)	♠ K 8 5 2	♡ K 7	◇ 8 5	♣ A J 7 6 4
e)	♠ K 8 5 2	♡ 7 5	◇ K J 7 5	♣ 6 4 3

With a) 1NT may seem an ideal response but the correct bid is
1♠. He may have:

f) ♠ A Q 6 4   ♡ 8   ♢ A Q 4 3 2   ♣ Q 8 5

How are you going to find the obvious spade contract unless you
bid them? *He* certainly isn't strong enough to reverse into spades.
A 1NT response by you *denies* a four-card major. Your spades
may be poor but unless you are prepared to bid them opener will
have to alter his approach and the whole system falls apart.

Hand b) reinforces a message already met in chapter 4. You
should respond 1♡, the lower of two touching four-card suits
(although a good four-card major should be preferred to a poor
four-card diamond suit if the opening bid is 1♣). This ensures
that a 4-4 fit in either major will be uncovered. If opener has hand
f) he can rebid 1♠. Note that if you foolishly responded 1♠ you
would find your spade fit here but reverse his heart and spade
holdings and he would be forced to rebid 2♢. You would then
have to pass, leaving him in a decidedly inferior strain.

With c) it is correct to respond 1♠. Your clubs are better and
you technically have the requirements for a change of suit at the
two level, but you are only going to volunteer one bid with this
hand. You are therefore obliged to show your major. Just like
opener, responder must consider his second bid (if any) before
making his first reply. He normally needs a good ten points if he is
to volunteer two bids.

With d) you should respond 2♣. If opener rebids 2♢ you intend to reverse into 2♠. (This is a reverse because opener would
have to advance to the three level to give simple preference to
your clubs.) A responder's reverse at the two level is forcing for
one round, showing at least ten high card points and 5-4 shape.

With e) you have excellent support for partner's diamond suit
but you still have the responsibility to introduce your four-card
major. If opener rebids 1NT or 2♣ you will happily give preference to diamonds.

Suppose now that, as West, you are faced with this auction:

♠ A 8 6	West	East
♡ Q J 7 6	1◇	2♣
◇ A K 7 6	3NT	4♡
♣ A J	?	

Perhaps your natural reaction is to pass, grateful that the heart fit has been uncovered. Try to think a little more deeply. East obviously has four hearts but chose instead to respond with a minor suit. He must have a responder's reverse, in other words he is *strong*. With your beautifully fitting hand you are worth at least 6♡.

One final thought! A consequential gain from bidding poor four-card majors is seen if you finally land in 3NT, having talked the defenders out of the killing lead.

Quiz on Chapter 5

1) Your partner opens a weak 1NT. What do you call with these hands?

a)	♠ K 6 5 3	♡ 6 3		◇ A J 6 3		♣ 6 5 2	
b)	♠ K 6 5 3	♡ 6		◇ A J 6 3 2		♣ 6 5 2	
c)	♠ K 6 5 3	♡ 8 7 5 3		◇ A J 6 3 2		♣ –	
d)	♠ K 6 5 3	♡ K 6 5 3		◇ Q 8 6 5		♣ 5	
e)	♠ 7 6 5 3	♡ A Q 7 6 3	◇ 8 6				♣ 6 4	
f)	♠ K J 8 7	♡ K 6		◇ K 7		♣ J 7 6 5 4	
g)	♠ A Q 8 6 5	♡ 8 6		◇ K J 6		♣ A 8 6	
h)	♠ A Q 8 6 5	♡ 8 6		◇ K J 6		♣ J 8 6	
i)	♠ K 8 6 4	♡ A 7 6		◇ A Q 8		♣ 8 7 5	

2) With each of these hands you bid a Stayman 2♣ after your partner's 1NT opening bid. How do you continue after the replies shown in brackets?

a) ♠ K 10 6 5   ♡ 7 5   ◇ A Q 8   ♣ Q 8 6 4   (2◇) (2♡) (2♠)

b) ♠ K 10 6 5   ♡ 7 5   ◇ A Q 8   ♣ A 8 6 4   (2◇) (2♡) (2♠)

3) This time you have opened 1NT and responded 2♡ in answer to partner's 2♣ enquiry. What do you call after his continuations, shown in brackets?

a) ♠ K 8 6   ♡ A Q 4 3   ◇ K 9 8   ♣ 10 9 7   (2NT) (3♡)
                                                            (3NT)

b) ♠ K 8 6   ♡ A Q 4 3   ◇ K 9 8   ♣ Q 9 7   (2NT) (3♡)
                                                            (3NT)

c) ♠ K 7 6 5   ♡ A Q 4 3   ◇ K 7   ♣ 10 8 6   (2NT) (3♡)
                                                            (3NT)

d) ♠ K 7 6 5   ♡ A Q 4 3   ◇ K 7   ♣ Q 10 6   (2NT) (3♡)
                                                            (3NT)

4) How do you respond to your partner's 1◇ opening with the following hands?

a) ♠ A 8 6   ♡ J 8 6 5   ◇ 8 7 5   ♣ K 5 3
b) ♠ A 8 7 6   ♡ J 8 6 5   ◇ 7 6   ♣ K 6 3
c) ♠ 9 8   ♡ A 8 7 6   ◇ K 7 6 3   ♣ K J 9
d) ♠ Q 8 7 6   ♡ K 7 6   ◇ 7   ♣ A 9 8 7 5
e) ♠ A 8 7 6   ♡ J 10 8   ◇ 5   ♣ A Q 8 7 5

Answers to Quiz

1) a) Pass. While a 4-4 spade fit might be superior to 1NT, you cannot afford to investigate with Stayman because any response other than 2♠ would leave you stuck.

b) 2◇. Sign off. A 2♡ response to Stayman would leave you floundering.

c) 2♣. Safe this time, since you can happily pass any response including 2◇.

d) Pass. If you try 2♣ and pass a 2◇ response you might be in a 4-2 fit. Don't chase rainbows.

e) 2♣. If opener responds 2◇ you can sign off in 2♡, otherwise you can pass his response. Don't settle for a heart fit with no guarantee of a combined holding of eight cards when you can safely investigate a 4-4 spade fit. However, exchange your diamond and heart holdings and you would have to sign off in 2◇.

f) 2♣. Forget the clubs. If opener responds 2♠, show appreciation of your distribution by raising to 4♠, otherwise your second bid will be 2NT.

g) 3♠. This time you are looking for a 5-3 fit. Stayman is no help here.

h) 2♣. Difficult. You are not strong enough for the game-forcing 3♠. Equally you are too strong for a 2♠ signoff. There is no bid available to make a game invitation while showing *five* spades (unless you play transfers). The best compromise is to test whether opener has four spades, and if not settle for 2NT.

i) 2♣, with a view to playing in 4♠ if partner has four. Don't forget that he may be less balanced than you.

2) a) 2NT over 2♦. Game try.

2NT over 2♡. Game try, showing four spades (otherwise you wouldn't have used Stayman).

3♠ over 2♠. Game try, revealing that a 4-4 fit has been uncovered.

b) 3NT, 3NT, 4♠. All as in part a) except that this time you are strong enough to insist on game.

3) a) Pass in each case.

b) 3NT, 3NT, Pass. This time you are maximum so accept the invitations. Note that you lose nothing by trying 3NT when partner raises to 3♡. If you show your 4-3-3-3 shape partner may judge that the nine trick game is better if he has a similar shape, otherwise he can retreat to 4♡.

c) 3♠, Pass, 4♠. Holding both majors yourself you know a 4-4 fit exists immediately you hear partner's 2♣ bid. You dutifully respond your lower suit. If he denies interest in hearts by bidding no trumps, he must have been looking for spades. Being minimum you should not raise to game if he only invites.

d) 4♠, 4♡, 4♠. As c), except that with a maximum you accept any invitation to game.

4) a) 1♡. It is obligatory to bid your four-card major.

b) 1♡. Bid your *lower* four-card major. Partner will rebid 1♠ if he has four.

c) 1♡. Look for the 4-4 major fit before agreeing diamonds.

d) 1♠. You are only worth one bid so show your major.

e) 2♣. This time you are strong enough to bid naturally. Your next bid will be spades, a responder's reverse.

6. The Fourth Suit

Often, by the time opener makes his rebid, the mist surrounding the final contract is beginning to clear for responder. However sometimes further clarification is needed and to progress further a forcing bid is necessary. Imagine that you face this sequence as East:

	West	East
♠ A Q 7 6 4		
♡ J 2	1♡	1♠
◇ 7 4 3	2♣	?
♣ K J 5		

As you ponder the obvious continuations they all seem to have fatal flaws. You are too strong for false preference to 2♡ and a jump preference to 3♡ shows genuine three-card support. 2♠ shows a weak hand with a good six-card suit, obviously unacceptable. A raise to 3♣ shows four-card support. 2NT expresses your values well but is unacceptable without a diamond guard. Although a relatively weak suit shouldn't deter you from bidding no trumps early in the auction, if your bidding has pinpointed the lead of one particular suit you need a firm guard in that suit. The defenders might have led spades, hearts or clubs if your side hadn't bid them but after this bidding a diamond lead is almost inevitable. Three suits have been bid and your answer is to bid the fourth, 2◇.

To bid the fourth suit does not show high cards or length in the suit, indeed if you had good diamonds after this auction you would, no doubt, bid no trumps at an appropriate level. Neither are you, as is so often believed, showing 'half a stop' in that suit. This interpretation, while working admirably for those hands where you do possess Q x or J x x, fatally restricts the use of the bid and renders far too many hands unbiddable. You are simply requesting more information. Has he got a sixth heart, or three-card spade support, or perhaps a diamond guard? Obviously the player who bids the fourth suit is quite likely to be fishing for a no trump guard, but that should not deter his partner from bidding naturally.

It is universally accepted that the fourth suit is artificial and forcing but opinions differ on whether it is forcing for one round or further. A simple, but reasonably effective, method is to agree that if you bid the fourth suit at the two level your partner's rebid forces another bid from you unless it comes in one of the following categories:

i) He rebids his own first suit at the minimum level.

ii) He supports your suit at the lowest level.

iii) He rebids 2NT.

Of course, if a game-forcing sequence has already been established before the fourth suit was bid, all continuations will remain game forcing. Therefore you should have enough points to make 2NT a reasonable contract. Any jump bid after the fourth suit has been bid should be game-forcing. As with so many areas of bidding, experienced partnerships will wish to try to improve on this. What matters most is that both players are playing the same system, that it is simple to remember, and that it roughly corresponds to modern theory. Let us return to the previous hand and examine West's continuation with the hands below.

West	East	East hand
1♡	1♠	♠ A Q 7 6 4
2♣	2♦	♡ J 2
?		♦ 7 4 3
		♣ K J 5

West hands:

a)	♠ 8	♡ K 9 8 6 4 3	♦ Q 2	♣ A Q 8 2
b)	♠ 8	♡ K 9 8 6 4 3	♦ A 2	♣ A Q 8 2
c)	♠ 9 8 5	♡ A 10 8 6 3	♦ K	♣ A Q 8 2
d)	♠ K 8 5	♡ A 9 8 6 3	♦ K	♣ A Q 8 2
e)	♠ 9	♡ K 9 8 6 3	♦ K 9 6	♣ A Q 8 2
f)	♠ 9	♡ K 9 8 6 3	♦ A Q 6	♣ A Q 8 2
g)	♠ 9	♡ K 9 8 6 3	♦ Q 2	♣ A Q 8 6 2
h)	♠ 9	♡ A K Q 8 3	♦ 8 2	♣ A Q 8 6 2
i)	♠ 8	♡ A Q 9 8 6	♦ 8 6 2	♣ A Q 8 2
j)	♠ 8	♡ A K Q 8 6	♦ 8 6 2	♣ A Q 8 2
k)	♠ 8	♡ A 10 9 8 4 3	♦ A 6	♣ A Q 8 2

54

With a) he will bid 2♡ (not forcing) which you will pass. With b) he will jump to 3♡ (game-forcing) which you will raise to 4♡.

With c) he will bid 2♠ (not forcing), which you will pass. This usually shows a 3-5-1-4 distribution, occasionally 2-5-2-4 with a spade honour. With d) he will jump to 3♠ (game-forcing) which you will raise to 4♠.

With e) and f) he will rebid 2NT (not forcing and hence minimum) and 3NT respectively. These bids obviously show a diamond guard.

With g) or h) he will rebid 3♣ (forcing). Knowing that he has at least 5-5 shape you will raise to 4♣. He can then pass with g) and bid 5♣ with h).

Hands i) and j) give him a problem since he has nothing extra to show. With i) he does best to bid 2♡. Although this suggests a sixth heart it has the merit of keeping the bidding low. With j) he should raise the fourth suit by bidding 3◇, a game-forcing bid which returns the buck if the fourth suit is a minor. You can then try 3♡ which he will raise to 4♡, the correct contract despite only having seven trumps.

Hand k) gives him a more pleasant problem. He would like to show his sixth heart and his diamond guard but cannot do both in one bid. A forcing 3♡ is best with such a distributional hand.

A bid of the fourth suit at the three level by either player should be played as game-forcing. Suppose you, as East, have:

♠ 6 3	West	East
♡ K 9 4	1♠	2♣
◇ 7 4 3	2♡	?
♣ A K Q J 2		

The only thing you know about the final destination is that it will be at game level. At this stage 3NT, 4♡, 4♠ or 5♣ are all possible contracts. You will find out by bidding 3◇, intending to pass 3NT, raise 3♡ to 4♡, raise 3♠ to 4♠ or raise 4♣ to 5♣.

RAISING THE FOURTH SUIT

It is rarely the case that after three suits have been bid the best contract has the fourth suit as trumps, but it is not unknown. Should we use a raise of the fourth suit as an attempt to find a fit in that suit or should we use it artificially? As so often, the search for a 4-4 major fit takes priority. If the fourth suit is a major, a raise usually represents a genuine attempt to suggest that suit as trumps. To do this you must have sufficient values to accept the game try and four card 'support'. Consider the following auction.

West	East	West	East
♠ K J 6 2	♠ A Q 10 3	1♣	1♦
♡ A 7 4 3	♡ 8	1♡	1♠
♦ 5	♦ A J 10 4 2	2♠	4♠
♣ A K 4 2	♣ 9 7 6		

After West's 1♡ rebid East has the values for 2NT but that would be a lazy bid. He bids 1♠ with the intention of bidding 2NT next time. West could equally bid 2NT but, aware that a 4-4 fit may be available in spades, he makes the thoughtful bid of 2♠ and hence the correct contract of 4♠ is reached.

You should not automatically raise a 'major' fourth suit just because you have four of them.

a)	♠ Q 10 7 4	♡ A Q 9 4	♦ K J 6 3	♣ 9
b)	♠ A J 10 4	♡ A Q 9 4	♦ K J 6 3	♣ 9

With either of these hands you open 1♡ and rebid 2♦ over a 2♣ response. If partner continues with 2♠ you can raise to 3♠ with b) but 2NT is correct with a). Although he may have a responder's reverse with five clubs and four spades he is more likely to have:

♠ 8 6 2   ♡ J 6   ♦ A 7 5   ♣ A Q 8 6 4.

If you hold hand a) then any contract over 2NT is plainly unsound. 3♠ is correct with b) because you are strong enough to accept the game try. If he converts this to 3NT you will obviously pass.

Sometimes the fourth suit is a major in a sequence in which the bidder has already denied four cards in the suit, for example:

West	East	West	East
♠ Q 8	♠ A 5 3	1♦	1♡
♡ 8 4	♡ A J 6 3	2♣	2♦
♦ A Q J 6 5	♦ 10 8 2	2♠	3♠
♣ A K J 2	♣ 8 7 5	3NT	

If West had four spades he would have rebid 1♠ over 1♥ so East/West cannot have a 4-4 spade fit. East's 3♠ is therefore redundant for this purpose. Instead he is passing the buck back to West. He could have bid 3NT himself, but he is aware that there is no advantage in playing this contract from his side of the table with a holding like ♠ A 5 3. He is hoping that West can bid 3NT and West is delighted to do so, bearing in mind that a doubleton spade honour is the best that East can expect in the light of the previous bidding. If West could not bid 3NT East would have settled for 5♦.

Quiz on Chapter 6

1) You respond 1♠ to partner's 1♥ opening and he rebids 2♣. How do you continue with these hands?

a)	♠ A 7 6 3	♥ K J 7	♦ K 8 6 4	♣ 6 4
b)	♠ K 8 5 4	♥ J 7	♦ K J 7 2	♣ K 10 3
c)	♠ K 8 6 5 3	♥ J 6	♦ 8 6 4	♣ K 10 5
d)	♠ K J 6 5 3	♥ 8 6	♦ 8 6 4	♣ A K 5
e)	♠ K 8 6 5 3	♥ K 6	♦ 8 6 4	♣ A K 5
f)	♠ K Q 10 9 5 4	♥ 6	♦ K 6 4	♣ 8 5 4
g)	♠ K Q 8 7 6 4	♥ 6	♦ A 8 6	♣ K J 5

2) You open 1♠ and rebid 2♦ over the 2♣ response. Partner continues with 2♥. What do you call with these hands?

a)	♠ A J 7 6 3	♥ A J 7	♦ Q 10 8 7	♣ 8
b)	♠ A J 7 6 3	♥ A J 7	♦ A J 8 7	♣ 8
c)	♠ A J 7 6 5 3	♥ Q 4	♦ K J 10 4	♣ 8
d)	♠ A J 7 6 5 3	♥ A 4	♦ K Q 10 4	♣ 8
e)	♠ A J 7 6 4	♥ 7 4	♦ A Q 7 6 3	♣ 6
f)	♠ A J 10 6 4	♥ 7 4	♦ A K Q 10 7	♣ 6
g)	♠ A J 10 6 4	♥ 7	♦ A Q J 7	♣ 5 4 2
h)	♠ A J 10 6 4	♥ 7	♦ A K Q 8	♣ Q 10 7

3) You open 1♥ and rebid 2♥ over partner's 1♠ response. He now bids 3♣. How do you continue with these hands?

a)	♠ 7	♥ A Q 8 7 5 3	♦ 8 7 5	♣ K Q 6
b)	♠ 8 6 4	♥ A Q J 7 6	♦ 9 7	♣ K Q 7
c)	♠ 9 7	♥ A Q J 7 6	♦ K 7 6	♣ Q 10 8
d)	♠ 9 7	♥ A Q J 7 6	♦ 8 7 6	♣ K Q 8

4) You open 1♠ and reverse into 3♣ over partner's 2◇ response. He now bids 3♡. How do you continue with these hands?

a) ♠ K J 8 7 6 4   ♡ A Q   ◇ 8   ♣ A K 7 6
b) ♠ A K 8 6 4   ♡ 6   ◇ Q 8 6   ♣ A K J 2
c) ♠ A K 8 6 4   ♡ K 2   ◇ 9 7   ♣ A K 8 2
d) ♠ A K 8 6 4   ♡ 8 6   ◇ 9 7   ♣ A K Q 4

Answers to Quiz

1) a) 3♡. Jump preference. Three-card heart support and not forcing.

b) 2NT. Don't use the fourth suit when you have an obvious natural bid.

c) 2♡. False preference. You are far too weak to bid 2◇.

d) 2◇. Too strong for false preference but lacking the three hearts necessary for jump preference. You will pass any non-forcing bid he makes.

e) 2◇. Similar to d) except this time you intend to play in game.

f) 2♠. Weak hand, good suit.

g) 2◇, to be followed by 3♠. An immediate 3♠ would not be absolutely forcing so you create a game-forcing situation by bidding the fourth suit first. If partner has two spades the spade game is likely to be far superior to 3NT, even though you have a diamond guard.

2) a) 2NT. Minimum with the hearts guarded.

b) 3NT. This time you are strong enough to insist on game.

c) 2♠. Not forcing as opener is rebidding his *first* suit at the lowest level. Usually shows six spades.

d) 3♠. Game-forcing. If responder has the values for 2NT there should be a playable game contract available.

e) 3◇. Forcing, (even though you would rather it was not) because opener is rebidding his *second* suit. You will opt out at the first opportunity.

f) 3◇. This time you intend to play in game.

g) 3♣. Not forcing, because you have supported his suit at the lowest level.

h) 4♣. Game-forcing.

3) a) 3♡. Partner has created a forcing situation despite your minimum rebid and it is difficult to see the bidding dying before game is reached. Your responsibility is to provide him with extra information. Here you should stress your sixth heart.

b) 3♠. Three-card spade support may be just what he needs.

c) 3NT. You have a diamond guard so show it.

d) 3◇. Partner has made a forcing bid even though your rebid has shown a minimum opening so you should feel free to use the fourth suit. See what he has to say. You will raise 3♡ to 4♡ or 3♠ to 4♠.

4) a) 3NT. With two heart guards this is slightly more helpful than 3♠.

b) 4◇. Forcing, of course, and suggesting that you have three diamonds (or at worst a good doubleton) as well as five spades and four clubs.

c) 3NT. Your heart guard is the one feature you haven't yet shown.

d) 3♠. What else? Ideally you should have a sixth spade for this bid, but you must pick the least unattractive option. At least your spades are strong and should play reasonably opposite a small doubleton.

7. Methods of Hand Evaluation

THE VALUE OF A FIT

Do you sometimes wonder why experts sail into unbeatable slams with 25 points in the combined hands when it would never have occurred to you to proceed beyond game? They realise that the 4-3-2-1 point count method of evaluating a hand is not infallible. It is a blunt tool which works fairly well on balanced hands but considerably less well on distributional hands. With these hands it tends to undervalue aces and overvalue queens and jacks.

For example, how do you, as West, continue this auction?

		West	East
♠	K 10 9 8 6 4	1♠	3♦
♥	A 4 3	4♦	4♠
♦	K Q 8	?	
♣	4		

If you balance your 12 points (14 including spade length) against East's 16 and pass, the point count is blinkering you. Count your combined tricks! If he has three aces and nothing else you can see six spade tricks, five diamond tricks (if he chooses to force in a suit missing the king and queen he assuredly has five) and two aces. That adds up to a grand slam. If, to take the other extreme, he had forced with 3♣ and persisted with 4♣ over your 3♠ rebid you would be happy to find a makeable game. The hands fit badly and even a combined 28 points may be insufficient.

Although it is not so easy to be scientific at a lower level the same criteria apply. With a good fit bid aggressively but with a misfit be cautious. You have already seen that it is safer to respond at the two level with minimum values if you have some fit with partner's suit. Here are some further examples.

Suppose you open 1♠ with:

a) ♠ K Q 10 8 6 3   ♥ A Q 3   ♦ 5   ♣ Q 10 4

If partner responds 2♢ a rebid of 2♠ is ample, but if he responds 2♣ your hand looks altogether more promising and a jump to 3♣ is justified. Your ♣ Q 10 4 will probably be invaluable in the quest to establish his suit. Note that you are assuming that if he has a minimum response at the two level his clubs will be of reasonable quality.

b) ♠ A 3   ♡ J 6 4   ♢ 9 8 2   ♣ K J 7 6 5
c) ♠ A 3   ♡ J 6 4   ♢ K J 2   ♣ 9 8 6 3 2

Opposite an opening bid of 1♠ a response of 2♣ is reasonable with b) but such a response with c) gives opener a totally misleading picture of how he should value his points. 1NT is vastly superior. Quite simply, b) is a better hand than c). It is always preferable to have your honour cards in a suit in which you also have length because they help you to establish your long suit.

ACOL LIGHT OPENING BIDS
It is a well-known feature of Acol that it is permissible to make light opening bids, especially third in hand. This is *not* an excuse to open with any rubbish.

a) ♠ A K 8 7 5   ♡ 7 4   ♢ 9 7   ♣ K J 10 8
b) ♠ 9 8 7 5 4   ♡ A K   ♢ 9 7   ♣ K J 10 8

Hand a) is a reasonable 1♠ opening bid at any vulnerability and in any position. Hand b), while containing the same high cards, is *never* an opening bid. Those who think it clever to open 1♠ with this miserable collection should ask themselves two questions. Firstly, will it help partner judge how to bid if the auction gets complicated? We suggest that if you open 1♠ with b) and he ends up sacrificing in 4♠ doubled over 4♡ you will not look forward to the post mortem. Secondly, do you want a spade lead if your opponents buy the contract and your partner has the opening lead?

A third question to consider is whether you have an easy rebid.

c) ♠ A Q 8 6   ♡ 8 7   ♢ 7 3   ♣ A J 6 5 4
d) ♠ 7 3   ♡ 8 7   ♢ A Q 8 6   ♣ A J 6 5 4

If you open 1♣ with c) you have an easy 1♠ rebid. If a good fit in either suit exists it will be discovered and a 1NT contract is also left open if responder dislikes both of your suits. If, however, you open 1♣ with d) you are all too likely to hear a major suit response. You will then have to rebid 2♣ and possibly play there with four diamonds and only one club in dummy.

It is worth recalling that an agreement to play a weak no trump does not oblige you to open the bidding every time you hold a balanced hand with twelve points.

e)   ♠ Q 5 3   ♡ J 4 3 2   ◇ K 6 2   ♣ A Q 5
f)   ♠ 6 5 2   ♡ Q 10 9   ◇ K J 9 8   ♣ A Q 10

To open a vulnerable 1NT with e) is asking for -800. Hand f), with the good diamond holding and useful intermediate cards (tens and nines), is worth at least one extra point.

Even some hands which seem to have thirteen points are not worth opening.

g)   ♠ Q 6 4 3 2   ♡ K   ◇ Q 7 5 4 2   ♣ K Q

If you count length points for the two five-card suits hand g) seems to be worth fourteen, but this is an illusion. Whatever you open will deceive partner as to where your values lie and may force you into a rather ugly rebid. You have no good intermediate cards and combinations like singleton K or doubleton K Q are simply not worth their point count unless partner has bid that suit strongly. If you want a quick rule of thumb, deduct a point for any singleton honour except the ace and for doubleton holdings like K Q or Q J. If partner's bidding subsequently makes your holding look helpful you can always upvalue the hand. Now recount your points for hand g) and you will find that you have only a rather unattractive twelve count. You should pass.

THE LOSING TRICK COUNT
How do you respond to a 1♠ opening bid with:

a)   ♠ K 7 6 5 2   ♡ A 5   ◇ 4   ♣ 9 7 6 4 2?

If you use the standard point count you have seven high card points, two extra for the singleton diamond and one for the

doubleton heart. You raise to 3♠ and partner naturally passes
with:

b) ♠ A J 8 4 3   ♡ J 7 4   ♢ Q 6 3   ♣ A 5

Ten tricks roll in and you have missed another game contract.
You don't even have the excuse that the hands fit miraculously
since three of opener's points, the ♡J and ♢Q, are waste paper.
The root of the problem lies in your method of hand evaluation.
You should have bid 4♠, expecting partner to succeed with most
minimum opening bids. Once you have found an eight-card (or
better) trump fit you have a far better method of judging your
potential, the LOSING TRICK COUNT (LTC). This is how a simple
version of it works.

To calculate how many losers you have in a suit with three or
more cards calculate how many of the top three honour cards you
are missing. For a doubleton the critical cards are the ace and
king. Any singleton is a loser except the ace. Thus you never have
more than three losers in any suit. Most of the time it doesn't
matter whether the holding is in the trump suit or a side suit.
However it is assumed that a player who wishes to use the LTC
has at least three trumps, therefore a short suit will not be
trumps. A small singleton in a side suit is only one loser because it
is assumed that there will be enough trumps to take care of
subsequent leads in the suit. Obviously a small singleton trump is
a liability and renders the hand totally unsuitable for the LTC.

Here are some examples of calculating losers in a suit.

No losers:
    Void, A   A K   A K Q   A K Q 7   A K Q 7 5 etc.

One loser:
    Singleton (except singleton ace),   A 6   A Q   K 6
    A K 6   A Q 6   K Q 6   A Q J   A K J   A K 7 6
    A K 7 6 4 etc.
    It is also correct to count A J 10 as only one loser, although the
    king and queen are both missing.

Two losers:
    7 6   Q 6   A 8 7   A J 7   K 8 7   K J 7   Q J 7
    A 9 7 5   A 9 7 5 3   Q 8 6 5 2 etc.

A suit of Q 3 2 or Q 4 3 2 appears to have only two losers but is usually counted as three losers unless it is the trump suit, or unless it is 'balanced' by an ace in another suit.

Three losers:
   8 7 5   J 10 6   8 7 5 2   J 5 3 2   8 7 5 3 2 etc.

Taking the hand as a whole, you should also subtract a loser for a known nine-card trump fit if you are supporting partner's suit.

Obviously this is all very rough and ready. If partner opens 1♠, either hand c) or hand d) seem to contain eight losers, two in each suit.

c)   ♠ Q J 3 2   ♡ Q J 2   ◇ Q J 2   ♣ Q J 2
d)   ♠ A J 9 8   ♡ A J 9   ◇ A J 9   ♣ A J 9

The point count, backed up by common sense, tells you that hand c) is only worth 3♠ whereas d) merits a slam try. There are modifications to the LTC that can partially take account of this but formulae are really no substitute for common sense. The hands quoted above are extreme, and extreme cases make good ideas look foolish. After all, the traditional point count hardly describes the power of a hand with all thirteen spades. Most hands have some features that are undervalued by the LTC and some that are overvalued.

e)   ♠ 9 8 6 2   ♡ Q 4   ◇ K Q 7   ♣ A 9 7 5

Hand e) has eight losers in support of spades; three spades, two hearts, one diamond and two clubs. A finer appreciation might value ♡ Q 4 as 1¾ losers but ◇ K Q 7 as 1¼ losers. These changes have no overall effect, leaving three red suit losers.

The LTC is only used when a good trump fit (at least eight cards) has been found. Responder than assumes that opener had seven losers for his opening bid (although it must be stressed that he counted his points, not losers, when deciding whether to open). Responder adds his own total of losers to seven and subtracts the total from 24. The resulting figure gives the approximate number of tricks that the combined hands should take if opener is minimum. Let us return to hands a) and b).

| a) | ♠ K 7 6 5 2 | ♡ A 5 | ◇ 4 | ♣ 9 7 6 4 2 |
| b) | ♠ A J 8 4 3 | ♡ J 7 4 | ◇ Q 6 3 | ♣ A 5 |

With a) responder has six losers; one spade (two for the missing A Q minus one for a 5-4 trump fit), one heart, one diamond and three clubs. Add six to seven, making thirteen. Now subtract from twenty-four and you get eleven. The combined holdings are nearer to eleven tricks than nine! As it happened opener had eight losers, two spades (he doesn't subtract one for the nine-card fit as he bid the suit first), three hearts, two diamonds (only two because the unsupported queen is 'balanced' by the ♣A or the ♠A), and one club but ten tricks are easily available.

You soon learn the magic figures. Provided you have a suitable fit you should raise partner's opening major to the two level with nine or ten losers, to the three level with eight losers and to game with seven losers. If you open 1♠ and partner raises to 3♠ (eight losers) you should raise to game with six losers. A word of warning though, the LTC does not allow for serious duplication of values. If responder counts a side suit singleton as one loser and opener subsequently counts K Q J 6 in the same suit as one loser the partnership will probably get too high. This is equally the case if you are counting points. It cannot be stressed too often that if, because of previous bidding, you suspect that such duplication exists you should bid cautiously. Frequently you cannot tell; however, even if you do bid to a poor game the defenders may come to your rescue.

West	East	West	East
♠ A Q 6 3 2	♠ K 10 5 4	1♠	3♠ (1)
♡ 5 4 2	♡ A 8 7	4♠ (2)	No
◇ K Q J 6	◇ 8		
♣ 4	♣ 10 8 7 5 3		

1) Eight losers—two spades, two hearts, one diamond, three clubs.
2) Six losers—one spade, three hearts, one diamond, one club. Obviously a heart lead beats 4♠ but, failing that, declarer is able to establish his diamond suit and discard East's heart losers. Exchange West's diamond and heart holdings and eleven tricks are likely on any lead despite the paucity of points.

Of course you don't have to rely exclusively on the LTC. When deciding at what level to support partner you can use the point count with fairly balanced hands like e) and the LTC with distributional hands like a) which are undervalued by the traditional point count. If, having applied your chosen method, you are still in doubt you can resurrect the other method.

The LTC works best when deciding whether to bid marginal games or whether to sacrifice over the opponents' game. It should *not* be used for slam bidding where controls and trick-taking potential are all important.

Finally, at the risk of repetition, the LTC must only be used when you have established at least an eight-card trump fit.

PLAYING TRICKS
In Chapter 8 we will discuss the requirements of opening bids at the two level and above, some of which are defined in terms of PLAYING TRICKS rather than points. You calculate your playing tricks as follows:

i) Suits with at least three cards:

3 tricks:	A K Q			
2½ tricks:	A K J	A Q J		
2 tricks	A K x	A Q 10	A J 10	K Q J
1½ tricks	A Q x	K Q x	K J 10	
1 trick	A J x	A x x	K J x	Q J 10
½ trick	K x x	Q J x	Q 10 9	

Also you add length tricks as follows:

½ trick	Each four-card suit.
1½ tricks	Each five-card suit.
3 tricks	Each six-card suit.
4 tricks	Seven-card suit.
5 tricks	Eight-card suit etc.

ii) Doubletons and singletons:

2 tricks	A K		
1½ tricks	A Q		
1 trick	A x	K Q	Singleton A
½ trick	K J	K x	

Consider these hands:

a) ♠ A Q 10 7 5 4   ♡ A K J 9   ◇ A 6   ♣ 7
b) ♠ K J 10 3 2   ♡ A Q 10 6   ◇ A Q J   ♣ Q

Hand a) has 9 tricks:

Spades = 5 tricks	(A Q 10 = 2 Six-card suit = 3)
Hearts = 3 tricks	(A K J = 2½ Four-card suit = ½)
Diamonds = 1 trick	(A x = 1)

That is not to say that it is guaranteed to take nine tricks if partner has a misfitting Yarborough. However give him just ♠ K 3 and you will have good chances of making ten tricks in 4♠. Nine tricks represents the best available estimate of its potential if spades are trumps.

Hand b) has 8 tricks:

Spades = 3 tricks	(K J 10 = 1½ Five-card suit = 1½)
Hearts = 2½ tricks	(A Q 10 = 2 Four-card suit = ½)
Diamonds = 2½ tricks	(A Q J = 2½)

Just as with the losing trick count, this is not a foolproof method and you must feel free to adjust your total if you are consistently undervaluing or overvaluing your holdings.

c) ♠ A K J 10 9   ♡ A J 9 8   ◇ Q 10 7   ♣ K

Hand c) has 5½ tricks:

Spades = 4 tricks	(A K J = 2½ Five-card suit = 1½)
Hearts = 1½ tricks	(A J x = 1 Four-card suit = ½)

However each holding is potentially worth more. ♠ A K J is preferable to ♠ A Q J, ♡ A J 9 8 is better than ♡ A 4 3 2 and your minor suit holdings may promote a trick in partner's hand. A better estimate would be 6½ tricks.

QUICK TRICKS

When responding to strong distributional hands (see chapter 8) it is sometimes useful to have a guide to how helpful your contribution will be. Once again the emphasis is on aces and kings, with a queen only counting if it is supported by a higher honour.

The quick trick count is summarised below:

A = 1,   K = ½ (unless singleton),   A K = 2,
K Q = 1,   A Q = 1½.

Quiz on Chapter 7

1) Which of these hands are worth an opening bid as dealer with both sides vulnerable? Consider also whether they would be worth an opening bid third in hand.

a)	♠ J 8 7 5 3	♡ A 7	♢ Q J 6	♣ K 8 5
b)	♠ 8 6 5 4 2	♡ A K	♢ 9 8 7 5	♣ K Q
c)	♠ 8 6 4 3 2	♡ A K	♢ Q 10 8 7	♣ K Q
d)	♠ A K 8 6 5 2	♡ 9 7	♢ K 10 8 7	♣ 2
e)	♠ A Q 9 8 7	♡ K 9 8 7 5	♢ 8 6	♣ 2
f)	♠ 8 6	♡ 2	♢ A Q 9 8 7	♣ K 9 8 7 5
g)	♠ A Q 6 5 2	♡ 8 6	♢ K 7 6 4 2	♣ 2
h)	♠ Q 8 5	♡ K 8 7 5	♢ 7	♣ A J 9 7 5
i)	♠ 7	♡ Q 8 5	♢ K 8 7 5	♣ A J 9 7 5

2) Your partner opens 1♡ with just your side vulnerable. For each of these hands think out your response, and the reasons governing your choice (i.e. number of losers if appropriate).

a)	♠ 7 5 4 2	♡ A 9 5 2	♢ 7 4	♣ A Q 7
b)	♠ J 8 5 2	♡ A 8 7 5	♢ K 8 6	♣ 8 6
c)	♠ 3	♡ Q 9 8 6 5	♢ 8 5	♣ A 8 6 5 3
d)	♠ A 8 6	♡ Q 10 7	♢ 6	♣ 9 7 6 5 3 2
e)	♠ 9 8 6	♡ Q 7 5 3	♢ A	♣ 8 7 5 4 2
f)	♠ 9 7 5	♡ Q 7 5 3	♢ 7	♣ A 10 6 5 3
g)	♠ 9 7 5	♡ K 7 5 3	♢ 7	♣ Q 10 6 5 3
h)	♠ A J 10 9	♡ K J 9 7	♢ 7	♣ J 10 9 5
i)	♠ A J 10	♡ K 10 7 5	♢ K 10 9	♣ 8 7 4
j)	♠ –	♡ 8 7 6 4 3 2	♢ A 8 6 3	♣ 7 5 3
k)	♠ 5	♡ J 9 8 6 5	♢ 7 6 3	♣ 10 8 7 5

3) You open 1♠ and partner raises to 2♠. How do you continue with these hands?

a)	♠ A K 8 7 5 3 2	♡ 6	♢ A 8 6 4	♣ 5
b)	♠ A K 8 7 6 5	♡ 6	♢ A 8 6 4 2	♣ 5
c)	♠ A Q 8 5	♡ K 8 6	♢ 9 8 6	♣ A K Q

4) With both sides vulnerable your partner opens 1♠ and rebids 2♡ over your 2♣ response. How do you continue with these hands?

a) ♠ Q 8 7   ♡ 8 5   ◇ A 7 5   ♣ K J 8 6 2
b) ♠ Q 8 7   ♡ K 10 9 2   ◇ 7   ♣ A 9 7 5 3
c) ♠ Q 8 7   ♡ Q J 4   ◇ 7   ♣ A 8 7 6 4 2
d) ♠ Q 8 7   ♡ 7   ◇ Q J 4   ♣ A 8 7 6 4 2

Answers to Quiz

1) a) Pass in either position. Don't make borderline opening bids with a bad suit. The main purpose of a light third hand opening is to guide partner if he has to make the opening lead.
   b) Pass in either position. This hand is barely worth twelve points. It would be far stronger if your honour cards were in your long suits.
   c) 1♠ in either position. This hand also has unattractive features but it is now a bit too strong to risk passing.
   d) 1♠ in either position. An excellent suit and an easy rebid.
   e) 1♠ in either position. This hand has substantial playing strength if partner has a fit with either major.
   f) Pass in first position. Borderline openings are more attractive if you can see the prospect of a major suit contract. 1◇ in third position to indicate a lead.
   g) Pass in first position. 1♠ in third position. This indicates a good lead and has pre-emptive value.
   h) Pass in first position. 1♣ in third position. You will rebid 1♡ over a 1◇ response or pass a 1♠ response.
   i) Pass in either position. The lack of an attractive rebid over a 1♠ response tips the scales against a third hand opening of 1♣.

2) a) 3♡. Either 8 losers (3 spades, 2 hearts, 2 diamonds, 1 club) or 11 points (including one for the doubleton diamond). Either method of evaluation points to 3♡.
   b) 2♡. Either 9 losers (3 spades, 2 hearts, 2 diamonds, 2 clubs) or 9 points (including one for the doubleton club). Again the two methods agree.
   c) 4♡. 6 losers (1 spade, 2 hearts (-1 for nine-card fit),

69

2 diamonds, 2 clubs). The point count would grossly under-value such a distributional hand.

d) 2♡. 8 points. It is not appropriate to apply the losing trick count to what might be a seven-card fit. In any case it is not permitted to jump to 3♡ with only three-card support.

e) 2♡. 8 losers (3 spades, 2 hearts, 3 clubs) or 8 points (including 2 for the singleton diamond). The point count wins here.

f) 3♡. Again 8 losers (3 spades, 2 hearts, 1 diamond, 2 clubs) or 8 points. This time the verdict goes to the LTC because the ♣A (which heads a long suit) is a better card than was the singleton ♢A in example e).

g) 2♡. 9 losers this time because the unsupported ♣Q is not balanced by an ace.

h) 4♡. 7 losers (1 spade, 2 hearts, 1 diamond, 3 clubs).

i) 3♡. 8 losers or 11 points.

j) 4♡. 7 losers (3 hearts (-1 for ten card fit), 2 diamonds, 3 clubs). The LTC is the natural method of evaluation for such a distributional hand. If partner has strong spades the duplication might defeat you but you must be aggressive in bidding vulnerable games.

k) 2♡. Only 9 losers, despite the absence of points.

3) 1) 4♠. 4 losers. Partner has nine or ten losers but game will be playable opposite most ten-loser hands.

b) 4♠. 5 losers. You will be very unlucky to fail.

c) 2NT. Two reasons not to use the LTC here. Firstly, you may be in a 4-3 fit. Secondly, it is easier to use the point count for a balanced hand.

4) a) 3♠. Partner has shown at least five spades. With 11 points and 8 losers, 3♠ seems clearcut.

b) 4♡. Which count influences you, 7 losers or 11 points? With all your high cards working well the choice is obvious. The 4-4 fit may play slightly better than the 5-3 fit so prefer 4♡ to 4♠.

c) 4♠. Only 11 points but the hands fit beautifully. Allow your 7-loser hand to tempt you to bid game. This should not be confused with a delayed game raise, showing four spades and a hand too strong to immediately raise 1♠ to 4♠, because partner's rebid guarantees five spades.

d) 3♠. This time a poor fit. Your diamond honours are likely to be waste paper. Whatever method you use cannot be an alternative to good judgement.

8. Strong Two Opening Bids and Pre-empts

THE 2♣ OPENING BID

If you are lucky enough to be dealt a hand with 23 or more high card points, or 10 playing tricks (as described in chapter 7) you will usually open with the conventional 2♣ bid. Responder bids a conventional 2◇ with fewer than eight points, otherwise he bids naturally, although he follows the general principle of not introducing a bad suit when the bidding is likely to end up at slam level. Consider these hands after partner has opened 2♣:

a)	♠ K 9 8	♡ Q 6 5 3	◇ 8 4	♣ A 9 7 2
b)	♠ K 9 8	♡ Q 6 4 3	◇ 8	♣ K J 9 3 2
c)	♠ A Q 9 7	♡ Q 6 4 3	◇ 9	♣ 9 7 5 2
d)	♠ K 9 8	♡ A J 10 4	◇ 8	♣ 7 6 4 3 2

With any of these you would be keen to bring the heart suit into play after a 1♣ opening but only d) merits a 2♡ response to 2♣. When a positive response faces an Acol 2♣ opening bid the final destination is frequently a slam, and there is too much danger that opener will give immediate support with ♡ K x x x, leading to a very poor 6♡ contract. Once a suit has been agreed it is hard to adjust to an alternative denomination, yet in each case 6♠, 6♣ or 6NT may be laydown. Respond 2NT with a), 3♣ with b) and 2♠ with c).

A 2♣ opening bid is totally game forcing, unless opener rebids 2NT (balanced 23-24 high card points) after a 2◇ response. Opener's rebid is based on natural principles so, unlike an Acol 2♠ opening bid, a rebid of 2♠ after a 2♣ opening and a 2◇ response can be made on a good four-card suit.

ACOL TWO BIDS (2◇, 2♡, 2♠)

The opening bids of 2◇, 2♡ and 2♠ are generally known as ACOL TWO bids and the necessary requirements have more to do with playing tricks than high card points. If a hand satisfies the following three conditions, you can afford to open with an Acol two bid.

1) The hand has at least eight playing tricks.
2) The hand has sufficient defensive strength to give you confidence that the contract belongs to your side, hence you can afford to bid constructively rather than pre-emptively.
3) Your suit has length (at least five cards) and strength. To open 2♡ your suit should be as good as ♡ A Q J 3 2 for a five-card suit or ♡ A J 9 4 3 2 for a six-card suit. With a doubleton honour partner should feel confident that the trump suit should provide at least five winners and concede at most one loser. The distinctive feature of an Acol two bid is the emphasis on a strong suit.

Each of the hands below has eight playing tricks but they are totally different in character.

a) ♠ A Q 3 2   ♡ A K 3   ◇ A K 7   ♣ A K 9
b) ♠ K Q J 10 6 4   ♡ A 8   ◇ A J 5   ♣ A 4
c) ♠ K Q J 10 9 8 7 6 5   ♡ 7   ◇ 6   ♣ 8 4

Hand a) has outstanding playing strength and defensive strength. With 27 high card points it is clearly worth a 2♣ opening bid. You have no worries about opponents' interfering, indeed, you will be glad to teach them a sharp lesson if they try to outbid you. Also, despite your outstanding hand, you have no suit that remotely qualifies for an Acol two bid.

Hand b) is a typical 2♠ opening bid, containing good spades and reasonable defensive values. In contrast, c) has no defensive values and your main ambition must be to make it hard for your opponents to find their fit. You should open 4♠.

If you are in doubt as to whether or not to open an Acol two bid, ask whether partner is likely to pass a one bid with hands that would make game probable. Also there is no harm in counting your points. If you have more than 20 you should resolve a marginal decision in favour of a two opening.

Note that an Acol two bid has eight *or more* playing tricks. Despite having 12½ playing tricks there is a lot to be said for opening d) with 2♠ and leaping to 6♡ on the second round.

d)   ♠ A K Q J 5 4   ♡ A Q J 5 4 3   ◇ A   ♣ -

This focuses partner's mind on the two bid suits, giving the message that honours in the majors are gold-plated but other cards are useless. With the ♡K he should certainly raise to 7♡ or 7♠. Note *there will be a second round!* An Acol two bid is forcing until suit agreement is reached. Partner has a negative 2NT response available if he has a weak hand. With the hand below East must have felt very apprehensive when West opened 2♠, but he made the disciplined denial bid of 2NT and the hand took on a rosier hue when he heard West's second suit.

West	East	West	East
♠ A K J 4 3	♠ 9	2♠	2NT
♡ A K 8 6 4	♡ 9 7 3 2	3♡	4♡
◇ A 8	◇ 10 7 5		
♣ 4	♣ 8 6 5 3 2		

After an Acol two bid, a game-forcing sequence is created unless responder bids 2NT. After a 2NT response the auction can die if opener can do no more than rebid his suit at the three level, if he introduces a new suit and responder gives simple preference, or if he introduces a second suit and responder gives a simple raise.

To make a positive response in a new suit you need at least 1½ quick tricks (described in chapter 7). Note that the emphasis is on aces and kings rather than points. This is because an Acol two hand is usually distributional, with the result that minor honours in the side suits tend not to be too helpful.

Finally note that after a 2♡ opening bid a raise to 3♡ is *stronger* than a jump to 4♡. The explanation is the quaintly named '*Principle of Fast Arrival*.' Suppose your partner opens 2♡.

e)   ♠ Q 8 6 4   ♡ K 6 5   ◇ Q J 7   ♣ J 3 2
f)   ♠ A K 6 4   ♡ K 6 5   ◇ K 7 6 5   ♣ 3 2

Hand e) is worth a positive response, but with a hand lacking in controls and shape you don't want to encourage him to proceed beyond game level. If you leap to 4♡ you deprive him of bidding space, thus passing the message of no slam interest. This rather destructive bid denies an ace. In contrast, f) has excellent controls and you will be delighted to co-operate in the search for a slam. Respond 3♡ (forcing, of course) to invite cue bidding. Once game values have been established, if you choose to take the route of 'fast arrival' you are passing a message of weakness in the context of what you are known to hold.

THE 2NT OPENING BID

An opening bid of 1NT shows a balanced hand, therefore the suit opening bids have to cater for all other hands in the 12-19 point range. This leaves an opening bid of 1♡ covering a multitude of different hand types, from a strong balanced hand with four poor hearts to a bare opening bid with six hearts. We have already decided upon much stricter parameters for a 2♡ opening, therefore we cannot be too fussy as to with what we open 2NT. This bid shows 20-22 high card points, may well include a five-card major, six-card minor, singleton honour or two-suited hand with 5-4-2-2 shape. All the hands below pose similar problems for dealer. None of them is strong enough for a 2♣ opening, yet there is great danger of a missed game if he opens at the one level. Each should be opened 2NT!

a)   ♠ A Q 8 6   ♡ A   ◇ K Q 8 6   ♣ K Q J 6
b)   ♠ K J 6 5 3   ♡ A 9   ◇ K Q 9   ♣ A K J
c)   ♠ K J 7 6 4   ♡ A Q   ◇ A K Q 6   ♣ Q 10
d)   ♠ K Q 3   ♡ K 6   ◇ A 6   ♣ A K Q 10 8 6

Responder cannot sign off opposite 2NT as all suit responses at the three level are forcing. 3◇, 3♡ and 3♠ fulfil the same purpose as the same bids after a 1NT opening. The 3♣ bid is best used as initially asking opener whether he has a *five*-card major, opener rebidding 3◇ without one. The bidding then proceeds with both players bidding their four-card suits in ascending order up to 3NT so that a 4-4 major fit isn't lost, for example:

75

West	East	West	East
♠ K J 6 4	♠ Q 10 7 5	2NT (1)	3♣ (2)
♡ A Q	♡ K 6 4 3	3♢ (3)	3♡ (4)
♢ J 7	♢ 9 5 2	3♠ (5)	4♠ (6)
♣ A K Q J 4	♣ 10 8		

1) 20-22 points. Not the ideal shape but not strong enough for 2♣ and too strong for 1♣.
2) Asking for a five-card major.
3) No five-card major.
4) Four hearts.
5) Four spades. Denies four-card heart support.
6) The correct contract!

Common sense suggests that you can apply the same structure of bidding when opener rebids 2NT after a 2♣ opening bid and a 2♢ response.

OTHER STRONG HANDS

However much we widen the scope of the 2NT opening bid, we cannot cater adequately for all hands in the 20-22 point range. Consider these hands:

a)	♠ Q 6 5 3 2	♡ —	♢ A K Q 5	♣ A K Q 6
b)	♠ A K 7 6	♡ 6	♢ A K 7 6	♣ A K 9 3
c)	♠ Q 7 5 4 3 2	♡ A	♢ A K	♣ A Q J 5
d)	♠ A 4	♡ 8	♢ A K J 5	♣ K Q J 10 6 4

With a), 2♠ is ruled out by the poor quality of your spades, and 2NT by the void. You must open 1♠ and hope you get an opportunity to make a game-forcing jump shift on the next round. With b), you can either stretch to 2♣ or open 1♢ or 1♣. Hand c) gives you no alternative to 1♠. With d) you would like to open 2♣ showing at least 8 playing tricks, however this bid doesn't exist, therefore open 1♣.

PRE-EMPTIVE OPENING BIDS

With a few conventional exceptions, opening bids from 3♣ upwards are pre-emptive. They carry a precise message for partner, namely a good suit but usually without the high card points that would merit an opening bid. If you pre-empt, almost all your high cards should be concentrated in your suit. This knowledge leaves partner in a very strong position as he is the one person at the table who knows the precise combined values of his partnership. He should be able to work out accurately the correct contract for his side, or if opponents compete he will be able to judge whether to double, pass or sacrifice. Once you decide to pre-empt you should pre-empt to the highest level that you dare, in order to put maximum pressure on your opponents. You use the same method of calculating playing tricks as you use for a strong two opening. At equal vulnerability (love all or game all) you should be within three tricks of your contract. If vulnerable against non-vulnerable opponents (known as RED, the traffic light signal for stop) you need an extra trick. Reverse the vulnerability (known as GREEN, more traffic lights) and one fewer trick will suffice. For obvious reasons, this is known as the rule of two, three and four. Consider the following hands as dealer at love all:

a) ♠ 8 6   ♡ A K J 7 6 4 3   ◇ 9 6 5   ♣ 2
b) ♠ A 7   ♡ J 9 7 6 5 4 2   ◇ K 8 6   ♣ 2
c) ♠ Q 9 7 4   ♡ A J 10 7 6 4 3   ◇ 8   ♣ 2
d) ♠ 8   ♡ A J 10 7 6 4 3   ◇ Q 9 8 4   ♣ 6
e) ♠ 7 4   ♡ K Q J 9 8 6 5 4   ◇ 6 3   ♣ 2
f) ♠ 7   ♡ K Q J 9 8 6 5 4   ◇ K Q 5   ♣ 2

Hand a) has 6½ tricks, an ideal 3♡ opening bid. However b) is totally unsuitable for a pre-emptive 3♡ because your hearts are too poor and you have too many high cards in the other suits. You mustn't encourage partner to sacrifice in 5♡ if your opponents bid 4♠! You should also pass with c). Your heart suit is worthy of a pre-empt, but your hand might also be very valuable in a spade contract. It is almost never right to pre-empt in the first or second position if you also have a four-card major, or if the hand looks to have potential to play in another denomination. Partner may have a strong hand including a good five-card holding in your second suit, but be put off by a misfit with your main suit. If you were third in hand, a 3♡ opening would be acceptable because partner's strength is limited by his pass as dealer. You are less concerned about losing a minor fit so open 3♡ with d).

With e) you have seven playing tricks, an eight-card suit, and no defensive values. This makes it perfect for a 4♡ opening, putting maximum pressure on your opponents. Note that if opponents then bid 4♠ you *must pass!* A pre-empter must never bid again unless partner's bidding makes it necessary. You have given the message to partner, now let him decide. Hand f) has opening values but tactical considerations make a 4♡ opening reasonable. If you can make 4♡ and your opponents can make 4♠ the sooner you bounce the bidding, the better. The risk of missing a slam is less than the danger of giving them room to explore. Third in hand, the danger of missing a slam would be negligible (partner cannot have three aces) so 4♡ is clearcut.

If your partner pre-empts, your point count is a very poor guide to your prospects. Generally speaking you should try to count tricks, just as you do as declarer when dummy goes down! Bearing in mind that partner's most likely holding in a side suit is a small doubleton, queens and jacks are useless unless they are supported by higher honours in the same suit and control cards in the other side suits. Suppose partner, as dealer at love all, opens 3♡ and your right hand opponent passes.

	♠	♡	◇	♣
g)	6	Q 9 7 5	8 7 5 3	A 8 6 4
h)	A K 6 4	2	A 8 5 3	A 9 4 3
i)	K Q J 5	7	K Q 7 5	K Q 8 7
j)	A Q 10	—	K Q J 10 7 6	K Q J 9
k)	A K J 7 5 3	—	A K Q 5	A Q J
l)	A K 7 4 3 2	5	A 9 7	A 6 3
m)	K 7 6	K 5 3	A Q 6	K 7 5 2

With g) you should raise to 5♡! Your left hand opponent probably has a very strong hand and your opponents can undoubtedly make 4♠, maybe even 6♠. The only thing in your favour is that they don't necessarily know that, so once again pre-empt to the maximum. On the other hand if you hold h) you must raise to 4♡, expecting partner to make it. His six playing tricks and your four quick tricks make the necessary ten. To bid 3NT would be absurd, as without access to his hand his heart suit would be useless. Exchange the ♡2 for the ♣2 and 4♡ would still be correct.

With i) you should pass, even though you have one high card point more than h). There will probably be four losers in 4♡ (three aces and one trump, or two aces and two trumps) and 3NT will not play well, having to constantly lead the side suits from your hand. However 3NT is correct with j) as you expect to make it with the tricks in your own hand. With k) try 3♠, (forcing). If necessary you will settle in 4♡ but if partner raises 3♠ to 4♠ you will bid 6♠. Holding l) forget the spades and raise directly to 4♡. Without entries to partner's heart suit, 4♠ may have too many losers, but your eight-card heart fit should make 4♡ a safe contract. Finally, despite your 10-card heart fit, 3NT is probably the best contract if you hold m). Not only do you need one fewer trick, but by bidding 3NT you protect your fragile tenaces from the opening lead. It is not difficult to count nine tricks, seven hearts if partner has the ♡A, the ◇A and the ninth on the opening lead. Paradoxically, the time to convert your partner's pre-emptive opening to 3NT is often when you have a good fit, as this will help communications with his long suit.

Quiz on Chapter 8

1) As dealer at game all, what do you open with these hands?

a)	♠ A K 6 4 2	♡ A K 6 5	◇ A Q	♣ K 9
b)	♠ A 8 6 4 2	♡ A K 6 5	◇ A K	♣ K 9
c)	♠ A K 6 4 2	♡ A K 6 5	◇ A K	♣ 9 6
d)	♠ A 8 6 4 2	♡ A K Q 5	◇ A K Q	♣ 9
e)	♠ A 8 6 4 2	♡ A K Q 5	◇ A K 5	♣ 5
f)	♠ A 8 6 4 2	♡ A K Q 5	◇ A Q 5	♣ K
g)	♠ 8 6	♡ A K Q 9 7 6 5 4	◇ 6 5	♣ 7
h)	♠ A K	♡ A K Q 8 3	◇ A Q 5 3	♣ 9 6
i)	♠ A K 7 5	♡ K 8 6	◇ A K 10 6	♣ A Q
j)	♠ 7	♡ K 9 7 5	◇ 9	♣ K J 10 7 5 4 2
k)	♠ 6	♡ 9 6	◇ 10 5	♣ A Q J 9 7 6 4 3
l)	♠ 8	♡ 8 5	◇ K 6 4	♣ K Q J 7 5 4 2
m)	♠ 8	♡ 8 5	◇ A 6 4	♣ K Q J 7 5 4 2

2) Which of these sequences are forcing?

	West	East		West	East		West	East		West	East
a)	2♠	2NT	b)	2♠	2NT	c)	2♠	2NT	d)	2♠	2NT
	3♠	?		3♡	?		3♡	3♠		3♣	4♣
							?			?

	West	East		West	East		West	East		West	East
e)	2♠	3♣	f)	2♠	4♠	g)	2♠	3♠	h)	2♣	2♢
	3♠	?		?			?			2NT	?

3) Your partner opens 2NT. How do you plan to discover whether your side has an eight-card major suit fit with these hands?

a)	♠ 7 5 4	♡ Q 10 6	♢ K J 6 4	♣ 8 6 4
b)	♠ 7 5 4	♡ Q 10 6 2	♢ K J 6	♣ 8 6 5
c)	♠ 7 5 4	♡ Q 10 6 4 2	♢ K J 6	♣ 8 6

4) As dealer at love all, your partner opens 3♣ and your right hand opponent passes. What do you call with these hands?

a)	♠ K 8 5	♡ 8	♢ 9 7 6 4 2	♣ Q 9 6 4
b)	♠ A Q 7	♡ K Q 8 6	♢ K 8 7 6 3	♣ 2
c)	♠ A 5 3	♡ A K J 7 5 4	♢ A Q 7	♣ 2
d)	♠ A 7 5	♡ A 7 4	♢ Q 5 3 2	♣ K 3 2

Answers to Quiz

1) a) 2♣. Game forcing. 23 or more high card points.

b) 2NT. Not strong enough for 2♣ but too strong for 1♠. If you have an eight-card major fit with your partner the 3♣ response should ensure that you find it.

c) 2♠. 8 playing tricks (3½ spades, 2½ hearts and 2 diamonds.)

d) 2♣. Only 22 high card points but look at the alternatives! The spade suit is not good enough for an Acol 2♠, 2NT with a small singleton is not an attractive proposition and 1♠ risks playing a laydown game in a part-score.

e) 1♠. You have no alternative.

f) 2NT. The least of evils.

g) 4♡. 8 playing tricks but no defensive strength.

h) 2♡. The excellent five-card suit makes 2♡ preferable to 2NT.

i) 2♣. Intending to rebid a non-forcing 2NT over a 2◇ response.

j) Pass. Don't pre-empt if you also have a four-card major, unless you know partner has a weak hand. 3♣ would be reasonable third in hand.

k) 4♣. 7½ playing tricks, a good eight-card suit, and nothing outside.

l) 3♣. Just one good side card shouldn't deter you from pre-empting.

m) 1♣. Too strong for 3♣. Again 3♣ would be reasonable third in hand.

2) a) Not forcing, because opener simply repeated his suit at the lowest level after a negative response.

b) Forcing. A new suit at the three level in an uncontested auction is always forcing.

c) Not forcing. East has been forced to bid and has only given simple preference.

d) Not forcing. Responder has to bid and gives just a courtesy raise of opener's second suit.

e) Forcing. A positive response after an Acol two bid is clearly game-forcing.

f) Not forcing. East probably has eight scrappy points with poor controls.

g) Forcing. This sequence is *stronger* than f). East is expecting West to start cue bidding.

h) Not forcing. The only sequence after a 2♣ opening that is not game-forcing.

3) a) Respond 3♣, asking for a five-card major. Rebid 3NT over 3◇ (denying a five-card major), raise 3♡ to 4♡ or 3♠ to 4♠.

b) Respond 3♣. Over 3◇ continue with 3♡, showing a four-card suit. Alternatively raise 3♡ to 4♡ or 3♠ to 4♠.

c) Respond 3♡, showing a five-card heart suit. With three-card support opener will not allow the bidding to come to rest in 3NT; however, with or without three hearts he can rebid 3♠ to search for a 4-4 spade fit.

81

4) a) 5♣ or even 6♣. Pre-emptive, before they find their heart fit.

b) Pass. 3NT will *not* play well despite your reasonable point count.

c) 3♡. Hoping partner can raise to 4♡.

d) 3NT. Unless they can take five quick diamond tricks this should succeed.

9. Strong Hands

RESPONDER MAKES A JUMP SHIFT

How do you respond to a 1♦ opening bid if you are lucky enough to hold:

    ♠ K 8 5   ♡ A Q 6 5   ♦ A 5   ♣ K Q 3 2?

Elementary books state that you can bid 2♡ (a JUMP SHIFT) with 16 points. However, once you have created this game-forcing situation opener concentrates on keeping the bidding low to create room for discussion. Because limit bids no longer operate he cannot easily show you extra values.

a) ♠ Q J 10   ♡ 2   ♦ K 9 8 7 4 2   ♣ A J 10
b) ♠ A 7   ♡ 8 2   ♦ K Q J 8 7 2   ♣ A J 5

He will rebid 3♦ with a) or b). This leaves responder wondering how to show his extra two points, a dilemma frequently solved by an agricultural leap to 6NT. When dummy produces a) it is plain that 3NT would have been quite high enough! The advantage of a 1♡ response is that it is much easier to persuade opener to show his strength with a limit bid. Holding a) he would rebid 2♦ and you would then do best to close the auction with a leap to 3NT. Holding b) he would rebid 3♦ and you could bid a slam with complete confidence. Inexperienced players feel uneasy about a simple 1♡ bid because they don't know how to keep the auction alive after a rebid in clubs or spades. Having digested the chapter on the fourth suit, that should be no trouble to you now.

Responder should only use an immediate jump shift if he has a good idea of the final destination of the auction. Otherwise his best tactic with a very strong hand is to make a series of forcing bids without jumping. When all available information has been prised out of opener he can take control of the auction, revealing his true colours. We recommend that you reserve an immediate jump shift for two types of hand.

Firstly you might have an outstanding suit.

c)   ♠ K 6 2   ♡ A 4   ♢ A Q J 10 8 4   ♣ Q 7

Hand c) is well worth a jump to 2♢ over a 1♣ opening. Your next bid will be 3♢ and partner will realise that a singleton honour or small doubleton will be perfectly acceptable trump support.

Secondly you might have a reasonable suit (usually, but not always, five cards or more) as well as a good fit for opener's suit.

d)   ♠ K 6   ♡ A 4   ♢ A Q 7 4 3   ♣ K J 7 2

With hand d) you also jump to 2♢ over 1♣, intending to agree clubs as trumps on the next round. In either case partner will realise that queens and jacks in the major suits are likely to be of little use but he will recognise the value of the ♢K if he has it.

It is worth mentioning that cue bidding sequences develop easily after a jump shift, making it easy to bid slams on minimal values if the hands fit well.

RESPONDER GIVES A DELAYED GAME RAISE
The DELAYED GAME RAISE (DGR) is rather like a weaker version of the jump shift.

a)   ♠ 7   ♡ J 9 8 6 4   ♢ A 8   ♣ 9 8 7 6 5
b)   ♠ 9 7   ♡ A J 8 6   ♢ A 10 8   ♣ K Q 10 6
c)   ♠ A 8   ♡ A J 8 6   ♢ K Q 10   ♣ 9 7 6 4

With each of these hands you have seven losers in support of partner's 1♡ opening and you intend to play at game level. However your motives and ambitions are contrasting. If you hold a) you are reasonably optimistic of his prospects in 4♡ unless the hands contain too much wasteful duplication. You certainly don't want him to start searching for a slam with a balanced eighteen points because the chance of a perfect fit is too small. As much as anything, you want to pre-empt the bidding in your known fit before your opponents can compare notes. It is quite possible that you can make 4♡ while they have an unbeatable game in spades, given the space to find it. You must bid an immediate 4♡.

If you hold hand b) you expect game to be routine and have no wish to discourage partner from a slam investigation if he has undisclosed strength. Since you have no fear of opponents making game you can proceed slowly. Temporise with 2♣ intending to leap to 4♡ next time, a delayed game raise. You are passing the message of strong clubs as well as a good hand. Opener will realise that a singleton club in his hand is a liability, not an asset. That is why your response to 1♡ should be 2♢ rather than 2♣ with hand c).

Sometimes opener's rebid can prevent responder from giving the full message of the DGR, namely four-card support and game values. This is when his rebid guarantees five cards in his first suit.

d) West	East	e) West	East	f) West	East	g) West	East
1♡	1♠	1♡	1♠	1♡	1♠	1♡	1♠
1NT	4♡	3NT	4♡	2♡	4♡	2♢	4♡

The sequences d) and e) must be DGR's. West has shown no more than four hearts so East must have four to carry the bidding past 3NT. If you fail to raise partner's major immediately when you are known to have four-card support the *only* explanation is a DGR. Thus, logic dictates that sequence e) must be forcing. A slam looks extremely probable with a 3NT rebid facing a DGR.

However in auctions f) and g) West's rebid has shown five hearts, therefore East will want to bid 4♡ with either hand h) or i).

h)	♠ A Q 10 6	♡ K J 6 5	♢ A 6	♣ 9 7 5
i)	♠ Q 8 6 4	♡ 9 7 6	♢ A Q 8	♣ K Q 6

With h) he would always have intended to bid 4♡ on the second round. With i) the newly acquired knowledge that West has five hearts deflected him away from his intended 3NT rebid. After sequence f) West doesn't need to know since he has announced his 12-14 points and is expected to pass. Auction g) is slightly more awkward as West could have quite a strong hand, keen to progress if East has h) but not if he has i). To differentiate between them East should jump straight to 4♡ with the weaker hand (i) and temporise with 3♣, intending to bid 4♡ on the next round, with the stronger hand (h). This is another example of fast arrival showing a weaker hand.

ACE ASKING BIDS (BLACKWOOD AND GERBER)

If we were asked by a novice for one tip on how to improve, a good reply would be: 'Give up Blackwood!' There is nothing wrong with Blackwood, indeed it is an excellent convention if used properly. In practice, however, it results in endless confusion between players who are never quite sure whether or not 4NT is Blackwood. There is a lot to be said for agreeing with your partner that 4NT is *always* Blackwood. It might be inefficient but at least you will always be on the same wavelength. Even this, however, does not necessarily eliminate the temptation to use Blackwood with totally unsuitable hands. Bridge players love gadgets and tend to use them because they give a scientific aura to an auction.

A typical misuse of Blackwood occurred recently when an opponent held:

a) ♠ A 8 6 4   ♡ A 6 3   ◇ J 7   ♣ A K 8 2

On hearing his partner open 1♠ he launched into 4NT which produced 5◇ (one ace). He then started to think, always a sign of a weak player because a strong player works out how he intends to continue before using Blackwood. He choice of 6♠ was pure guesswork!

b) ♠ K Q J 7 5   ♡ J 8 7   ◇ A 3   ♣ Q 6 3
c) ♠ K Q J 7 2   ♡ K Q J 10 7   ◇ A 3   ♣ 3

Opener held b) and when the clubs failed to break 3-3 ten tricks were the limit. He might equally well have held c). He would then have been itching to bid the laydown grand slam but unable to do so because responder had taken control of the auction. If he bid 7♠ he would risk finding responder with d), a far more suitable hand for Blackwood than a).

d) ♠ A 10 9 8 6 4 3   ♡ A   ◇ K Q J 10   ♣ Q

The 6♠ bid *demanded* that opener shut up, presumably because an ace was missing. Responder, holding a), had no right to take control of the auction depriving his partner of the chance to contribute. Despite his aces he had no idea where twelve tricks would come from. He should have started with 2♣. Opener would have rebid 2♠ with b), after which responder is worth no more than 4♠. Tricks are needed as much as aces if you contract to make a slam. On the other hand if opener held c) he would have announced his playing strength with a game-forcing jump to 3♡ on the second round. It is then possible to construct several auctions leading to the laydown grand slam, for example:

Opener	Responder
1♠	2♣
3♡	3♠ (Agreeing spades)
4♢ (Cue bid showing ♢A)	4♡ (Cue bid showing ♡A and slam interest)
4NT (Blackwood)	5♠ (Three aces)
5NT (How many kings?)	6♢ (One king)
7NT (I can count thirteen tricks)	

Hand c), unlike a), is ideal for Blackwood because it is possible to count tricks, provided partner has the required number of aces. The possession of all four aces (and perhaps all four kings) is *not* a guarantee of twelve tricks. Neither is the knowledge that you have a combined 32 points unless you have a good trump fit with cross ruffing possibilities or a long suit that will provide a source of extra tricks. If the hands fit poorly or are balanced you need at least 34 points to make 6NT an attractive proposition. Technically you should not have two losers in any suit if you use Blackwood, although plenty of slams are bid and made when the defenders could have cashed two tricks in a side suit but failed to divine the killing lead. If you adhere too rigidly to this requirement many hands become unbiddable so we will risk the wrath of the purists by not stressing it. The real humiliation is to bid freely to a slam and then contemplate dummy with the thought that whatever they lead and however they defend, you haven't got a prayer. Our advice to inexperienced players is to bid a small slam only if you are fairly sure and to bid a grand slam only if you are very sure. There is nothing more frustrating than to fail by one trick in a grand slam, only to find that nobody else in your duplicate game has ventured beyond game.

Have we given you the impression that Blackwood is the number one menace? We must have forgotten Gerber, surely the most prolific source of misunderstandings known to man! Let this masterpiece, all too typical of the average pair, speak for itself.

West	East	West	East
♠ A J 4 2	♠ K Q	1NT	2♣ (1)
♡ A 6 3	♡ K 10 9 2	2♠	4♣ (2)
♢ A 9 5 2	♢ 7	4NT (3)	5♣ (4)
♣ 9 7	♣ K Q 10 8 6 3	5♢ (5)	6♣ (6)
		6♢ (7)	No!

Explanation according to:

West	East
(1)	I'd better see if he has four hearts.
(2) Gerber. He likes my spades.	I can't bid 3♣ because that is a sign off.
(3) I must show my three aces.	My partner has bid Blackwood.
(4) More Gerber. He is asking for kings.	I haven't got any aces.
(5) I haven't got any kings.	This isn't possible.
(6) More Gerber, asking for queens.	What else can I do?
(7) No queens either. All very scientific.	I give up. I'll play with the wife next week.

A free and frank exchange of views then followed! Seriously, if you must play Gerber then you must discuss the precise sequences in which 4♣ is Gerber. For example does the sequence 2NT pass 4♣ ask for aces or show clubs?

We don't need to define when 4NT is Blackwood because it really doesn't matter, provided you have agreed *something* specific with your partner. However if you want a sensible but simple rule here goes. 4NT is Blackwood if *any* of these conditions is satisfied.

1) A suit has been bid and supported. (i.e. *both* partners have bid it.)
2) The previous bid was a suit and 4NT is a jump.
3) The previous bid was a jump to the four level.

e)	West	East	f)	West	East	g)	West	East	h)	West	East
	1♠	3♣		1♠	4NT		1♠	2♡		1♠	2♣
	4♣	4NT					2♠	4NT		2♢	4NT

i)	West	East	j)	West	East	k)	West	East	l)	West	East
	4♠	4NT		1♠	2♢		1NT	4NT		1♠	2♢
				4♠	4NT					3♠	4♣
										4NT	

e) satisfies condition 1) since clubs have been bid and supported.

f), g), and h) satisfy 2) since 4NT is a jump bid following a suit bid. The trump suits are probably spades, spades and diamonds respectively but all West really knows is that East feels capable of taking control of the auction.

i) and j) satisfy 3). In both cases West shows excellent spades and little interest in any alternative denomination. Even if East were void in spades it would be necessary to play in spades since there may be no entries to West's spade suit in no trumps.

k) asks Wests to pass with a minimum no trump opening or bid 6NT with a maximum. 4NT is a jump but the previous bid was also no trumps.

l) is not Blackwood according to our stated conditions, but it all depends on the meaning of 4♣. If you think that East has shown six diamonds and five clubs, no suit has been agreed and 4NT is a natural bid. However on the grounds of frequency, most experts consider that the best use of 4♣ is a cue bid agreeing spades. Because spades have been agreed they would then consider 4NT to be Blackwood. With clever ideas like this you must make a choice. If you want to improve on the basics you can do so, but only if you and your partner are prepared to put in a lot of work. Our basic definition is immeasurably better than the reality of so many partnerships, namely confusion.

CUE BIDDING

Frequently a trump suit has been agreed and one, or both, players have good reason to believe that values for a slam might be present but neither feels able to take control of the auction with Blackwood. The accepted method of communicating slam interest to partner and inviting him to contribute is to make a 'cue bid'. There are many different styles of cue bidding. We will suggest a simple method which, no doubt, you will improve upon as you gain experience. A bid is a cue bid if all of the following conditions apply:

i) A trump suit has been explicitly agreed (both players bidding it).

ii) The bidding cannot die below game, i.e. the issue is game or slam, not part score or game.

iii) If the agreed suit is a minor, the bidding has passed 3NT. This is because even if you find a 4-4 minor suit fit it is often still necessary to investigate the nine trick game.

You should only cue bid second round controls (kings and singletons) when previous bidding clearly shows that you haven't got the first round control in the suit. You should normally cue bid your cheapest first round control.

a) West	East	b) West	East	c) West	East	d) West	East
1♠	2♠	1♠	3♠	1♢	2♣	1♡	3♣
3♢		4♢		2♡	3♢	3♢	3♡
				3♠		3♠	

a) 3♢ is a trial bid inviting game, not a cue bid, because the auction can die in 3♠.

b) 4♢ is a cue bid, showing first round control in diamonds (ace or void) and denying such control in clubs.

c) 3♠ is the normal fourth suit bid, no doubt hoping to hear 3NT. Although a minor suit has been bid and supported, the bidding is still below 3NT.

d) 3♠ is a cue bid, because a major suit has been bid and supported.

What sort of hand could West have for auction b)?

e)	♠ A Q 8 7 5	♡ K 8 5	◇ A 8 6 ♣ Q 7
f)	♠ A Q 8 7 5	♡ A Q 7 2	◇ A 8 ♣ K 6
g)	♠ K Q 8 7 5	♡ 8 6	◇ A K Q J 7 ♣ 6
h)	♠ A 10 8 6 5 4 3 2	♡ 7	◇ A K Q 2 ♣ —

He cannot have e) since that would justify no slam interest over partner's known 10-12 points or eight losers.

He should not have f) either. Hand f) has no suit with two top losers and two aces cannot be missing. He can justify bidding 6♠ on general strength but it is most unlikely that he could discover enough to bid a grand slam with confidence.

He could have g). He would then be hoping to hear a return cue bid of 4♡, after which he would bid 4NT, intending to bid 6♠ unless two aces were missing.

He could even have h). This hand becomes a minor miracle if partner supports spades and he would leap to 7♠ if responder cue bid 4♡. Responder must bid 4♡ automatically if he has the ♡A because the bid is below game in the agreed trump suit. He has already disclosed his full values by his limit bid and if opener is still keen, he must co-operate. If his only ace was the ♣A he would have the right to bid 4♠, leaving it to opener to go further if he wished.

Finally a hand to demonstrate just how effective cue bidding can be if approached systematically and logically.

West	East	West	East
♠ 6 2	♠ A K Q 10 8 7 5	1♡	2♠
♡ A K 10 6 5 3	♡ Q J	3♡	3♠
◇ 8 6	◇ A 7	4♣ (1)	5◇ (2)
♣ A 7 2	♣ 5 3	5♡ (3)	5♠ (4)
		6♡ (5)	7NT (6)

1) East's spades must be excellent indeed if he makes a jump shift without heart support. A small doubleton is ample support.
2) Slam try. ◇A or void, no ♣A.
3) The ♡A.
4) I cannot go further. This strongly implies two losing clubs.
5) West could bid 6♣, but then East could not uncover the

vital ♡K. 6♡, having committed the partnership irrevocably to a small slam, is suggesting a grand slam. West knows that East lacks the ♣A, hence any grand slam try would be illogical unless he had this card. West is effectively showing the ♣A and ♡K in one bid.

6) East can now count thirteen tricks thanks to his partner's illuminating cue bidding. A perfect grand slam despite only 27 high card points.

Quiz on Chapter 9

1) Your partner opens 1♣. How do you respond with these hands? How do you then continue after a minimum club rebid?

a) ♠ A Q J 6   ♡ A Q 7 6   ◇ K J 10   ♣ A 7
b) ♠ A Q J 7 6   ♡ A Q J 7 5   ◇ A 7   ♣ 4
c) ♠ A 8   ♡ A K J 7 5 3   ◇ 9 8 6   ♣ K 6
d) ♠ A 8   ♡ A Q 10 9 7   ◇ 8 6   ♣ A Q 8 6
e) ♠ A Q 10 5   ♡ A Q 8 6 4   ◇ K 8   ♣ K 5
f) ♠ A K 7   ♡ K Q 7   ◇ A Q 5   ♣ Q 10 9 7
g) ♠ 5   ♡ J 8 6 4 3 2   ◇ A K   ♣ A Q 7 5

2) How do you respond to partner's 1♠ opening with these hands?

a) ♠ K 7 5 3 2   ♡ —   ◇ 8 6 4 3 2   ♣ K 8 6
b) ♠ K J 7 4   ♡ K 8 6   ◇ A K 7 5   ♣ 9 5
c) ♠ K J 7 5   ♡ 5   ◇ J 7 6 4 3   ♣ A K 6
d) ♠ A Q 8 6   ♡ K 7 5   ◇ 8   ♣ A Q J 7 5

3) You open 1♡ and hear your partner jump shift to 3♣. He then raises your 3♡ rebid to 4♡. What do you call with these hands?

a) ♠ A 8 7   ♡ K Q 7 6 4 3   ◇ 7   ♣ K 8 5
b) ♠ A 8   ♡ K Q 8 7 6 5   ◇ 9 4   ♣ K 5 3
c) ♠ Q J 6 2   ♡ K Q 8 6 5   ◇ K Q J   ♣ 6

4) In these auctions, is the 4NT bid Blackwood?

a)	West	East	b)	West	East	c)	West	East	d)	West	East
	1♡	4♠		1♣	3NT		2NT	4NT		2NT	3♡
	4NT			4NT						4♡	4NT

e)	West	East	f)	West	East	g)	West	East	h)	West	East
	1NT	3♠		1♡	2♢		1♡	2♢		1♡	2♢
	4♣	4NT		3♣	3♢		2♠	3♡		2♡	3♣
				4NT			4♣	4NT		3NT	4♣
										4NT	

5) You respond 1♠ to your partner's 1♢ opening and he jumps to 3♠. How do you continue with these hands?

a)	♠ A J 7 5	♡ 8 6 3	♢ 5 2	♣ A 6 3 2
b)	♠ K Q 7 4	♡ 9 8	♢ A Q 8 7	♣ K Q 4
c)	♠ K Q 6 5 4 2	♡ K Q J 5	♢ K 7	♣ 4
d)	♠ K Q 8 7 5 4	♡ K Q J 8 5	♢ —	♣ A 8
e)	♠ A K Q 7 5	♡ K Q J 6 5	♢ 8	♣ Q 8

6) Over your 1♡ opening bid partner leaps to 2♠. You raise to 3♠ and he continues with a cue bid of 4♢. How do you continue with these hands?

a)	♠ K J 6 3	♡ A K Q 7 5 2	♢ -	♣ K Q 3
b)	♠ J 7 5	♡ A Q J 6 3	♢ K J 10	♣ 8 6
c)	♠ J 7 5	♡ Q J 8 7 4	♢ K J 6	♣ A 5
d)	♠ J 8 7	♡ K Q 8 7 5	♢ K Q 2	♣ A 8
e)	♠ K J 7	♡ A K Q J 7	♢ 9 8 6	♣ A 7

Answers to Quiz

1) a) 1♡, and rebid 6NT over a 2♣ rebid.

b) 1♠, and rebid 3♡ over 2♣. Don't make an immediate jump shift with a two-suited hand.

c) 2♡, and rebid 3♡ over 3♣. An excellent heart suit.

d) 2♡, and raise 3♣ to 4♣, thus showing that your jump shift was based on good club support and a fair heart suit. Cue bidding can then commence.

e) 1♡, and reverse into 2♠ over 2♣. If you hear of three-card heart support you will Blackwood your way into 6♡.

f) 1♢, and Blackwood your way into 6♣ (or 6NT) over 2♣.

$1\diamond$ is a harmless little lie. All you really want is to keep the auction alive to hear if partner's rebid is really exciting.

g) $1\heartsuit$, and jump to $3\diamond$ over $2\clubsuit$. By the time you have later supported clubs partner should get the message of a good hand with at most one spade. Don't jump shift with such a poor heart suit.

2) a) $4\spadesuit$. Pre-emptive. You have little defensive strength and don't want competition.

b) $2\diamond$, followed by $4\spadesuit$. A DGR.

c) $2\clubsuit$. Start the DGR sequence in a suit where you have high cards. You don't want partner to be put off a slam by shortage in diamonds.

d) $3\clubsuit$. This is too strong for a DGR.

3) a) 4NT. Don't count your points. Look at the fit! Your $\clubsuit$K probably makes the club suit solid. If partner has three aces you will bid $7\heartsuit$.

b) $4\spadesuit$. The cue bid is better than Blackwood with your two losing diamonds.

c) Pass. More points than a) or b) but the wrong cards. Partner has gone out of his way to stress clubs. Your singleton is not going to help him establish the suit. No doubt your spade and diamond honours are useless opposite shortage.

4) a) Yes, after a pre-empt at the four level. West may have:

$\spadesuit$ K 10 5 $\heartsuit$ A K Q 8 6 4 $\diamond$ 6 $\clubsuit$ A 8 6

b) No. West is just looking for a couple of extra points from East. He may have:

$\spadesuit$ K Q 8 $\heartsuit$ K J 5 $\diamond$ K 7 5 $\clubsuit$ A Q J 6

c) No. 4NT is a jump but the previous bid was also no trumps. East may have:

$\spadesuit$ A J 3 $\heartsuit$ J 7 5 $\diamond$ A Q 10 $\clubsuit$ 6 5 4 2

d) Yes. Hearts have been bid and supported. East may have:

$\spadesuit$ K 7 5 $\heartsuit$ K Q 8 6 3 $\diamond$ 10 $\clubsuit$ K J 7 6

e) Yes. Spades have been bid and supported. 4♣ was a cue bid agreeing spades, not a club suit, because West has been clearly instructed not to proceed beyond 3NT unless he can diagnose an eight-card spade fit. Perhaps East has:

♠ K Q 10 8 4   ♡ K Q 9   ◇ K Q 3   ♣ K 5

f) Yes. Note that the 3♣ bid was game-forcing (a reverse following a response at the two level). Perhaps West has:

♠ 5   ♡ A K Q J 9   ◇ K Q 9   ♣ A 9 7 6

g) Yes. Hearts are the agreed trump suit. 4♣ was a cue bid. East may have:

♠ K 8   ♡ K Q 6   ◇ A Q J 7 5   ♣ 9 7 4

h) No. East has a strong minor two-suited hand but West has a glaring misfit.

♠ K Q 10 9   ♡ K Q 10 7 6 4   ◇ 8   ♣ J 5

Note that the 4♣ bid was forcing. Unless 3NT has been doubled, a retreat into 4♣ or 4◇ is always forcing.

5) a) 4♠. You have an obvious raise to game but no slam interest. A cue bid, encouraging partner to proceed beyond game, would be treacherous.
b) 4◇. Cue bid, showing first round diamond control and denying first round club control. If partner can bid 4♡ you will follow up with 5♣, showing second round control.
c) 4NT. Ideal since you can see plenty of tricks and you do not have two immediate losers in any suit. If he obliges with four aces, you can underwrite 7NT.
d) 4♣. Blackwood is useless at this stage because if he shows two aces you will not know whether they include the useless ◇A or whether he has the two major suit aces that make 7♠ excellent. If partner now proceeds with 4◇ (the ◇A) or 4♡ (the ♡A but not the ◇A) or 4♠ (neither red ace) you can subsequently employ Blackwood with confidence. It is comparatively rare to use Blackwood with a void.
e) 4NT, intending to bid 6♠ over 5♡ or 7♠ over 5♠. Yes, it is possible that you could reach 6♠ with two losing clubs, but can you suggest a better alternative?

6) a) 6♠. Partner has denied the ♣A so 7♠ is impossible but he must have just about every other important missing card. If you bid 5♡ and subsequently raise his 5♠ to 6♠ he may read your 5♡ as a grand slam try and assume you have the ♣A. When you know the final contract, bid it before accidents occur.

b) 4♡. You have no great enthusiasm but it is your duty to cooperate below game level. If he then bids 4♠ you can pass with a clear conscience.

c) 4♠. You have a weak hand and there is no justification for pushing the bidding to a higher level.

d) 5♣. This time you have every reason to enthuse.

e) 4NT. Provided he has two aces you can practically count thirteen tricks. It is time for you to take control.

Part Two—The Contested Auction

10. Overcalls

THE DIFFERENCES BETWEEN OVERCALLING AND OPENING

In deciding whether or not you should open the bidding your main criterion is your point count. You may decide to open with a shapely eleven points but unless your hand is severely devalued by an unattractive feature such as a singleton king you will not pass with 13 points. The logic behind this is that if both partners pass with 13 points 'game' hands may be passed out. However, once your opponents have opened the bidding the probability of your side buying the contract diminishes and the factors which govern your decision whether to intervene must reflect this. An overcall has to cater as well as possible for three very different distributions of the remaining points. They can be summarised as follows:

D1) Your side has the majority of points. You will either outbid the opposition or double their contract.

D2) Your opponents have the majority of points. They can outbid you but your overcall might suggest a profitable defence to partner. Alternatively your partner might be able to find a cheap sacrifice bid over their final contract.

D3) The points are evenly split. It is likely that each side can make a part score if its chosen suit is trumps; indeed it is even possible that both sides can make game! In this case you do not want to sell out cheaply. Your opponents might outbid you but sometimes you will succeed in pushing them too high.

Each of these distributions makes its own demands on the use of the overcall. Clearly D1) means that you must not pass with a very strong hand. Equally D2) indicates that if you have a strong suit you should try to bid it for lead-directing reasons, even if your hand is weak. D3) is best served by adopting a positive attitude, aware of danger but willing to take reasonable risks to enter the bidding. The principles outlined in this chapter try to harmonise these conflicting needs. You will find that if your opponents open first there are many hands with up to 15 points that you must pass because they do not fit into any available defensive bid. This does not result is missed games because the two defenders are allocated very different roles. Suppose that South opens 1♡. The first defender to speak is West (known as the IMMEDIATE hand because he speaks immediately after the opener). The last defender to have the chance to speak (if North passes) is East. He is known as the PROTECTIVE hand for good reason. West may have been forced to pass with quite a respectable hand. East cannot afford that luxury. He must try to dredge up a bid if he has ten points to protect his partner's possible strength. All defensive bids promise less when they are made by a protective hand. Chapter 12 deals with protective bidding, in the meantime what we have to say applies only to the immediate hand.

Overcalling a suit bid with your own suit
Provided you have a strong suit you can make a one level overcall with a hand which is weaker than an opening bid by as much as a king. If your partner opens the bidding and you are on lead (your opponents having bought the contract) you *tend* to lead his suit unless you have an alternative that is clearly better. If, on the other hand, partner has overcalled and you fail to lead his suit you had better have a very good excuse ready for the post mortem. This should weigh heavily upon you when *you* are deciding whether to overcall. Ask yourself whether you want him to lead from a holding like K x in your suit. Consider these hands:

a)   ♠ J 9 6 5 3   ♡ A Q   ◇ K 9 7   ♣ Q 7 4
b)   ♠ A Q 10 9 6   ♡ 8 6   ◇ K 5 3   ♣ 9 7 4

Suppose as West you hold a) and you hear South open 1♣. You certainly do not want a lead from partner's ♠ K x. It is far too likely to waste a trick! You can pass with the knowledge that if North also passes, East will be aware of your problem.

Hand b) is three points weaker but the spades are much healthier. In the (quite likely) event that your partner has to make the opening lead you are very keen to guide him towards a spade. This hand comfortably fulfils the requirements for a minimum overcall of 1♠ over 1♣. Such an overcall at the one level shows roughly 8-15 high card points, occasionally less if you have strong tactical reasons or more if you have a two-suited hand (see chapter 11). If your hand is at the bottom end of this range your suit should be particularly good. An overcall at the two level is a little bit stronger, perhaps 10 (if you have a good six-card suit)—17 high card points at equal vulnerability.

There are two other criteria when you are considering a borderline overcall.

Firstly there is the vulnerability. You should bear in mind that if you overstep the limits of prudence your opponents are well placed to double you for penalties (whether or not they are playing SPUTNIK doubles). Paradoxically some of the most profitable penalties are available against low level contracts when a defender has taken a risk, only to find his partner with a complete misfit. At RED vulnerability you should err on the side of caution. Conversely you can be a little more frisky at GREEN vulnerability.

Secondly, an overcall made with sparse values can be doubly effective if it uses up a lot of bidding space. If you overcall a 1♣ opening with 1♠ you blot out the diamond and heart suits at the one level. Unless your opponents are playing SPUTNIK doubles they will find it hard to discover a 4-4 heart fit. Alternatively, unless they have discussed their methods thoroughly, they may have a misunderstanding and arrive in a poor 4-3 fit. If you make an overcall that bypasses one or two suits (particularly a major) you put pressure on opponents. Be prepared to lend them a little rope! It is amazing how effective a pre-empt at the one level can be.

Action by overcaller's partner

Throughout this section we will consider the options available to East after the following start to the auction:

South	West	North	East
1♣	1♠	No	?

We will assume that neither side is vulnerable, hence West holds roughly the values previously stated. The bids suggested would also be suitable if both sides were vulnerable. It is the *relative* vulnerability that counts.

If East intends to support West's suit he assumes that West has playing strength roughly equivalent to a light Acol opening bid (about 7½ losers). If East can see a misfit he must be aware that West's high card values could be considerably less than those required for a minimum opening bid, and that the playing strength that persuaded West to overcall may be useless. Thus he must tread cautiously. If only North/South are vulnerable East will allow for West holding perhaps two points less. Conversely if only East/West are vulnerable East will expect a slightly stronger hand.

Obviously if a pair chooses to lower significantly the strength required for an overcall, they must also change the behaviour of the overcaller's partner.

EAST SUPPORTS WEST'S SUIT

South	West	North	East
1♣	1♠	No	3♠

Since West has shown a five-card suit, three-card support is perfectly adequate. There are two entirely different types of hand with which East will wish to bid 3♠.

a) ♠ Q 8 5   ♡ 6 5 3   ◇ K Q 10 6   ♣ A 10 9

b) ♠ Q 10 8 7   ♡ 6 5 3   ◇ K 7 6 4   ♣ 9 8

If East has hand a) he wishes to bid 3♠ as a game try. If, however, he had hand b) he wishes to bid 3♠ pre-emptively. In this case if West has maximum overcalling values 3♠ might succeed. If West has only a minimum overcall North/South can probably make 4♡ and the pre-empt will make it hard for them to find their heart fit.

Plainly the bid cannot be used for both purposes. There is, happily, an excellent solution to this problem. Modern methods treat all direct raises of an overcalled suit as pre-emptive.

Suppose, as West, you hold hand c) after the above auction:

c)   ♠ A K J 6 2   ♡ K Q J   ◇ J 3 2   ♣ 4 2

Although you have maximum values for your overcall you must restrain the temptation to bid 4♠. If East holds hand b) you will be lucky to make nine tricks!

This leaves us with the problem of what to do with hand a) when you genuinely wish to make a game try. You hold the values that would justify raising an opening bid of 1♠ to 3♠ (except that you don't have a fourth spade, irrelevant here as you know partner has five.) The answer is to bid opener's suit at the lowest possible level and then bid spades next time. This handy little convention is called an UNASSUMING CUE BID. How should West proceed after this start to the auction?

South	West	North	East
1♣	1♠	No	2♣
No	?		

He initially assumes that East is suggesting game in his suit. With a minimum overcall he repeats his suit at the lowest level or finds an alternative rebid below this. To avoid having to consider the numerous sequences that can arise we suggest that if West's rebid is above 2♠ (the lowest level at which he can rebid his suit) he has accepted the game try and the bidding cannot die below game. If West wishes to accept the invitation he tries to find a more constructive bid than raising directly to game in his suit. This is because there are also hands where East may need to make this forcing bid without any real enthusiasm for West's suit. Perhaps East holds:

   ♠ 8 3   ♡ A Q 7 5   ◇ A Q 7 4   ♣ 9 6 3

He has a real problem in that his hand is worth a game try but he does not want to commit himself to playing in spades. His best option is to temporise with 2♣. If West discourages with 2♠ he will resignedly give in. If West rebids 3♠ he will raise to 4♠. However if West has a maximum overcall with a club guard but only five spades he should thoughtfully bid 2NT. East, with this hand, will gratefully raise to 3NT. Without the club guard, and lacking a sixth spade or second suit West can 'raise' the cue bid, keeping options open.

EAST BIDS NO TRUMPS

South	West	North	East
1♣	1♠	No	1NT

In this auction East shows at most two spades (frequently one or even none) and a guard in South's suit. Although East would assume that West had playing strength equivalent to a light opening bid (7½ losers) if the partnership had a good fit, he is rather more wary of a likely misfit. West may have little more than eight high card points and his length in spades may well provide no extra tricks. Hence the values he needs to bid no trumps are somewhat higher than he would need to respond no trumps to an opening bid of 1♠. It is generally accepted that a bid of 1NT shows 10-12 high card points, 2NT shows 13-14 high card points and a full 15 high card points are necessary to venture to 3NT. A good rule of thumb is that responder should bid one fewer in no trumps opposite an overcall than he would have done if his partner had opened the bidding.

EAST BIDS HIS OWN SUIT

South	West	North	East
1♣	1♠	No	2♦

An entirely new suit by East has historically been played as non-forcing (although many experts prefer to use it as a one-round force). East can bid 2♦ with:

♠ 4　　♡ Q 8 5　　♦ A K J 8 7 5　　♣ 9 6 4

This contract is likely to play at least as well as 1♠ and West will usually pass. If West does rebid 2♠, having heard that East strongly prefers diamonds, he will have very good spades.

Alternatively if West has a maximum overcall and respectable diamond support he may make a game try by bidding 3♢.

Replace East's club holding with ♣ A K 5 and he would jump to 3♢ over West's 1♠. This should be forcing for at least one round.

Action by opener's partner

South	West	North	East
1♣	1♡	Double	

At this point it is very tempting to launch into conventions at the expense of traditional theory. North's double has always been played for penalties, but most experts nowadays play it for takeout, a convention called a Sputnik or Negative double. This is a great improvement on traditional theory because it is a gadget which enables you to have your cake and eat it. Not only is it now possible to bid many hands that would otherwise have been rendered unbiddable by West's interference, but a penalty double actually becomes easier to find. However for the moment we will put this aside. When a partnership has mastered the basics, the players can choose for themselves whether they are willing to expend the time and effort necessary to investigate the Sputnik double. If your curiosity is stimulated, you will find the Sputnik double in appendix 1 at the end of this book.

We must start by making clear why this double is for penalties. Once a player has made a bid or double, any subsequent double by his partner is for penalties. Note that a pass does not come under the heading of 'bid'.

If North is considering a penalty double of West's 1♡ overcall his hand must satisfy three tests.

Firstly he must hold good quality intermediate cards in the suit. If North has about ten points including ♡ K J 9 8 5 West is going to have a pretty torrid time. Any finesses he tries in the trump suit will fail and no doubt South will take every opportunity to push a trump through West's exposed hand. This is an ideal suit for a penalty double. Change North's holding to ♡ A K 4 3 or even ♡ A K 4 3 2 and North should prefer to bid no trumps at an appropriate level. Despite having three extra points in hearts he only has two tricks in the suit. West probably has ♡ Q J 10 9 8 6 and will patiently draw North's tiny trumps.

Secondly North should not have good support for his partner's suit:

a) ♠ J 2   ♡ K Q 10 4   ◇ J 7 4   ♣ A 9 7 4

If he has hand a) he would do better to bid 3♣ or 2NT than double the 1♡ overcall. The penalty double looks attractive but if he leads the ♣ A, dummy produces four small clubs, West ruffs, and the contract may make with an overtrick. Four of his points and six of South's (the ♣ K Q J) will take no tricks. The more cards that North has in South's suit, the more likely this unpleasant turn of events becomes. Exchange North's spade and club holdings and a penalty double becomes far more attractive. Summing up, the fewer cards you have in partner's suit, the more attractive you should find a penalty double of the opponents' suit.

Thirdly North's hand should have no obvious alternative contract.

b) ♠ K Q J 10 8   ♡ K Q 10 4   ◇ 8 7   ♣ 9 7

If he holds b) he should bid his excellent spade suit before contemplating a penalty double of hearts at the one level. If South has a spade fit the spades may be useless in defence.

It is worth commenting that if North exercises discretion by not doubling 1♡ he will occasionally have the opportunity to double 2♡ later, safe in the knowledge that he has already disclosed his assets to South.

Once North makes a penalty double, South should be reluctant to remove it.

South	West	North	East
1♣	1♡	Double	No
？			

c)	♠ A 7 6 5	♡ 7	◇ Q J 8	♣ A J 7 6 3
d)	♠ 6 4 3	♡ —	◇ A J 7 5	♣ K Q J 10 8 4
e)	♠ 6 5 3	♡ —	◇ A 7 6	♣ A K Q 9 7 6 2

If South holds c) he should pass. He has the two and a bit defensive tricks that North has a right to expect and knows that North can see no obvious alternative contract. Admittedly North/South may have a 4-4 spade fit but even then defending 1♡ doubled may be quite lucrative.

The time for South to remove the double is when he has a great, undisclosed discrepancy between his playing strength and defensive values. With d) he only opened because of his excellent clubs. With a void in trumps and only one certain trick in defence of a heart contract he should rebid 2♣. Change the hand to e) and he should jump to 3♣. The reward (if any) from defending 1♡ doubled is unlikely to compensate for a missed game.

As far as possible most other bids from North retain the meaning they would have had if West had not overcalled.

South	West	North	East
1♣	1♡	?	

f) ♠ A Q 8 6   ♡ 9 7 4   ◇ Q 10 5   ♣ 9 8 4

g) ♠ Q 10 5   ♡ 9 7 4   ◇ A Q 8 6   ♣ 9 8 4

h) ♠ Q 10 5   ♡ 9 7 4   ◇ A Q 8 6   ♣ A 8 6

With hand f) North bids a forcing 1♠ but give him g) and he has a problem. Without the 1♡ intervention he could have bid 1◇ or 1NT, but this hand is too weak for a forcing 2◇, and to bid No Trumps after an overcall in hearts guarantees a guard in hearts. A No Trump call with a suit unguarded is a justifiable risk if the opponents have to make a 'blind' lead but when that lead is pinpointed by the bidding it is suicidal. North can come to no harm by passing. If South has a strong hand he will reopen the bidding, possibly with a takeout double (takeout since North has not bid, see chapter 11) or with 1NT (17-20 points).

Strengthen North's hand to the extent of hand h) and he can cue bid 2♡. A bid of the opponents' suit has a purpose similar to bidding the fourth suit in an uncontested auction. It is a one-round force, in this case showing at least the values to compete as far as 2NT. It suggests that North cannot think of anything else to bid and tends to show a balanced hand. It is frequently described as 'demanding that South bids no trumps with a heart guard.' This is not strictly accurate since is plainly possible to imagine hands with a heart guard that are totally unsuited to no trump play, e.g., opener may have:

♠ K J 6 4 3   ♡ A   ◇ 9   ♣ K Q 10 7 5 2

It is better to describe the 2♡ cue bid as 'requesting more information', but a bid of no trumps is generally welcome. With undisclosed values South should avoid a minimum rebid such as 2NT or 3♣ which can be passed.

Other natural overcalls

If West jumps to 2♠ over South's 1♡ he shows a hand on which he would open 1♠ and rebid 3♠ in an uncontested auction, about seven playing tricks. It is not forcing and shows a good six-card suit. Unless you adhere strictly to these narrow parameters partner will never know what to do. There are, of course, many hands with a good five- or six-card suit that are not suitable for a simple overcall or jump overcall. These are discussed in Chapter 11.

A 1NT overcall by West over South's 1♡ opening bid shows 16-18 points and at least one guard in hearts. To bid no trumps in this position is very dangerous, hence the need for a considerably stronger hand than is required for a 1NT opening. If North has ten or more points he will make a penalty double, armed with the knowledge that his side has the balance of points. West will probably then find himself with few, if any, entries to dummy to take vital finesses. Note that since North will normally double with ten points, if instead he chooses to bid a suit over a 1NT overcall he *denies* ten points. The logic of this is that if North introduces a suit at the two level it is not forcing, showing a goodish suit but little else.

Apart from his point count West's main requirement for his 1NT overcall is his heart holding. He cannot allow weaknesses in other suits to worry him, otherwise many strong hands will become unbiddable. Suppose he has:

♠ 7   ♡ A Q 8 6   ◇ A K 8 6   ♣ K J 10 6

He has no sensible alternative to overcalling South's 1♡ with 1NT. If East chooses to proceed, his bidding should have a similar structure to bidding over a 1NT opening bid, Stayman and sign-offs at the two level etc.

Quiz on Chapter 10

1) With neither side vulnerable South deals and opens 1◇. What should you, as West, call with these hands?

a) ♠ A Q J 8 5   ♡ 8 7   ◇ 8 7   ♣ 10 8 6 2
b) ♠ 8 7   ♡ A Q J 8 5 ◇ 8 7   ♣ 10 8 6 2
c) ♠ 10 8 6 2   ♡ 8 7   ◇ 8 7   ♣ A Q J 8 5
d) ♠ 9 8   ♡ 9 7 5   ◇ A J 5   ♣ A Q J 8 5
e) ♠ Q 9 6 5 3   ♡ A 7 4   ◇ A 7 4   ♣ 9 6
f) ♠ Q 9 6 5 3   ♡ A 4   ◇ A 7 4   ♣ A J 6
g) ♠ A K Q J   ♡ 8 7 5   ◇ 7 6 4   ♣ 8 6 2
h) ♠ A Q J 8 7 4 ♡ A Q 5   ◇ 9   ♣ K 7 5
i) ♠ K 7 3   ♡ A 8 6   ◇ K Q 9   ♣ A J 10 8
j) ♠ 8   ♡ A Q 10   ◇ Q 9 8 6 4 ♣ A K Q J

2) With both sides vulnerable, South as dealer opens 1◇, West overcalls 1♠, and North passes. What should you, as East, call with these hands?

a) ♠ K 9 7 5   ♡ 8 7   ◇ 9 5 2   ♣ Q J 7 5
b) ♠ A 8 7 4   ♡ Q 5   ◇ 6 4 3   ♣ A J 8 6
c) ♠ K 9 7   ♡ 8 7 4   ◇ 9 8 2   ♣ Q J 6 5
d) ♠ 9 5   ♡ A K 7   ◇ 8 6 4 3   ♣ A J 7 5
e) ♠ 9 5   ♡ A K 7   ◇ 8 6 4 3   ♣ A K 7 5
f) ♠ 9   ♡ A 8 7 5   ◇ Q J 7 5   ♣ 9 8 4 3
g) ♠ 8   ♡ A J 9 7   ◇ Q J 7 5   ♣ K 10 6 5
h) ♠ —   ♡ A K 7 4   ◇ Q J 6 4   ♣ K J 7 5 4
i) ♠ —   ♡ Q 9 5   ◇ 10 9 6 3 ♣ A Q J 4 3 2

3) You are West with neither side vulnerable. You overcall South's opening 1♡ with 1♠, North passes and East makes the cue bid of 2♡. What do you bid with these hands?

a) ♠ A Q 8 7 4   ♡ 8 2   ◇ A J 7   ♣ 9 3 2
b) ♠ A Q 10 7 6 4 ♡ 9 4   ◇ A Q   ♣ 9 7 6
c) ♠ A Q 8 7 4   ♡ A J 7   ◇ 9 8   ♣ 9 8 3
d) ♠ A Q 8 7 4   ♡ A Q 4   ◇ Q 6   ♣ 9 8 5
e) ♠ A Q 8 7 4   ♡ 8 6 3   ◇ Q 8   ♣ A Q 7
f) ♠ A Q 8 7 4   ♡ 9 7   ◇ K Q J 5   ♣ J 9

4) You are North with both sides vulnerable. South opens 1◇ and West overcalls 1♡. What do you call with these hands?

	♠	♡	◇	♣
a)	A 7 2	K Q 9 7 5	7	A 6 4 3
b)	Q 8 6	A Q 6 5	9 8 5	Q 7 4
c)	A 9 8	J 9 6	J 6 5	J 10 8 7
d)	A Q 9 6	7 5	8 6 3	Q 8 6 4
e)	A J 7	J 9 3	Q 9 7	A 9 7 6
f)	Q 5	K Q 10 5	K J 9 7	9 8 2
g)	A Q J 9 7	K Q J 2	9 8 6	8

5) You, as South, open 1♣ with neither side vulnerable. West overcalls 1♡ and North doubles. What is your second call with these hands?

	♠	♡	◇	♣
a)	A Q 9 8	7	K 9	A 9 8 6 4 3
b)	A 8 7 5	—	A 9 7 5	A J 9 6 4
c)	K 9	6	J 10 9	K Q J 10 7 5 2
d)	K J 10 9 7	5	5	K Q J 8 7 6
e)	K Q J 9 7	6	8	A K 10 9 7 5

Answers to Quiz

1) a) 1♠. You are slightly below the minimum values needed for an overcall at equal vulnerability but your excellent suit and the pre-emptive effect of your bid (shutting out the heart suit) make it just about worthwhile.

b) Pass. Still a good suit but no pre-emptive value. You might venture 1♡ at green vulnerability.

c) Pass. Despite the pre-emptive effect (shutting out both majors) partner has a right to expect much more than this for a two-level overcall at any vulnerability.

d) 2♣. A minimum two-level overcall with a five-card suit at equal vulnerability. Pass at red vulnerability.

e) Pass. With borderline values the poor quality of your spades should have the casting vote.

f) 1♠. Despite the poor spades you have a strong hand and you should try to find a bid at any vulnerability. Change the ♠3 into the ♡3 and you would have to pass and wait (hopefully) for partner to protect.

g) 1♠. Cheeky but fairly safe. They are hardly likely to be able to make a penalty double. Don't make a habit of overcalling with four-card suits, but here you desperately want a spade lead. If partner overbids to game opposite your nine-loser hand you will just have to apologise!

h) 2♠. A perfect strong jump overcall.

i) 1NT. The ideal hand.

j) 1NT. Far from ideal, until you consider the alternatives! You are far too strong to pass, your club holding is unsuitable for a two-level overcall, and a takeout double only prolongs the agony, as partner is bound to bid spades.

2) a) 3♠. Pre-emptive. Hopefully this will prevent North/South finding their heart fit.

b) 2♢. If West rebids only 2♠ you should pass. If he makes a higher rebid your next bid will be 4♠.

c) 2♠. Mildly pre-emptive.

d) 2♢. You will pass a rebid of 2♠, raise 2NT to 3NT or 3♠ to 4♠.

e) 2♢. As with d) except that this time the only unresolved question is 'which game contract?' If West rebids only 2♠ ask for more information with 3♢.

f) Pass. Before they double!

g) 1NT. Showing 10-12 points, a diamond guard, and at most two spades.

h) 2NT. This time 13-14 points. You do not wish to be in game opposite a minimum overcall with this revolting misfit!

i) 2♣. Not forcing. Better than staying in 1♠.

3) a) 2♠. Minimum overcall.

b) 3♠. Forcing. Accepting the game try and almost certainly showing six spades.

c) 2♠. Despite your heart guard this minimum overcall gives you no justification for making the game-forcing bid of 2NT.

d) 2NT. Forcing. If partner has genuine spade support he will, no doubt, convert to 4♠. Meanwhile you must make the bid most likely to help him if he has two small spades and about twelve points.

e) 3♡. Accepting the game try but denying a sixth spade, a secondary four-card suit or a heart guard.

f) 3◇. A maximum overcall with a second suit.

4) a) Double. The perfect hand! You have a misfit with South, good hearts, and no good suit of your own.

b) 1NT. Tends to show 7-10 rather than 6-9 because North can always pass with a poor six points and wait for South to re-open, if strong.

c) Pass. You would have scraped up a response of 1NT if West had passed 1◇, but you are now happy to pass.

d) 1♠. No reason not to bid this one naturally.

e) 2♡. You would have bid 2NT without the overcall but now you need reassurance in hearts. If partner rebids 2NT (heart guard, but minimum) you will pass.

f) 2NT. Your diamond fit is too good to contemplate a penalty double. 3◇ is a reasonable alternative.

g) 1♠. With this excellent suit you should look for your own fit first. In any case they may well be able to escape into a good club fit.

5) a) Pass. You have all the defensive values partner can expect and no exceptional playing strength.

b) Pass. Obvious, despite the heart void.

c) 2♣. Few defensive values. Good playing strength in clubs even opposite a void.

d) 1♠. Even less defensive strength.

e) 2♠. 1♡ doubled could make, while 4♠ is laydown for your side.

11. The Takeout Double

If South deals and opens 1♡, a double by West demands that if North passes East must 'take it out', however weak his hand. On the whole a double is for takeout if the following conditions both apply:

i) A suit bid below 3NT has been doubled.

ii) The doubler's partner has not previously bid or doubled. He may have passed.

Takeout doubles at the one level broadly fall into two categories.

Firstly there are hands where the doubler is genuinely willing to accept whatever suit his partner bids.

Secondly there are hands where the doubler intends to suggest a different strain (either no trumps or his own suit) if he doesn't like the denomination picked by his partner. If he does this he is showing quite a strong hand, at least an ace above a minimum opening bid. We will consider these hands later. In the meantime we will examine the takeout double where the doubler genuinely wants his partner to choose.

For West to double South's 1♡ he needs the values of an opening bid. If in doubt, he should be influenced by his holding in the unbid major suit (or suits if the opening bid was a minor) because East is far more likely to reply with a major suit.

a) ♠ A Q 9 7   ♡ 6   ◇ Q 8 6   ♣ K 10 9 8 4

West could reasonably double 1♡ with hand a), intending to pass East's response unless it is forcing. He would obviously prefer not to hear 2◇ but if East bypasses 1♠ and 2♣ to bid 2◇ he is quite likely to have a five-card suit. Exchange the spade and diamond suits and it would be wiser to pass.

b) ♠ A Q 7 6   ♡ 6 3   ◇ K 7   ♣ K 10 9 8 4

If West holds hand b) he should pass a 1♡ opening but replace the diamond suit with ◇ A Q doubleton and the hand is worth a double. This is a calculated risk because he must pass a 2◇ response. Before making a takeout double you must decide whether or not you are prepared to pass the least favourable response. If the answer is 'no' you must not double unless you have at least sixteen points.

TAKEOUT DOUBLES WITHOUT TOLERANCE FOR ALL THE UNBID SUITS

Suppose West makes a takeout double, listens to East's choice, and then ignores his choice by changing denomination, for example:

♠ A Q	South	West	North	East
♡ K Q 9 6	1♡	Double	No	1♠
◇ K Q 9	No	1NT		
♣ K J 6 5				

West is showing a hand too strong for an immediate 1NT overcall, balanced, with 19-20 points. If East had bid 2♣ or 2◇ West would have continued 2NT (19-21 points). Incidentally, this is why you were advised in Chapter 10 to overcall 1♡ with 1NT holding:

   ♠ 7   ♡ A Q 8 6   ◇ A K 8 6   ♣ K J 10 6

If you thought that you could start with a takeout double and subsequently remove 1♠ to 1NT you can now see that partner will expect a very strong hand.

How do you interpret West's manoeuvring in this sequence?

South	West	North	East
1♡	Double	No	2♣
No	2◇		

His hand is not balanced and doesn't seem to have clubs so it must be either two-suited or one-suited.

a) ♠ A Q 9 7 5   ♡ 9   ◇ A K 6 5 3   ♣ K 6
b) ♠ A Q 7   ♡ 8 5   ◇ A Q 10 8 6   ♣ A K 6

Is he trying to give you a choice between the other two suits with hand a), or is he proclaiming hand b) too strong for an immediate overcall of 2◇ and without the quality of suit required for a jump overcall of 3◇? You certainly can't have it both ways. Nowadays there is a wealth of conventional bids available to show two-suited overcalls (at least 5-5 in shape). If you don't use these, there is a lot to be said for starting such hands with a simple overcall in one of the suits. It is a bit nerve-racking to introduce hand a) with a 1♠ overcall, but in practice the bid is rarely passed out and you will usually get the chance to complete the description of your assets by bidding diamonds strongly next time. The more shapely your hand, the more you can assume that there will be further bidding.

It is hand b) which must be catered for by a takeout double followed by a change of suit. If you make a takeout double and then remove partner's minimum response to a new suit you are showing a hand too strong to make a direct overcall in that suit, i.e. about 17-20 points. It is not forcing but obviously highly encouraging. It is also possible to use this approach with some hands that are not strictly one-suited.

c) ♠ A Q 9 7   ♡ A Q 9 8 6 3   ◇ A 9   ♣ 6

With hand c) it is quite safe for West to double South's 1◇ opening bid. If East bids spades he will forget the hearts and raise spades, otherwise he will bid 2♡ next time showing a hand too strong to overcall 1♡. Incidentally if East responds 1NT, West's 2♡ continuation is encouraging, not a sign off.

If West's hand is so strong that he wishes to force a second bid out of East he must jump in his new suit. Change the hearts to ♡ A K Q 8 6 4 and he would double followed by a jump to 3♡. This shows a hand too powerful even for a strong jump overcall: an Acol two bid.

A good 'aide memoire' to help you with these sequences is to remember that any new denomination introduced after a take-out double shows a hand too strong to bid that denomination immediately.

Responses to a takeout double

It must be stressed firmly that a penalty pass is a very rare part of East's armoury. Consider these hands:

a) ♠ 7 4 3   ♡ A K 7 5 3   ◇ J 9 7   ♣ 9 7
b) ♠ 4 2   ♡ K Q J 9 8 7   ◇ 9 8   ♣ 8 6 2
c) ♠ 9 7 5   ♡ 8 6 5 4   ◇ 8 6 3   ♣ 4 3 2

If he passes West's double of 1♡ with a) he is quite likely to be sabotaging his partner's plan. Remember that West may have an Acol two bid in spades and that +300 from one heart doubled, minus two will be pretty poor compensation if 6♠ is laydown for his side. East's correct response is 1NT, showing 5-9 points.

The penalty pass can only be justified if he has a hand like b), with outstanding intermediate cards in opener's suit and without honour cards likely to help partner. A penalty pass *demands* that West leads a trump (if he has one) so that East can proceed with the task of drawing trumps. Of course it should not need stressing that East will *never* make a penalty pass just because he can't think of anything to bid. With c) he must grit his teeth and invent a suit. 2♣ is probably better than 1♠ because West, who clearly has a very good hand, is too likely to get excited if he thinks he has found a major suit fit.

When replying to a takeout double, East ignores the variety of hands that West may announce on the next round and faithfully assumes that his partner has a bare opening bid with tolerance for all the unbid suits until it is proved otherwise. If this is the case he is aware that West will be especially likely to hold good spades, the unbid major. The search for a 4-4 major suit fit is important, whether or not the auction is contested. Suppose West doubles South's 1♡ opening bid and North passes:

d) ♠ Q 9 8 5   ♡ A 7 5 3   ◇ J 5   ♣ 10 7 5
e) ♠ Q 9 8 5   ♡ 8 6   ◇ 9 5   ♣ J 9 8 6 4
f) ♠ K 9 8 5   ♡ 8 6   ◇ 9 5   ♣ K J 8 6 4

With d) East should bid 1♠, not 1NT. He is aware that his partner's most likely heart holding is a small singleton. Equally, with e) he will prefer 1♠ to 2♣. Since he is not strong enough to volunteer a second bid in a competitive auction he chooses the response most likely to help West. However with f) he starts with 2♣, expecting to complete the picture of his assets on the next round with a bid of 2♠.

The range covered by East's choice of suit at the lowest level is necessarily wide, showing 0-8 points. With 9-11 points (or a hand with eight losers) East should jump, even if his suit has only four cards. This is a limit bid and thus not forcing.

If East wishes to demand another bid from West he must use the cue bid of 2♡. This is forcing to suit agreement, thus 2♠ is forcing in g) but 3♠ can be passed in h).

g)	South	West	North	East
	1♡	Double	No	2♡
	No	2♠	No	?

h)	South	West	North	East
	1♡	Double	No	2♡
	No	2♠	No	3♠
	No	?		

Obviously, none of these guidelines is meant as a substitute for judgement. Suppose South opens 1♡, West doubles, North passes, and East holds these hands:

i)	♠ A Q 8 7 5	♡ 9 7 5	◇ 8	♣ 10 9 8 6
j)	♠ K 7 4	♡ K Q	◇ 9 7 5 3	♣ J 5 3 2

Hand i) is plainly far too strong for a 1♠ response despite containing only six high card points. The losing trick count (eight losers, not seven because a nine-card fit has not been proved) serves you better with this highly distributional hand. It is easy to imagine using a 5-4 spade fit to cross-ruff your way to ten or eleven tricks even if West has a minimum takeout double. East should bid 2♠, expecting that West will raise to game with thirteen points and 4-4-4-1 shape (this sort of hand will usually contain only six losers once West hears of East's spades). On the other hand only an avid point counter would jump to 3♣ with j). This nine-loser hand without a good suit can be introduced with 2♣. If West then passes you are unlikely to have missed anything.

Despite being requested to choose a suit, East will opt for a no trump bid sometimes. Any no trump bid obviously must take account of the fact that West's most likely holding in opener's suit is a singleton, hence East's holding should appear likely to provide a double guard. 1NT shows 5-9 points, 2NT shows 10-12, and 3NT shows 13+. Note that if partner makes a takeout double you require fewer points to respond no trumps than you would need if he had made a simple overcall. This is because an overcall can be made with much weaker hands than a takeout double if tactical considerations are right.

The picture changes somewhat if North bids after West's double. Once again South opens 1♡ and West doubles, but this time North bids 1♠. East is relieved of his obligation to speak with tram tickets. Indeed if he now chooses to bid he is making a FREE BID and thus showing at least six points (or equivalent playing strength). Thus all the bids showing 0-8 points now become 6-8. If East chooses to bid no trumps he is only expected to guard hearts (opener's suit) since West is assumed to hold the spades. Alternatively, East can double for penalties if he has spades.

Nowadays sequences like 1♡-double-2♡-double are frequently played for takeout on the grounds that if North/South have found a fit East will want to double for penalties only rarely. Such a double is called a RESPONSIVE double, but (keeping to our stated yardstick) you should treat this as a penalty double without specific partnership agreement.

THE DOUBLER RAISES HIS PARTNER'S CHOICE OF SUIT

We deal now with the doubler's subsequent action if he likes the suit chosen by his partner.

South	West	North	East
1♢	Double	No	1♠
No	?		

West must restrain his enthusiasm, remembering that in the worst scenario East could have a Yarborough with only three spades. A good rule of thumb is for West to imagine that he

116

opened the bidding with a minor suit and East responded 1♠ (in that case, of course, showing 6 points). West decides the level to which he would have supported East's spades and then bids one less. Thus a raise to 2♠ shows 16-18 (or 6 losers), 3♠ shows 19-21 (or 5 losers) and 4♠ shows 22+. Even this will take you too high if East really has got total rubbish, but you cannot cater for everything.

Common sense demands these values change if East's 1♠ is a free bid. If North had bid 1♡ over West's double then East's 1♠ takes on the values of a genuine response to a one level opening, therefore West would raise directly to 4♠ with 19 points.

Opener's partner calls

NORTH REDOUBLES
If West doubles South's 1♢ opening bid North has an additional bid available created by the double, i.e., the redouble. Before we try to consider the meanings of other bids he might make we must ascertain how best to use the redouble. West has taken quite a risk in entering the auction. If East is very weak and North is strong then East/West may suffer a very unpleasant penalty. Any bid of a suit or no trumps made by North lets them off the hook, hence it makes sense to use the redouble to announce to South that a juicy penalty *might* be possible. To this purpose North redoubles with any hand if he has a balanced, or semi-balanced, hand with nine or more points, unless he has four-card support for South. (As explained in chapter 10 you should announce your own fit before contemplating penalty doubles.) The shorter the holding that North has in South's suit, the better suited his hand is for a redouble.

North should not worry that South might be left to toil in a redoubled contract with an inadequate trump suit because it is practically impossible for East/West to pass this redouble out. Their main concern is to escape from a potential disaster with as much dignity as possible. East is expected to bid a five-card suit (or even a four-card suit if he can do so cheaply), however weak his hand. If he passes it only means that he cannot say anything. West is hardly likely to be in a position to make a penalty pass, bearing in mind his original double was for takeout. If East has a hand which would like to make a penalty pass of 1◇ redoubled, his best course of action is 1NT before West is forced to bid a bad five-card club suit.

North's redouble passes the message to South that East/West should not be allowed to play in any contract undoubled unless they have freely bid and supported a suit. North may have:

♠ A J 10 2   ♡ J 9 2   ◇ 8 6   ♣ A J 8 3

He is prepared to double spades or clubs and would be content to hear South double hearts. Suppose the auction continues as follows:

South	West	North	East
1◇	Double	Redouble	1♡
No	No	?	

North has not got the trump quality necessary to double 1♡ but he must not pass. His redouble has created a forcing situation for himself as well as for South. He should bid 1♠ (forcing), just as he would have done on the first round of bidding if West had been silent. As far as possible, most bids that are made by responder after he has redoubled retain the meaning they would have had on the first round without any intervention (including whether they are forcing). Alternatively suppose he faces this problem on the second round:

South	West	North	East
1◇	Double	Redouble	No
No	1♡	?	

He can pass, secure in the knowledge that South must bid or double. If East *voluntarily* raises to 2♡ and South passes then North can pass if he wishes. The fact that they are now freely supporting hearts, rather than scrambling around for a fit, implies they think they are off the hook.

North's redouble suggests a penalty double may be available, but there are some hands where South will not tolerate this, just as there are some hands where South will not pass a penalty double of an overcall. The types of hands are very similar. If he wishes to bid again because he is weak and shapely he does so immediately. If he wishes to bid because he is strong and shapely he passes first time and removes North's subsequent penalty double. Consider South's rebid with these hands after the auction below:

South	West	North	East
1◇	Double	Redouble	No
?			

a) ♠ 6   ♡ 7 6   ◇ K Q J 10 9 7   ♣ A J 7 5
b) ♠ 6   ♡ 4 3   ◇ K Q J 10 8   ♣ K J 10 8 6
c) ♠ 8   ♡ 6 5   ◇ K Q J 10 8 7 5   ♣ A 10 7
d) ♠ 6   ♡ 5   ◇ A Q J 9 7 6   ♣ A K 9 8 6

With none of these hands will he allow North to make a penalty double of a major suit, at least until he has put North into the picture about the nature of his assets. With the first three hands he only opened because of his playing strength, indeed his defensive strength is well below the two and a half tricks that North might expect. In each case he immediately removes the redouble, to 2◇, 2♣ and 3◇ respectively. If East had volunteered 1♡ or 1♠ South would still bid in the same way. This is not a free bid, it is an essential responsibility with a weak hand. If he mistakenly passes and tries to recover on the next round North will not believe he is weak.

With hand d) he has excellent playing strength and defensive values, indeed, a very strong hand. Whatever penalty North may extract from doubling a major suit may well not compensate for a missed game or slam. He passes the redouble and removes North's penalty double by bidding clubs. This sequence should be played as forcing to game.

NORTH SUPPORTS SOUTH'S SUIT

If South's 1◇ opening bid is doubled by West and North has a fit for South's diamonds the subsequent auction is likely to proceed with both sides finding a fit and each trying to push the other one level too high. It is in North's interest to be aggressive in supporting South before East/West have a chance to get together. Suppose he has:

♠ 5 3   ♡ 8 5   ◇ A 7 4 3   ♣ J 9 8 5 2

This is a hand which would be an obvious raise to 2◇ without the double. Even facing a minimum opening bid he would be happy to buy the contract in 3◇ rather than allow opponents to play in their chosen major at the two level. It is by no means unlikely that North/South can make 3◇ *and* East/West can make 3♠. If North ventures only 2◇, no doubt East or West will attempt to play in 2♡ or 2♠. North will then try 3◇, only to lose out to 3♡ or 3♠. North should exert maximum pre-emptive pressure at once by bidding 3◇.

The rule is that when supporting partner's suit North should bid one level higher after a takeout double than he would have done if there had been no double (assuming he has at least 4-card support). Hence a raise to 2◇ shows a hand that would otherwise have been passed and a jump to 3◇ shows a hand otherwise worth 2◇. The hand that genuinely merits a constructive bid of 3◇ can be shown by the conventional bid of 2NT. This is because North will redouble with hands that are suitable for a natural 2NT bid.

NORTH CHANGES DENOMINATION

After South's 1◇ opening bid is doubled by West, North introduces any strong, balanced hand (unless he has four-card support for South's diamonds) with a redouble. Traditionally he also introduced strong unbalanced hands with a redouble (unless he had diamond support), intending to bid his strong suit later. This allowed him to play a simple change of suit as non-forcing. However this practice has fallen from favour, mainly because East/West frequently find a strong fit and pre-empt violently, leaving North to bid his suit for the first time at an uncomfortably high level. Many players settle for a compromise by which a change of suit at the one level is forcing but a change of suit at the two level can be passed.

a)	♠ A J 9 8 6 2	♡ 5	◇ A K 6	♣ 9 7 5
b)	♠ 9 7 5	♡ 5	◇ A K 6	♣ A J 9 8 6 2
c)	♠ 9 7 5	♡ 5 3	◇ 4 2	♣ K Q 10 9 7 5
d)	♠ J 7 5 3	♡ Q 8 5	◇ 4 2	♣ A J 8 6
e)	♠ J 7 5 3	♡ 8 5	◇ A J 8 6	♣ 6 4 2

With hand a) North is not interested in a low level penalty double of the all too likely East/West heart contract. He does far better to bid his spade suit immediately, rather than have to make a decision over a 4♡ pre-empt by East. However with b) he must start with a redouble as a simple 2♣ response could be passed. A 2♣ response would show a hand like c) with a good long suit and not much outside. You certainly couldn't justify a change of suit at the two level with this hand if it were forcing, yet there is much to be said for introducing your suit early in a competitive auction.

North should also be aware that West is likely to have length in the three unbid suits for his double, hence he should avoid introducing feeble four-card suits. With hands d) and e) he would have been obliged to respond 1♠ without an intervening double, but now 1NT is best with d) and a raise to 3◇ is correct with e). Firstly, he has reason to avoid a weak 4-4 spade fit because there is a high probability that the outstanding trumps will break 4-1. Secondly, with hand e) he expects the opposition to bid hearts vigorously and wishes to show his diamond support before the bidding gets too high.

Other takeout doubles

We have so far only looked at hands where South has opened with a suit bid at the one level and West has doubled. In each of the following auctions a defender doubles a contract at, or below, the three level when his partner's only previous contribution has been a pass. All are, therefore, for takeout.

a)	1♡	No	2♡	Double
b)	1NT	No	2◇	Double
c)	1♡	No	1♠	Double
d)	1♡	1♠	No	No
	Double			

The doubles in auctions a) and b) should be taken to show support for all three unbid suits with special emphasis on the unbid major or majors, though if the doubler subsequently changes suit he would be showing a hand too strong for an immediate overcall; c) shows the minors and d) shows a hand like:

♠ 3   ♡ A Q 8 6 5   ◇ K 10 8 6   ♣ A Q J

There are, of course, a vast number of sequences which are well beyond the scope of this book. Equally there are some exceptions to the 'rules' we have given, for instance;

e)	1♡	No	1♠	No
	2◇	No	2♠	Double
f)	1♡	No	1NT	Double

The double in auction e) can hardly be for takeout. There is only one unbid suit and if you really want to give partner a choice between clubs and clubs, why not bid . . . clubs? Despite satisfying all the conditions for a takeout double it is clearly for penalties. He has spades and that is why he didn't bid on the first round.

Auction f) contains a rare example of a double of no trumps for takeout, purely on the grounds of frequency of use. Since your opponents seem to have at least eighteen points between them you will rarely be able to extract much of a penalty from 1NT doubled. Far more common is the type of hand where you would happily have made a takeout double of 1♡, e.g.:

♠ A Q 8 6   ♡ 9   ◇ A 10 8 7   ♣ K J 8 7

If nothing else, these exceptions show you how much there is to know. For the moment if you abide by the general principles you won't go far wrong.

THE PENALTY DOUBLE OF 1NT
This really has no place in a chapter on takeout doubles, but we will give it an airing, if only because there are so many misapprehensions.

If South opens with a weak 1NT either defender can double with 16 points. It can sometimes be a worthwhile gamble to double with less, if you are on lead and you have a lead that is likely to be successful.

a) ♠ K J 6   ♡ Q 8 5   ◇ A Q 8 3   ♣ K 8 4
b) ♠ A 7 4   ♡ 5 3   ◇ A K Q 9 7 5   ♣ 9 7
c) ♠ A 8   ♡ K 8 6   ◇ K Q J 10 8 6   ♣ 8 6

With hand a) you should pass whether you are East or West. There is probably no lead you can make without giving away a trick and if declarer knows who holds all the missing points you are likely to be endplayed continually. If you hold b) or c) you can make a good case for doubling, but only if you are on lead. If partner has to make the initial attack he has no reason not to lead his own suit, and it may well then be too late to establish anything from your attractive diamond suit.

The possibility of a long running suit should be in North's mind as he considers whether or not to sign off over the double.

d) ♠ Q 8 6   ♡ Q 7 5 3   ◇ 7 5   ♣ K 8 6 4
e) ♠ Q 7 6   ♡ Q J 8 6 4   ◇ 7 5   ♣ K 8 6
f) ♠ 6 5 3   ♡ 9 7   ◇ 8 6   ♣ A K J 9 7 2

With hand d) he has no sensible alternative but to pass, although if he has a five-card suit it is usually wise to sign off. If he passes with hand e) because his side have at least half of the points, he is playing Russian roulette. His tricks are slow. By the time the defenders have cashed a long suit it will be aces and kings that take the remaining tricks, not queens and jacks. A 2♡ bid is clearcut.

With f) the decision is close. A sign off in 2♣ is the safe course. Alternatively a vulnerable pass could result in +580 or −500. How strong are your nerves?

If North passes, the traditional theory that East removes his partner's double with any hand lacking five points is patently absurd. Much depends on the vulnerability. Let us quote two extreme cases.

g) ♠ 6 4 3 2   ♡ 9 8 6   ◇ 7 5 3   ♣ 6 4 2
h) ♠ K Q J 10 8 6 3   ♡ 6 3   ◇ 4 3 2   ♣ 7

At red vulnerability it would be unthinkable for East to remove West's double with g). Firstly, West may be able to beat 1NT on his own. Secondly, even if 1NT doubled is laydown with two overtricks it is better to concede 380 than 800 (quite likely if West has a doubleton spade). Even if North redoubles for business, East should allow West to rescue at the two level into a five-card suit if he considers it desirable. Removing a penalty double requires at least a five-card suit.

Conversely with h) East should aim for the vulnerable game by bidding 4♠ rather than struggle to extract a small penalty from non-vulnerable opponents. His lack of entry cards may make the establishment of his spades impossible unless they are trumps.

Unfortunately there are no easy rules to guide East. In each case he must balance the likely consequences of the alternative actions before deciding.

Quiz on Chapter 11

1) You are West. South opens 1♣ as dealer with neither side vulnerable. What do you call with these hands?

a)	♠ A Q 3	♡ K 9 7 4	◇ J 8 6 4 3	♣ 8
b)	♠ A K 3	♡ K 8 6 4	◇ Q 9 7 6 5	♣ 8
c)	♠ A J 10 9 6	♡ K 9 7 5	◇ A 7	♣ 8 6
d)	♠ A Q J 7 5	♡ A Q J 7 5	◇ 9 7	♣ 7
e)	♠ A K Q 9 7	♡ A K Q 9 7	◇ 9 7	♣ 7
f)	♠ A 5 3	♡ Q 8 6	◇ A 8 7 4	♣ A J 9
g)	♠ A K 8	♡ Q 8 6	◇ A 8 7 4	♣ A J 9
h)	♠ A K 8	♡ K J 9	◇ A 8 7 4	♣ A J 9
i)	♠ A K J 8 6	♡ A J 9 6	◇ K 9	♣ 8 5
j)	♠ K 9	♡ A K Q 8 6 4	◇ K 9 8	♣ 9 4
k)	♠ A 7	♡ A K Q 8 6 4	◇ A J 8	♣ 9 4

2) You are East with both sides vulnerable. West has doubled South's opening bid of 1♣ and North passed. What do you call with these hands?

a)	♠ 8 7 4	♡ 10 9 7	◇ 6 3	♣ J 6 5 4 3
b)	♠ Q 9 7 5	♡ 8 6	◇ 10 8 6	♣ A J 6 4
c)	♠ Q 9 8 5	♡ 9 7	◇ Q 8 7 5	♣ 9 8 6
d)	♠ 9 8	♡ 8 6 4	◇ 8 6 2	♣ A K 6 5 3
e)	♠ 9 8	♡ 8 6 4	◇ J 8	♣ K J 10 9 8 5
f)	♠ Q 10 7 5 4	♡ 9 7	◇ A Q 7	♣ 8 5 3
g)	♠ A J 9	♡ Q 9 7	◇ A 10 8	♣ 9 8 6 4
h)	♠ A 9 8 6	♡ A Q 6 5	◇ K 7 8	♣ 9 7

3) How would your answers to question 2 have differed if North had bid 1♡ instead of passing?

4) You are North with neither side vulnerable. South opens 1◇ and West doubles. What do you call with these hands?

a)	♠ A J 9 4	♡ K J 9 8	◇ —	♣ A 9 7 5 4
b)	♠ A J 9 8	♡ Q 10 9 7 6	◇ 7 5	♣ K 4
c)	♠ —	♡ A Q 10 9 7 5	◇ Q 10 8	♣ K 6 5 4
d)	♠ 8 7 5	♡ K J 10 8 6	◇ 6	♣ Q 9 7 5
e)	♠ 8 7 5	♡ 8 6 3	◇ 8	♣ A J 10 5 3 2
f)	♠ 9	♡ 5 4 2	◇ Q 6 5 3	♣ 9 7 5 3 2
g)	♠ 7 4	♡ 9 7 3	◇ K 8 6 3	♣ A 6 3 2
h)	♠ 10 8	♡ A Q 8	◇ Q 10 8 6	♣ K 7 5 3
i)	♠ 9 7 5	♡ K 5 4 2	◇ 8 6 4	♣ K 7 5
j)	♠ K 7 5	♡ K 5 4 2	◇ 8 6 4	♣ K 7 5

5) You are South with both sides vulnerable. You open 1♡, West doubles, North redoubles and East bids 1♠. What do you call with these hands?

a)	♠ A 6	♡ A Q 8 7 4	◇ Q 7 4	♣ 10 9 4
b)	♠ A 7	♡ A Q 8 7 4	◇ K 8 6	♣ A Q 8
c)	♠ 6	♡ A Q J 7 5 4	◇ Q 10 7 6 4	♣ 6
d)	♠ 6	♡ K Q 9 7 6 2	◇ K Q 8	♣ J 7 2
e)	♠ 6	♡ A K Q 7 5 4	◇ 9 8	♣ K Q J 10

Answers to Quiz
1) a) Pass. You are simply too weak.

   b) Double. Minimum values for an immediate takeout double, although you might be tempted with one less point if your shape was perfect, i.e., 4-4-4-1.

125

c) 1♠. To double is tempting as you would like to uncover a heart fit, however partner is quite likely to bid 1♦ with a four-card suit. This will leave you in a silly contract because you are not strong enough to correct to 1♠.

d) 1♠. You hope the bidding will return to you at a reasonable level so that you can bid your heart suit. With two five-card suits you bid the higher first for the same reason that you would open this hand with 1♠ rather than 1♡. You can subsequently bid your second suit without reversing. Of course, if you play 2♣ as a Michaels cue bid showing the major suits that is even better.

e) Double. A rare example of a genuinely two-suited hand being introduced by a takeout double. Holding a hand with this playing strength you cannot risk 1♠ being passed out. 2♠ might seem superficially attractive, but it actually increases the chance of three passes. If East responds 1♦ you will keep the auction going with a forcing 2♠, intending to complete the picture of your hand with 3♡.

f) Pass. Don't worry! If North passes and partner cannot protect you haven't missed much.

g) 1NT. 16-18 points.

h) Double, followed by 1NT. 19-20 points.

i) Double. If East bids 1♦ your rebid is 1♠. If he bids 1♡ you should raise to 2♡.

j) 2♡. A perfect strong jump overcall.

k) Double, followed by a forcing jump in hearts to show a hand with at least eight playing tricks.

2) a) 1♡. Horrid, but inescapable. Not 1NT which shows 5-9 points.

b) 1♠. Prefer the major suit to 1NT.

c) 1♠. Prefer the major to the minor, though if you had a five-card diamond suit you should choose to show it as 1♦ is a cheaper bid than 1♠.

d) 1NT. This is not a suitable hand for a penalty pass.

e) Pass. This hand is worth four tricks in defence, but is likely to be totally useless if partner picks the trump suit.

f) 2♠. Ideal.

g) 2♣. You have the values to force as far as 2NT but you

don't know what to do, so see what partner has to say. If he bids a suit (forcing) you will give a single raise (not forcing).

h) 2♣. This time with more enthusiasm. You are going to play in game, but if you try to pick a suit you may commit yourself to a 4-3 fit with a 4-4 fit available in the other major.

3) Hands a) and c) are too weak for a free bid, hence you would have passed. You would also have passed with hand e), but this is obviously not a penalty pass now.

With hand h) you would make a penalty double. There are not enough points in the pack for all this. If North is psyching with a weak hand, but with a club fit, you may still find your own heart fit!

Note that if you, quite reasonably, choose to bid 1NT with d) partner will expect you to have the clubs guarded, but not necessarily the hearts. It is presumed that he has the hearts for his double.

With hand g) you again bid 2♣. Pick the lower of the two cue bids.

4) a) Redouble. This is going to be a bloodbath if partner allows you to double whatever contract they stumble into. If South does remove the redouble by rebidding 2♢ you might well pass despite your points. He would be announcing a sub-minimum hand and you can see a ghastly misfit.

There is an alternative to redouble! Since you are desperate to make a penalty double however weak South's hand is, you can pass and then make a penalty double. That makes it less likely that he will bid before you have a chance to double. The disadvantage is that he may feel that your failure to redouble first time makes your subsequent double only tentative. Why not agree with your partner that pass followed by double is an instruction to leave the double at all costs?

b) Redouble. You will happily double a major suit or accept partner's double of 2♣. If East bids 2♣ and South passes, you must settle for 2♡.

c) 1♡. Forcing. Introduce your suit before the spade pre-empt.

d) 1♡. Not as powerful as c) but your suit is worth a mention.

e) 2♣. Not forcing, showing your good suit before the bidding gets too high.

f) 2◇. You hardly expect this little pre-empt to sabotage their efforts to find a major fit but South, knowing that you have a very weak hand with diamonds, may find a good sacrifice if they bid game.

g) 3◇. A hand that would have been worth 2◇ without the double.

h) 2NT. This time you have a genuine raise to 3◇. If South does not wish to advance further he can sign off in 3◇.

i) Pass. You would have dredged up a 1♡ response without the double, but your suit is too poor now, bearing in mind that West is quite likely to have four hearts also.

j) 1NT. Redouble is an alternative, but your intermediate cards are so poor that you would not wish to make a low level penalty double of any suit contract.

5) a) Pass. Your defensive strength will not disappoint North if he doubles 1♠.

b) Pass. Forcing. You will obviously accept North's penalty double or play in a game if he cannot double.

c) 2◇. Weak, distributional, and lacking defensive values.

d) 2♡. As above.

e) Pass. You want to convey the picture of a hand with good playing values but unsuitable for defence. Wait for North to have his say and then remove to clubs (forcing to game).

12. Protective Bidding

We have concentrated so far on competitive auctions which begin with West joining in over South's opening bid. West has been pretty choosey about when he bids, indeed he has turned up his nose at several hands that would have merited an opening bid.

a) ♠ J 8 6 5 3   ♡ 9 7 4   ♢ K Q 7   ♣ A Q
b) ♠ A Q 7 6   ♡ 6 3   ♢ K 9 8 5 4   ♣ K 7
c) ♠ A 8 6   ♡ A J 4 3   ♢ K 8 5   ♣ Q 8 6
d) ♠ J 8   ♡ A Q J 9 5   ♢ K Q 5 4   ♣ 7 5

With each of these hands West must pass South's 1♡ opening bid. The spades are too poor for a minimum overcall with hand a). With b) a takeout double is all too likely to lead to a stupid 2♣ contract, while a 2♢ overcall is not to be recommended with poor diamonds and a good four-card spade suit. There is no bid that could remotely be considered with c) or d).

Clearly, if West and North both pass East cannot afford to be so fussy, otherwise good game contracts will be lost, with only the miserable compensation of a few undoubled undertricks. Equally important are the numerous hands when the points are equally divided and both sides can make a part score. With these hands East/West need, at some stage, to push themselves aggressively into the auction. Even if they cannot buy the contract they may succeed in pushing North/South to a contract they cannot make. A partnership which is unduly cautious in the competitive auction allows golden opportunities to slip away by default.

If South's opening 1♡ bid is passed round to East, he should therefore adopt a very positive stance. His hand is called the PROTECTIVE hand. This means that if he passes, the opponents will have bought the contract of their choice. With most ten point hands he should try to find a bid. In deciding whether to bid he should apply the following rule of thumb. He mentally adds a king to his assets and if the resulting hand would have merited a bid in the immediate position, he makes that bid. This is, in fact, *less* dangerous than taking action with a stronger hand in the immediate position. East *knows* his partner has some high cards, otherwise North/South would hardly be passing out 1♡.

Obviously West must not get over-excited if East makes a protective bid, even if his own hand is quite strong. Generally West requires about three extra points to make any encouraging response to a protective bid. East is partly bidding West's hand for him. If both partners bid the same high cards, chronic overbidding will result.

THE PROTECTIVE SUIT OVERCALL
This can be very weak indeed.

a)	♠ A Q 8 6 5	♡ 6 3	♢ 10 9 7	♣ 9 7 4
b)	♠ 8 6	♡ 9 7	♢ Q 9 8	♣ A Q 7 6 4 2
c)	♠ J 9 7 5 4	♡ 5 4 2	♢ A Q 8	♣ K 7
d)	♠ A Q J 8 6	♡ 9 7	♢ A K 7	♣ 9 7 5
e)	♠ A Q J 8 6 5	♡ 9 7	♢ A Q 8	♣ 7 5

Hand a) is a minimum protective 1♠ overcall of South's 1♡ opening and b) is a minimum overcall at the two level, both at equal vulnerability. Neither should East be too squeamish over suit quality. Hand c) is worth a protective 1♠ in preference to passing out 1♡. The bid might attract an unfavourable lead, but it is more likely to start a competitive auction in which either North/South will get too high or East/West will successfully commandeer the contract.

Hand d) is too strong for a protective overcall and East should start with a double, intending to remove West's response to 2♠. Hand e) is worth a protective jump overcall of 2♠.

THE PROTECTIVE 1NT
This bid breaks all the rules so carefully documented for an overcall of 1NT in the immediate position. It has to do this if we are to require East to show signs of life with balanced eleven point hands. Traditionally, a protective no trump has shown

11-14 points, but this leaves a very wide range of stronger balanced hands and nothing like enough bidding sequences available to describe them. Therefore we recommend you play that 1NT in the protective seat shows 11-16 points. It also does not promise a sure guard in opener's suit. If this sounds suicidal remember that partner is marked with some points because of the lack of bidding by North/South. He is quite likely to have something useful in the danger suit and he has the advantage of sitting over opener's honour cards.

a) ♠ A 8 2   ♡ Q 10 8 7   ◇ K Q 9   ♣ J 8 6
b) ♠ 8 7 3   ♡ J 7 3   ◇ A K 8 6   ♣ K 10 7
c) ♠ 2   ♡ A Q J 6   ◇ A 9 7 6   ♣ 9 7 6 3

With hands a) and b) East must overcall South's 1♡ with a protective 1NT. If this still leaves you feeling worried ask yourself what alternative you have. If West has a balanced fifteen points he will hardly thank you for passing. Remember also that North has announced that he holds practically nothing. It is always easier to play a contract if you know the location of the missing high cards.

However the circumstances of hand c) are deeply suspicious. If West has spades and a fair hand he would probably not have passed. It is likely that either he is very weak or he also has reasonable hearts. In either case North/South probably have a better contract available than 1♡, possibly even 4♠. You should pass before they find it. Even in the protective seat it is often prudent to pass out hands where too much of your strength is concentrated in opener's suit.

Because East's protective 1NT covers such a wide range of points, West must make a game try with ten high card points. To cope with this it is helpful to adapt the answers to the Stayman response.

South	West	North	East
1♡	No	No	1NT
No	2♣	No	?

With 11-13 points East answers at the two level as usual, allowing the partnership to stop in, or below, 2NT if West judges it appropriate. With 14-16 points he bids 2NT (game forcing), then a 3♣ continuation by West can again ask for a four-card major. Stayman adapted in this way is called the Crowhurst convention.

This leaves balanced hands of over 16 points, which must be introduced by a double followed by a no trump rebid.

THE PROTECTIVE TAKEOUT DOUBLE
If South's 1♡ opening is passed round to East he can, and should, double with as little as:

    ♠ K 10 9 2   ♡ 2   ♢ A 6 3 2   ♣ J 10 9 3

West, heeding the 'three extra points' rule, needs 12-14 points to jump in his choice of suit, 8-12 for 1NT or 13-15 for 2NT. If he has 12 or more points but no obvious bid, he can temporise with 2♡ to see what East has to say. East would continue with 2♠ which is forcing to suit agreement.

It is worth considering how West would react with the four hands introduced at the start of this chapter.

Hands a) and b) seem to have the correct point count for 2♠, but both of them have considerable potential with a likely spade fit and heart shortage opposite. In both cases West should start with 2♡ to ascertain the nature of East's protective double and over East's 2♠ rebid should raise to 4♠. Opposite a four-card spade suit a) has 7 losers (really less with the minor suit honours situated over the opening bidder) and b) only 6 losers. Since East will have a singleton or a void in hearts if he has a minimum protective double, there seem to be no wasted points. Again the losing trick count can lead to excellent game contracts with minimum values if a good fit is held. Hand c) is worth only 2NT (which is quite high enough with these combined hands) and d) will tempt West into a penalty pass as his excellent hearts are sitting over declarer.

East can, of course, also use an initial takeout double with stronger hands, in particular hands too strong to make a simple overcall. If he doubles and subsequently changes suit he can be relied upon for about three points less than if West had carried out this manoeuvre in the immediate position.

OTHER PROTECTIVE SITUATIONS

One area where the expert consistently outscores his less knowledgeable contemporaries is in contesting part score hands. You peacefully defend a contract of 2♥ in a teams of four match only to find that your opponents at the other table successfully bought the contract in spades or pushed your team mates into 3♥, one level too high. Each time you lose 5 or 6 IMPS because the other team were more aggressive than you, and it mounts up. Occasionally they concede a large penalty but not nearly often enough to compensate you for all the little swings you lost. Frequently you can see that your team could have done better, but only with hindsight. Some hands you could have doubled and collected 200 rather than bid on. However, such an aggressive policy, if regularly applied, would have resulted in doubling them into game on other occasions. If they consistently put you under pressure it is inevitable that you will misjudge some hands. Such pressure play is undoubtedly successful as long as you do not let the occasional 'disaster' worry you. The key to bullying opponents in this way is to strain every muscle in search of a competitive noise if opponents have found a fit and are about to pass it out at a low level.

Suppose you are West after the following start to the auction:

South	West	North	East
1♥	No	2♥	No
No	?		

a)	♠ Q 8 7 6 3	♥ 8 5	◇ A Q 5	♣ 8 7 4
b)	♠ K 8 6 4	♥ 4	◇ K 9 7 6	♣ Q 10 9 5
c)	♠ K Q 7	♥ K 9 5	◇ K Q 9	♣ 10 8 7 4

Both a) and b) are miserable collections but you know partner has some values, in fact your side may have half the points in the pack. Also the fact that your opponents have found a fit makes it mathematically more likely that you also have a fit. With hand a) you should protect with 2♠ and with b) you reopen with a takeout double. Even if North/South can extract a penalty it may be very difficult for them to judge it. This is obviously a part score hand and East will realise that the eleven or so points he holds are not a reason to try for game. If you had a genuine overcall or takeout double you would not have passed first time. Such action usually starts a keenly fought battle which ends at the three-level. If North/South buy the contract in 3♡ at least you will have improved your chances of beating them.

Hand c) is stronger but with such a flat hand there is little point in protecting. You have no reason to believe that your high cards will score any better if your side declares the contract than if North/South play in 2♡. Balanced hands are best passed out at this level.

After the above sequences West is known to be weak, so East should not find it hard to know what to do. However, consider East's dilemma here:

South	West	North	East
1NT	No	2♢	No
No	Double	No	?

West plainly doesn't have the sixteen points necessary to double 1NT but he could hold either of these hands.

d)   ♠ A Q 8 6   ♡ A 10 9 8   ♢ 5   ♣ K J 10 9
e)   ♠ J 10 9 7   ♡ K 9 8 6   ♢ 8   ♣ A 9 8 6

This, in turn, makes it hard for East to know how to react if he has ten points and a four-card major. He will find it hard to make a game try {catering for d)} without getting too high if West has e). On the whole we advise caution. A protective hand must be allowed to compete without partner killing him for his enterprise. Forget the occasional 'super fit' game and concentrate on the battle for the part scores.

Quiz on Chapter 12

1) South, as dealer with both sides vulnerable, opens 1♡ and this is passed round to you as East. What should you call with these hands?

a)   ♠ K 8 6   ♡ K 10 8   ♢ 9 8 6   ♣ A Q 8 5
b)   ♠ K 7 4   ♡ 10 8 5   ♢ K 8 6   ♣ A Q 8 5
c)   ♠ A Q 7   ♡ K 10 8   ♢ A 8 6   ♣ A J 8 5
d)   ♠ K 6   ♡ K Q 10 9 6 ♢ K 8 7   ♣ 9 8 6
e)   ♠ J 10 8 7 4   ♡ 7 5   ♢ A 9 8   ♣ K J 7
f)   ♠ A K 8 7 5 3   ♡ A 8   ♢ Q 10 9   ♣ 8 7
g)   ♠ A K J 6 4   ♡ A 8   ♢ K 10 9   ♣ 8 7 5

2) With neither side vulnerable you are West. South deals and opens 1♠, you pass and North's raise to 2♠ is passed back to you. What do you call with these hands?

a) ♠ Q J 10 9 7   ♡ A K   ◇ A 9 8   ♣ 8 6 4
b) ♠ Q J 5   ♡ K 8 6 3   ◇ A Q 10   ♣ Q 9 6
c) ♠ 7   ♡ K 9 8 5   ◇ A 8 6 4   ♣ Q 10 9 8
d) ♠ 8 4   ♡ A Q 9 8 6   ◇ K 10 9 7   ♣ 8 6
e) ♠ 9   ♡ K 10 9 7 6   ◇ A J 10 8 6   ♣ J 7

Answers to Quiz
1) a) 1NT. Perfect.
   b) 1NT. Uneasy with no heart guard, but the best available bid. Remember partner could be quite strong.
   c) Double, and bid no trumps as cheaply as possible next time.
   d) Pass. Partner must be short in hearts and is therefore probably weak. No doubt North/South have a far better resting place available than 1♡.
   e) 1♠. You have a poor suit but it is losing tactics to sell out to 1♡.
   f) 2♠. Too strong for a protective 1♠.
   g) Double, followed by 2♠. Again too strong for a protective 1♠.

2) a) Pass. Of course you can beat 2♠ but double would be for takeout.
   b) Pass. Too shapeless to compete.
   c) Double. Since North/South have the spade suit it is quite likely that they will outbid you in 3♠ but your enterprise may well have pushed them from a safe contract into a precarious one. Of course, there is an element of risk but the ultra-cautious player is seldom a winner.
   d) 3♡. As above.
   e) Double. If East bids 3♣ you try 3◇. Common sense rules out the possibility of your having a strong overcall in diamonds, after all you did pass first time. Therefore you must be showing a two-suited hand with diamonds and hearts.

13. Competitive Bidding

COMPETING OVER PRE-EMPTS

For most of the decisions we have so far examined there has been established theory for guidance. However, when both sides start bidding aggressively you tend to arrive quickly at a point when any one of several choices could be correct, and moreover a choice that could be a winner could also lead to a disaster. The purpose of pre-emptive bidding is to cause problems to opponents. How do you, as North, bid this hand at RED vulnerability if West opens 3♠?

♠ 8 6   ♡ A J 10 6 5 3   ◇ A Q   ♣ K J 7

The alternatives are Pass or 4♡. 4♡ is risky! Suppose partner has:

♠ K J 7   ♡ 7   ◇ J 8 6 4 3   ♣ 6 5 3 2

East will have a strong hand with good hearts, and his Double could lead to a penalty of 1100. To add insult to injury, West would have failed in 3♠. On the other hand Pass is risky! Suppose the distribution is:

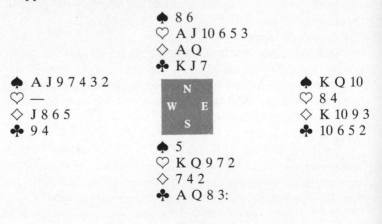

```
                      ♠ 8 6
                      ♡ A J 10 6 5 3
                      ◇ A Q
                      ♣ K J 7
♠ A J 9 7 4 3 2                        ♠ K Q 10
♡ —                  N                 ♡ 8 4
◇ J 8 6 5         W      E             ◇ K 10 9 3
♣ 9 4                S                 ♣ 10 6 5 2
                      ♠ 5
                      ♡ K Q 9 7 2
                      ◇ 7 4 2
                      ♣ A Q 8 3:
```

East will raise pre-emptively to 4♠ which cannot be beaten, yet 6♡ is laydown for your side!

The key to this hand is FIT. You have already met competitive auctions in which your knowledge of a fit makes you keen to play the hand rather than defend. One example is found in chapter 11 where it was seen that if you, as responder, have four-card support for partner you bid one level higher after a takeout double. Equally in chapter 10 you saw that you should generally avoid making a low level penalty double of an opponent's suit overcall until you have disclosed your four-card support for partner. In these situations you *know* of the fit. After West's 3♠ pre-empt above, you must make a momentous decision without any idea of partner's strength or shape. While there is no infallible rule it is probably true to say that most players are too cautious in these situations. −1100 looks bad, yet −420 rather than +1430 is just as bad. We remind you of the advice given in chapter 2 when discussing the weak no trump; 'If you are dominated by fear at the bridge table you will never be a winner.' A more constructive attitude by North would be this:

'West has, perhaps, 7 high card points. I have 15. That leaves 18. Suppose they are evenly split. South may have:

♠ J 7   ♡ K 4 2   ◇ J 9 7 2   ♣ A 10 3 2

4♡ should make and we are unlikely to beat 3♠ by more than one trick, if that! Yet unless I take the initiative the hand will undoubtedly be passed out!' If in doubt be guided by the quality of your suit, just like any other overcall.

Note that over a pre-empt you must partly bid partner's hand for him, just as in the protective position. Thus if he has a few points he shouldn't get too excited. Suppose your left hand opponent opens 3◇, your partner bids 3♠, and right hand opponent passes. You hold:

♠ 8 6 4   ♡ K 8 4 2   ◇ 9 7   ♣ Q 7 4 2

You should pass. Partner is *not* announcing nine playing tricks. He is praying that you have a few of the missing points. He will probably struggle to make 3♠.

One final point. Why could both sides make such high level contracts on the deal shown above? Because each side had a *fit in two suits*. North/South had hearts and clubs while East/West had spades and diamonds. If your bidding discovers a fit in two suits that is a very powerful reason for *playing* the hand.

HIGH LEVEL COMPETITION IF BOTH SIDES HAVE A FIT

There is a well known saying that gives advice when both sides have a known fit: 'When in doubt bid one more.' There is a lot of truth in this, if only because even if you are wrong your opponents may misjudge and overreach themselves. Generally it pays to be aggressive. Suppose at *game all* your opponents are in 4♠ and you are heading for −620. You misjudge and bid 5♡, heading for −800. However you have put pressure on them and, being unsure, they bid 5♠. You write down +100. Bridge is a *pressure game!*

Bidding 'one more' is a useful rule of thumb but you must also cultivate sufficient judgement to balance your PLAYING STRENGTH against your DEFENSIVE STRENGTH. Consider the East hands below after the following sequence at love all:

South	West	North	East
1♠	2♡	4♠	?

a)	♠ 7	♡ K 7 5 2	◇ A 7 5 3	♣ 8 6 4 2
b)	♠ 7 2	♡ K 7 5 2	◇ A 7 5 3	♣ 8 6 4
c)	♠ 7 5 2	♡ K 7 5 2	◇ A 7 5 3	♣ 8 6
d)	♠ K	♡ K 7 5 2	◇ A 7 5 3	♣ 8 6 4 2
e)	♠ A 5 2	♡ Q J 10 2	◇ A 7 5 3	♣ 8 6
f)	♠ Q J 10	♡ A 7 5 2	◇ A 7 5 3	♣ 8 6

If you have listened to the auction carefully you will realise that your side are unlikely to have more then four spades. The points appear to be evenly split, yet North has jumped to the four level. He almost certainly has five spades and good shape. This makes your combined *playing strength* greater with a) and c) than with b). Two small spades are bad news in this type of auction. Conversely if you had four spades you could be practically certain that partner would ruff the opening lead. Note that if you hold hand c) the 4♠ bid has *improved* the playing strength of your combined hands, confirming that partner has a singleton spade or a void.

The *playing strength* of d) is exactly the same as in a) but *defensively* your hand may be worth one extra trick if North holds the ♠A. Your ♠K is most unlikely to make a trick if it is visible to the whole world in dummy but could well score on a finesse if opponents play in 4♠. This is an argument against bidding 5♡. Kings, queens and jacks in the opponents' suit point towards defending rather than bidding on when the auction gets high.

Hands e) and f) have similar shape and point count but have different character. With e) all your honour cards are likely to be useful in a 5♡ contract (your ♠A is probably opposite a singleton) but only the ♠A and ◇A will score against 4♠. You have four useful playing cards but only two defensive tricks. Hand f) is more defensive. Your ♠ Q J 10 will be useless in 5♡. You have three defensive tricks but only two useful playing cards.

You will notice that we haven't yet told you what to bid on any of these hands. It doesn't matter if your judgement differs slightly from ours as long as you understand the principles governing your judgement. However, for completeness sake we will tentatively suggest the following:

a) 5♡   b) Pass   c) 5♡
d) Pass   e) 5♡   f) Double.

Occasionally your bidding discloses the magical *fit in two suits* discussed earlier. Consider your bidding as North at love all:

♠ 9 7 5	South	West	North	East
♡ Q 10 7 4	1♡	No	2♡	2♠
◇ K J 7 6 3	3◇	4♠	?	
♣ 5				

5♡ is clearcut. Not only do *you* have a fit in hearts and diamonds, you know that East/West have a fit in spades and clubs. Suppose the complete deal is:

$\spadesuit$ 9 7 5
$\heartsuit$ Q 10 7 4
$\diamondsuit$ K J 7 6 3
$\clubsuit$ 5

$\spadesuit$ Q 10 8 2
$\heartsuit$ J 9 2
$\diamondsuit$ 5
$\clubsuit$ 10 9 7 3 2

$\spadesuit$ A K J 6 4
$\heartsuit$ 6
$\diamondsuit$ Q 9 4
$\clubsuit$ K Q J 6

$\spadesuit$ 3
$\heartsuit$ A K 8 5 3
$\diamondsuit$ A 10 8 2
$\clubsuit$ A 8 4

You can certainly make 5$\heartsuit$, or 6$\heartsuit$ if partner can find the $\diamondsuit$Q. On the other hand, do you have sufficient faith in your combined defensive powers to feel sure that you will find the club ruff to defeat 4$\spadesuit$? If partner starts with two top hearts that will be the end of the defence.

YOUR FIRST BID IN LOW LEVEL COMPETITION

In many of these examples you are faced with an overcall which removes your natural bid. You are then faced with the choice of passing with useful values or overbidding at a higher level. How do you resolve this? These decisions are difficult at times, and have given rise to a wealth of excellent conventional ideas such as SPUTNIK DOUBLES. However we now dispense with these and examine how general principles guide you. Broadly speaking you can afford to overbid slightly to show a fit, whereas with a misfit you should be inclined to pass. Examine the North hand below in the context of the following auctions at *Game All*.

$\spadesuit$ 9 5 $\heartsuit$ Q 8 7 5 $\diamondsuit$ A 10 6 4 $\clubsuit$ J 7 3

	South	West	North	East
a)	1$\heartsuit$	No	?	
b)	1$\heartsuit$	1$\spadesuit$	?	

c)	1♡	2♠	?
d)	1♡	3♠	?
e)	1♣	No	?
f)	1♣	1♠	?
g)	1♣	2♠	?

a) and b) 2♡ is obvious.

c) Better to overbid your hand by a trick with 3♡ than pass, possibly losing your heart fit for ever. Partner might overbid to game, but on the other hand if you pass East might raise to 3♠ and partner, with a strong hand and good hearts, may be unable to compete.

d) Pass, although you can look wistfully at 4♡.

e) 1♢.

f) 2♣. You cannot introduce new suits at the two level with this weak hand. Giving three-card support is better than passing. Partner will be aware that you might have had this problem so, if he is strong enough to bid on, you should be in a position to investigate a 4-4 heart fit.

g) Pass. You haven't discovered any great fit so you have no reason to 'push'.

If nothing else, you will see from these examples that the worth of your hand is not governed only by your point count but also by *fit*.

Quiz on Chapter 13

1) At Game All your right hand opponent opens 3♡. What do you call with the following hands? Assume Double is for takeout and 3NT is natural.

a)	♠ K Q J 9 3	♡ 7 4	♢ A 7 5	♣ K Q 5
b)	♠ K 9 7 5 3	♡ 7 4	♢ A Q J	♣ K Q 5
c)	♠ K Q J 9 3 2	♡ 7	♢ A Q J	♣ K Q 5
d)	♠ K J 6 4	♡ 7	♢ K Q 7 5	♣ A K 8 6
e)	♠ K 7 5	♡ A Q 6	♢ A K 7 5	♣ Q 7 4
f)	♠ Q 8	♡ K 6	♢ A K Q 8 6 5 3	♣ 8 6

2) At Love All your left hand opponent opens with a preemptive 3♡, which your partner doubles (for takeout). Your

right hand opponent passes. What do you call with these hands?

a) ♠ Q 8 5 2   ♡ A 9 6   ◇ 8 6 3   ♣ 8 4 2
b) ♠ 8 4 2   ♡ A 9 6   ◇ 8 6 3   ♣ Q 8 5 2
c) ♠ K Q 7 5   ♡ 8 6 4   ◇ K 10 4 3   ♣ 10 7

3) What do you call with this hand at Love All after each of these bidding sequences?

♠ K 7 5 3   ♡ Q 10 6 4   ◇ K 3 2   ♣ 9 4

	South	West	North	East
a)	1♠	2♣	?	
b)	1♠	3♣	?	
c)	1◇	2♣	?	
d)	1◇	3♣	?	

4) At Game All South opens 1♡, West (your partner) overcalls 1♠ and North leaps to 4♡. As East what do you call with these hands?

a) ♠ A 8 6 4   ♡ 8 7 2   ◇ K Q J 6   ♣ 10 5
b) ♠ A 8 7 4   ♡ K Q J   ◇ 9 8 7 5   ♣ 10 5
c) ♠ K Q J 4   ♡ A 7 2   ◇ 9 8 7 6   ♣ 10 5

Answers to Quiz

1) a) 3♠. A minimum three-level overcall, about an ace above a minimum opening bid, or slightly less if you have a good six-card suit.

b) Pass. The same point count but a much weaker suit. This would be worth a protective 3♠.

c) 4♠. Assume partner has a few points. He cannot be expected to raise 3♠ to 4♠ with just the ♣A, yet that would make game very probable.

d) Double (for takeout). You could double with three points less in the protective position.

e) 3NT. 18+ points. Dangerous, but so is Pass!

f) 3NT. Fewer points but a worthwhile gamble with a running diamond suit. If you are doubled in a voice of thunder prudence dictates you retreat to 4◇.

2) a) 3♠. Not quite enough for 4♠.

b) 3NT. If you could bid your suit below 3NT you would do so, but you can't. You may not make 3NT, but on the other hand you may not make 4♣ either. The ♡A is a very good stop in this type of auction because you can hold up twice and probably isolate the weak pre-emptive hand.

c) 4♠. Just about worth it. Your three honour cards all seem to be useful.

3) a) 2♠. The overcall has not removed any significant bidding space.

b) 3♠. Stretch one level higher to show your fit.

c) 2◇. The only alternative is Pass, unless you play Sputnik doubles!

d) Pass. Totally fixed. Stretching a level with only three-card support is *not* to be encouraged.

4) a) 4♠. You have good *playing* cards, particularly if partner has some length in diamonds.

b) Double. Three *defensive* tricks, only one *playing* trick. Don't forget partner's likely heart holding is a singleton.

c) 4♠. Good *playing* cards, only one *defensive* trick. One of your opponents is likely to have a singleton spade.

APPENDIX 1

The Sputnik Double

If South opens 1◇ and West overcalls 1♠, North can make a penalty double if he is using traditional methods. The double is for penalties because South has already bid. The requirements for such a penalty double (as described in chapter 10) are so stringent as to make its use rare. North must not have four cards in his partner's suit *or* a good suit of his own *and* his spades must be very strong. It is not surprising that bridge players have sought after a more efficient use of this double! Such a use is easily found and is played by an increasing number of players. It rejoices under a suitably technological name, the SPUTNIK DOUBLE (sometimes called the negative double).

The Sputnik double is a takeout double, and its most important use is to compensate for the bid that the overcall has ruled out, namely 1♡. It might seem that North can pass and wait for South to protect but North/South will have serious problems if East raises spades pre-emptively before they get together. This Sputnik double shows four hearts and opener will initially assume that responder has 7-10 points. If responder has only six points he can make such a double provided he is confident that he can cope with any rebid by opener. Equally there is nothing to stop responder from making a Sputnik double with far stronger hands in order to search for a 4-4 heart fit. He can then bid aggressively on the second round to clear up the misapprehension he has created.

	South	West	North		South	West	North
a)	1♣	1♡	Double	b)	1◇	1♡	Double

A Sputnik double emphasises the unbid major, even if no space has been stolen. In each of the above sequences North is showing four spades, while at the same time suggesting that if South doesn't like spades he is prepared to consider alternative contracts. Therefore if North chooses to bid 1♠ in preference to a Sputnik double he doesn't want to give partner as much freedom to decide the final contract. Presumably he either has five spades, or is worried by a probable rebid after a Sputnik double.

   ♠ A K J 5   ♡ 6 4 3 2   ◇ 9 6 4   ♣ 7 5

If West overcalls South's 1♣ opening bid with 1♡, North will choose 1♠ with the hand above as he does not want to encourage South to rebid 2◇. Note that such a rebid would *not* be a reverse after a Sputnik double as South has a right to assume that North is willing to hear a bid in either unbid suit. It is more like making a single raise in responder's suit than reversing into a new suit.

	South	West	North			South	West	North
c)	1♣	1◇	Double		d)	1♡	1♠	Double

Sequence c) has two unbid majors. The Sputnik double should guarantee a four-card holding in at least one of them.

If both majors have been bid (sequence d)) North's double should show both minors or one minor and heart tolerance (so that he can retreat to 2♡ if South bids the wrong minor).

You can play Sputnik doubles up to any level and it is common to play them up to 2♠.

	South	West	North
e)	1◇	2♣	Double
f)	1♠	2♣	Double
g)	1♣	2♠	Double

The higher the level of the overcall, the more points you need for a Sputnik double. In sequences e) and f) North/South are very likely to find a playable spot at the two level, hence North can double with as little as six points if he has a particularly suitable shape.

   ♠ K 7 6 3   ♡ J 8 6 4   ◇ Q 7 4   ♣ 9 7

North could well hold this hand for sequence e). He has *both* majors *and* a good fit for South's diamonds. However reverse the diamond and club holdings and he should pass. As always, a marginal bid is more attractive if you are prepared for all outcomes. Counting points is no substitute for common sense.

The Sputnik double in sequence g) forces the bidding to the three level, therefore North should have at least nine points.

RESPONSES TO A SPUTNIK DOUBLE

When the double guarantees a known suit, opener tries to make the rebid he would have made if responder had bid that suit. Suppose South opens 1◇, West overcalls 1♡ and North doubles (showing four spades).

a) ♠ K J 7 4	♡ 8 7	◇ A K 9 8 7	♣ J 3
b) ♠ K J 7 4	♡ J 7	◇ A K 9 8 7	♣ K 7
c) ♠ 8 7	♡ A Q 5	◇ A K 9 8 7	♣ Q 9 8
d) ♠ Q 7	♡ A Q 5	◇ A K 9 8 7	♣ Q 9 8
e) ♠ Q 7 5	♡ 9 8 5	◇ A K Q 7	♣ A J 3

Holding hand a) South would have raised a 1♠ response to 2♠, a minimum spade bid. The minimum spade bid available now is 1♠. Hand b) would have qualified for a jump rebid in spades, so South jumps to 2♠. Hands c) and d) are ideal for no trump rebids (1NT and 2NT respectively). Inevitably some hands give a headache, for instance hand e). South would happily have rebid 1NT without the intervention but after the 1♡ overcall the lack of a heart guard rules out that bid. 1♠ seems the least flawed rebid.

When the double doesn't guarantee a suit South may have to improvise. Suppose South opens 1◇, West overcalls 2♣ and North doubles (showing at least one major suit). With hand a) South should prefer 2♠ to 2◇, after all North should have anticipated such a rebid when he made the double. Similarly 3♠ would be correct with hand b).

NORTH WANTS TO MAKE A PENALTY DOUBLE

If you had exchanged the penalty double for this new 'takeout' double the gain would have far outweighed the loss. However you *haven't* lost the penalty double, indeed you have given yourself a new penalty double as South can choose to convert North's Sputnik double with a penalty pass. If North has a hand which is suitable for a penalty double he passes! This pass is virtually forcing on South. Consider the implications of an auction in which West overcalls South's 1♣ opening with 1♠ and North passes. North has *either* a weak hand *or* a penalty double of spades. South must cater for the penalty double *unless* he has such a strong holding in the overcaller's suit that North cannot have a penalty double. This is not quite as suicidal as it sounds. If South has a minimum opening bid then the failure of East/West to bid beyond 1♠ marks North with some values. Note that East cannot make a trap pass with a strong hand in the hope of catching South. If South's spade holding allows him to pass, East would then have a tough time explaining the resulting missed game to West!

a)   ♠ K J 7 2   ♡ Q 8   ◇ J 7   ♣ A K 8 7 5
b)   ♠ K Q 7   ♡ Q 4 3   ◇ J 7   ♣ A K 8 7 5
c)   ♠ 7   ♡ 9 8   ◇ A J 8 6   ♣ K Q J 10 9 6
d)   ♠ 7   ♡ K 8 7 5   ◇ A 7 6   ♣ K Q J 7 5
e)   ♠ 7 4   ♡ K 8 6 5   ◇ A 8   ♣ K Q J 7 5

If South holds a) or b) his spade holding makes it virtually impossible that North has a hand suitable for a penalty double of a 1♠ overcall. Since the only other possibility is a weak hand, South can pass with a clear conscience.

Holding c) South suspects that North is hoping to hear a reopening double and is planning to convert it with a penalty pass. However, with so little defensive strength, he is not prepared to accept such a penalty double (using the same yardstick as described in Chapter 10). Therefore he must not reopen with a double. His correct rebid is 2♣. He certainly cannot pass as North may be very strong indeed!

With d) or e) South reopens with a takeout double. If North has a hand suitable to make a penalty pass, South will be content.

Quiz on Sputnik Doubles

1) At love all South opens 1♣ and West overcalls 1♡. What should you, as North, call with these hands?

a) ♠ Q 7 5 3   ♡ A 8   ♢ 7 5 3 2   ♣ J 8 3
b) ♠ Q 7 5 3   ♡ 8   ♢ A 7 5 3   ♣ J 8 6 5
c) ♠ Q 9 7 5 3   ♡ A 8   ♢ 7 5 3   ♣ J 6 4
d) ♠ Q 9 3   ♡ 7 6 4 3   ♢ A 5 3   ♣ Q 7 4
e) ♠ Q 9 3   ♡ 7 6 5 3   ♢ A 8 5 3   ♣ Q 9
f) ♠ Q 9   ♡ A Q 9 8 6   ♢ K 9 7   ♣ 7 5 3

2) At game all South opens 1♢ and West overcalls 2♣. What should you, as North, call with these hands?

a) ♠ A 8 5 3   ♡ Q 9 6 3   ♢ Q 5   ♣ 9 6 4
b) ♠ K Q 8 7   ♡ J 10 8 6   ♢ 7 6 4   ♣ 5 2
c) ♠ A J 6 4   ♡ 8 7 5   ♢ A J 8 6   ♣ 9 7
d) ♠ J 8 6 4   ♡ 9 8 5   ♢ A J 6   ♣ 9 8 5
e) ♠ A 8 5 3   ♡ Q 9 6 3   ♢ 5   ♣ 9 6 4 2
f) ♠ A 8 5 3   ♡ Q 9 6 3   ♢ 7 6 5 2   ♣ 9
g) ♠ A 9 8 6   ♡ 8 7 5   ♢ 5   ♣ K Q 10 7 6
h) ♠ K 7 5 3   ♡ A Q 9 7 5   ♢ J 5 3   ♣ 6
i) ♠ K 8 6 5   ♡ Q 9 7 5 4   ♢ J 5 3   ♣ 9

3) At love all you, as South, open 1♡ and West's overcall of 1♠ is passed round to you. What do you call with these hands?

a) ♠ 9   ♡ K Q 8 6 4   ♢ A K 6   ♣ A Q 5 3
b) ♠ 9   ♡ K Q 9 8 5   ♢ A K 7   ♣ 8 7 5 3
c) ♠ A Q 7 5   ♡ K Q 8 7 5   ♢ J 4   ♣ 7 5
d) ♠ 9 7   ♡ K Q 8 6 4   ♢ K 8 6   ♣ A 7 2
e) ♠ 9   ♡ K Q J 8 6   ♢ A J 9 7 6   ♣ 8 5

4) At game all you, as South, open 1♢ and North doubles West's 1♠ overcall. What do you call with these hands?

a) ♠ 9 8   ♡ K 7 6 5   ♢ A Q J 7 4   ♣ Q 6
b) ♠ 9 8   ♡ K 7 6 5   ♢ A Q J 7 4   ♣ A J
c) ♠ 9 8 6 4   ♡ K 8   ♢ A Q J 7 4   ♣ K 8
d) ♠ 9 8 6   ♡ K 8 7   ♢ A K Q J 7   ♣ A Q
e) ♠ A Q 6 3   ♡ 9   ♢ K 8 7 6 4   ♣ K 7 2

Answers to Quiz

1) a) Double. Showing four spades and 6+ points.

b) Double. You should investigate a 4-4 spade fit before supporting clubs, just as you would in an uncontested auction.

c) 1♠. Forcing. You are not prepared for a 2◇ rebid after a Sputnik double.

d) 2♣. You should not double without four spades or bid 1NT without a heart guard.

e) Pass. If South reopens with a double you will bid 2◇ (remember that if you play Sputnik doubles South *has* to reopen unless his hearts are good. Therefore he might have no more than a minimum opening bid).

f) Pass. If South's reopening bid is a double, your pass will leave West regretting his intervention.

2) a) Double, and pass if South makes any minimum rebid.

b) Double. You only have six points but you can happily pass any rebid.

c) Double. Then raise 2◇ to 3◇, give preference to 3◇ over 2♡ or raise 2♠ to 3♠.

d) 2◇. Your hand is too weak to investigate the spade fit with a Sputnik double.

e) Pass. A 2◇ rebid after a Sputnik double would embarrass you.

f) Double. You are prepared for any response.

g) Pass. Waiting, like a vulture, for a reopening double!

h) 2♡. You are strong enough to bid this hand naturally.

i) Double. You are not strong enough to investigate a 5-3 heart fit but a Sputnik double should enable you to find a playable spot.

3) a) Double. If North makes a minimum response you will make one further game try.

b) Double. This shows no extra values. If North removes this double he must have a hand too weak to make an initial Sputnik double.

c) Pass. Your own spade suit tells you that North cannot have a penalty double of spades. Therefore he must be weak.

d) Double. Just in case North can make a penalty pass.

e) 2♦. With a weak, distributional opening you would not accept a penalty double of spades. Your obligation to reopen remains, just in case North has such a penalty double, but you must not double and give North the opportunity to pass.

4) a) 2♡. You would have raised a 1♡ response to 2♡.

b) 3♡. Again the bid you would have made if North had responded 1♡.

c) 2♦. Your natural rebid, now that a spade rebid is absurd.

d) 2♠. You would welcome the news of a no trump guard so you can play in 3NT.

e) 1NT. The overcall has stolen your natural rebid and this seems the most descriptive solution. This doesn't show 15-16 points as it would in an uncontested auction.

APPENDIX 2

Transfer Bidding

1) After a 1NT opening

If you ask the average club player to give the main advantage of transfer bidding you will probably be told that it usually gets the contract played by the 'right' hand. There are two reasons why it pays to have the stronger hand as declarer. Firstly, holdings like K x or A Q are protected from the opening lead. Secondly, defending is harder if most of the opposing values are concealed in declarer's hand rather than visible in dummy to everybody. Transfer bidding has the merit of increasing the probability that the no trump opener becomes declarer.

However, the greatest advantage of playing transfers is that many more sequences become available, leading to accurate bidding of many hands that were unbiddable with traditional methods. Consider the problems you face if your partner opens 1NT and you hold these hands:

a) ♠ 3 2   ♡ A J 6 5 3   ◇ A Q 6   ♣ 8 5 3
b) ♠ A 5 3   ♡ A J 7 6 5   ◇ A 9 8 5   ♣ 6
c) ♠ 8 6 2   ♡ A Q 7 5   ◇ 7   ♣ A K J 5 4
d) ♠ K Q 7   ♡ A Q 8 4   ◇ 9 7   ♣ A K J 5

Holding a) you want to show five hearts and make a game *try*. The accepted method of doing this is to start with a Stayman 2♣ and bid 3♡ on the next round. However, this bypasses 2NT, which might be the last playable contract if opener has 12 points and only two hearts.

Holding b) you start with 3♡ but what if opener rebids 3NT? If you remove this to 4◇ you may have left behind the best contract. On the other hand, if you pass, the defenders may cash five or six club tricks when 5◇ would be laydown! You need a way to show both suits *below* 3NT.

Holding c) you can investigate a heart fit with Stayman but if that fails to materialise you cannot show your clubs by bidding 3♣ because that would be a sign-off. Alternatively, you could start with 3♣, but if that produces 3NT you cannot safely probe for a 4-4 heart fit.

If you consider b) and c) together you will see that traditional responses to 1NT are not very helpful if you hold 5-4 shape.

Holding d) you are near the slam zone, having a combined 31-33 points. A 4-4 fit could be worth that vital extra trick. Stayman will uncover such a heart fit, but a club fit will be much harder to find.

Any good system of transfer bidding solves these problems, and at very little cost. The only price you have to pay is that you lose the opportunity to sign off in 2◇. The system we outline here is the 'lowest common denominator' of transfer systems, incorporating all the basic principles but leaving you to add the details.

THE 2◇ RESPONSE TO 1NT

This guarantees five hearts and requires opener to bid 2♡. You could have any of these hands. Opener has no way of knowing which until he hears your continuation.

a) ♠ 7	♡ K J 7 6 4	◇ J 8 6 4	♣ 8 7 4
b) ♠ 3 2	♡ A J 6 5 3	◇ A Q 6	♣ 8 5 3
c) ♠ 3 2	♡ A J 6 5 3	◇ A Q 6	♣ K 8 5
d) ♠ 3 2	♡ A J 8 6 5 3	◇ A J 8	♣ 8 5
e) ♠ 3 2	♡ A J 8 6 5 3	◇ A K 8	♣ 8 5
f) ♠ A 5 3	♡ A J 7 6 5	◇ A 9 8 5	♣ 6
g) ♠ A J 6 4	♡ K J 7 6 4	◇ A 4	♣ 9 7

With a) you will pass 2♡. You are using the transfer as a sign off.

With b) {which was hand a) in the previous section} you will continue with a non-forcing 2NT, showing five hearts and the values to make a game *try*.

Hand c) merits a continuation of 3NT. The message is similar to b) but this time you must insist on game.

With d) raise 2♡ to 3♡. Since you have already shown five hearts by bidding 2◇, you are now showing a sixth heart and leaving partner to choose between a final contract of 3♡ or 4♡.

Hand e) is strong enough to rebid 4♡. You could have immediately bid 4♡ over 1NT but it might be advantageous to make partner declarer if he has vulnerable tenaces in the black suits.

With f) {which was hand b) in the previous section} or g) you intend to follow up by bidding your four-card suit. This is forcing for at least one round and should be game-forcing if the second suit is bid at the three level.

South	West	North	East
1NT	No	2◇	No
2♡	No	3◇	No
?			

The idea that opener can bid a non-forcing 3♡ here is quite absurd. You are forcing him to bid game (3NT) if he has a misfitting minimum with two hearts and three diamonds. Why would you want to play in a part-score if he has a *better* fit? Opener should normally bid 3♡ rather than 4♡ if he has three card support, leaving an extra round for cue bidding if responder has a slam in mind.

THE 2♡ RESPONSE TO 1NT
As you would expect, this guarantees at least five spades and requires opener to bid 2♠. The continuations follow similar principles to those described above.

THE 2♠ RESPONSE TO 1NT
This bid can be used in a number of different ways but it seems best to reserve it for hands with enough values to investigate a slam but without a five-card suit. It is obviously game-forcing and initiates a sequence in which both players bid their four-card suits in ascending order until either a fit is found or 3NT is reached.

If opener's 1NT is minimum he rebids 2NT over 2♠ and

responder starts bidding four-card suits. If opener's 1NT is maximum he launches into his lowest four-card suit immediately over 2♠.

We can now see how responder (East here) should deal with hand d), at the start of this appendix.

West	East	West	East
♠ J 8 4	♠ K Q 7	1NT	2♠
♡ K J 7 6	♡ A Q 8 4	3◇ (1)	3♡ (2)
◇ A K Q 3	◇ 9 7	4♡ (3)	5♣ (4)
♣ 8 7	♣ A K J 5	5◇ (4)	6♡ (5)
		No	

1) Shows 13½-14 points and four diamonds. Denies four clubs.
2) Four-card heart suit.
3) Heart support.
4) Cue bids, showing first round control.
5) Note that the 4-4 fit allows declarer to make *five* heart tricks and hence avoid the club finesse. This sequence, unlike one starting with Stayman, would also have uncovered a 4-4 club fit.

Since opener is obliged to rebid 2NT over a 2♠ response if he has a minimum no trump opening it is also possible to use 2♠ for 11-12 point balanced hands without a four-card major. If opener's rebid is 2NT responder passes. If opener bids his lowest four-card suit responder signs off with 3NT. This releases the 2NT response to 1NT. We suggest you use this as a transfer to 3♣, allowing you to sign off in clubs or diamonds at the three level.

THE 2♣ RESPONSE TO 1NT
There is no pressing need to change Stayman sequences; however, there is one clever idea currently in use.

a) ♠ K J 6   ♡ A K 3   ◇ 7 5   ♣ A K J 5 4
b) ♠ 8 6 2   ♡ A Q 7 5 ·   ◇ 7   ♣ A K J 5 4

With hand a) you have a clearcut 3♣ response to 1NT using traditional methods. You hope to uncover a 5-3 club fit and eventually land in 6♣. There is nothing wrong with this, except that you sometimes want to investigate a club fit *after* failing to find a major fit with Stayman {e.g., hand b) which you originally saw as c) at the start of this chapter}. We suggest that, with one exception, you introduce all strong hands containing a five-card minor with Stayman, whether or not you have a four-card major. The exception is if you have a *five*-card major as well. Then you should start by transferring into your major and then bid your five-card minor twice.

c)	West	East	d)	West	East
	1NT	2♣		1NT	2♣
	2♦	3♣		2♠	3♦

e)	West	East
	1NT	3♣ or 3♦ or 3♡ or 3♠

Sequence c) is forcing, not a sign off. East has at least five clubs and obviously considers 5♣ or 6♣ a possible alternative to 3NT. He might also have a four-card major.

In sequence d) East has a similar hand with diamonds. If he has a major it doesn't seem to be spades!

The sequences in table e) now have no meaning. We are sure you can remedy that!

2) Other transfer sequences

It certainly makes sense to use transfer bids over a 2NT opening and any other sequence in which 2NT is the first natural bid in the auction. (e.g. 2♣ P 2♦ P 2NT). A 3♣ response should have the traditional Stayman (or Baron) meaning. 3♦ and 3♡ should show hearts and spades respectively.

Most partnerships abandon *all* conventions (even Stayman) when 1NT is doubled in order to allow responder to sign off in *any* suit at the two level.

It is also effective to use Stayman and transfers after a 1NT or 2NT overcall by your partner—but only as long as he is on the same wavelength. So many evenings which begin 'Transfers partner?' end in acrimony as a 3-2 trump fit proves insufficient for the job in hand! Conventional ideas need exhaustive discussion, otherwise they are best abandoned.

Quiz on Transfer Bidding

1) How do you respond with these hands if your partner opens 1NT?

a) ♠ Q 10 8 6 3   ♡ 7 3   ◇ K 7 6 4   ♣ 8 5
b) ♠ Q 10 8 6 3   ♡ K 7 6 4   ◇ 7 3   ♣ 8 5
c) ♠ A K 6 3   ♡ 8 6   ◇ A K J 4 3 ♣ 9 7
d) ♠ A K 2   ♡ A 5 2   ◇ A K J 4 3 ♣ 9 7
e) ♠ K Q 7 4   ♡ A 10 5   ◇ A 8   ♣ K Q 8 3
f) ♠ K Q 7   ♡ Q J 6   ◇ A K J   ♣ Q 7 3 2

2) Your partner opens 1NT and you bid 2♡. How do you continue after his enforced 2♠ rebid with these hands?

a) ♠ A Q 10 7 5   ♡ K 7   ◇ Q 10 8   ♣ 10 5 3
b) ♠ A Q 10 7 5   ♡ K 7   ◇ A 10 8   ♣ 10 5 3
c) ♠ A Q 10 7 5   ♡ K 7   ◇ A Q 8 6 ♣ 8 3
d) ♠ A Q 10 7 5   ♡ K 7   ◇ J 8 4 3 ♣ A 3
e) ♠ A Q 10 7 5   ♡ J 3 2 ◇ A 8 4 3 ♣ 4
f) ♠ A Q 10 7 5 2 ♡ J 3 2 ◇ K 5 3   ♣ 4

3) You open 1NT and dutifully rebid 2♠ when your partner responds 2♡. What do you call with these hands if his second bid is 2NT?

a) ♠ K 3   ♡ K Q 6   ◇ K 10 6 5   ♣ J 10 7 5
b) ♠ K 3   ♡ K Q 6   ◇ K 10 6 5   ♣ K 10 7 5
c) ♠ K 3 2 ♡ K 3   ◇ K 10 6 5   ♣ Q J 7 5
d) ♠ K 3 2 ♡ K 3   ◇ K 10 6 5   ♣ K Q 7 5

4) You open 1NT and your partner responds 2♠. What is your rebid with these hands?

a) ♠ K Q 6 3   ♡ K 3   ◇ Q 9 6 4   ♣ Q 10 8
b) ♠ K Q 8 6   ♡ K 3   ◇ A 9 6 4   ♣ Q 10 8

Answers to Quiz

1) a) 2♡. You intend to pass the enforced 2♠ rebid. It is arguable whether or not it is wise to sign off into a five-card major with 5-3-3-2 shape but it is *always* correct to sign off with 5-4-2-2 or 5-4-3-1 shape.

b) 2♣. Stayman, seeking a 4-4 heart fit. Obviously if opener's rebid is 2♢ you will sign off in 2♠.

c) 2♣. You will raise 2♠ to 4♠, otherwise you intend to continue with a game-forcing 3♢.

d) 2♣. You are not interested in the answer! You are simply using Stayman as a necessary starting point, prior to announcing your diamond suit.

e) 2♠. This will uncover a 4-4 fit in either black suit. If no such fit exists you should settle for 3NT.

f) 3NT. Even a 4-4 club fit is unlikely to make a slam desirable, so bid the obvious game contract.

2) a) 2NT. A hand with five spades and the values to raise 1NT to 2NT.

b) 3NT. As above, except this time you must insist on game.

c) 3♢. Game forcing and showing at least 5-4 shape.

d) 3NT. To bid 3♢, suggesting that 5♢ may be superior to 3NT, is foolish with such a poor suit.

e) 2NT. Not ideal, but you are not strong enough for a game forcing 3♢.

f) 3♠. Game try, showing a sixth spade.

3) a) Pass. Minimum with only two spades.

b) 3NT. Maximum with only two spades.

c) 3♠. Minimum, and hence declining the invitation to game, but opting for the 5-3 spade fit.

d) 4♠. Maximum with three-card spade support.

4) a) 2NT. Start by announcing your minimum no trump opening. Responder will now bid his lowest four-card suit.

b) 3♢. Maximum, denying four clubs and showing four diamonds.

Lisa Kleypas is the author of a number of historical romance novels that have been published in fourteen languages. She is also the author of the contemporary novels *Sugar Daddy* and *Blue-Eyed Devil*. In 1985, she was named Miss Massachusetts and competed in the Miss America pageant in Atlantic City. After graduating from Wellesley College with a political science degree, she published her first novel at age twenty-one. Her books have appeared on the *New York Times* bestseller list. Lisa is married and has two children.

SEDUCE ME AT SUNRISE

London, 1848 — for the last two years, following an attack of scarlet fever, Winifred Hathaway has been an invalid. She's been told she can do nothing but succumb to her illness, but her bright and optimistic nature means she will not accept such a fate. She has too much to live for, namely the handsome Merripen. A part of the Hathaway family since they took him under their wing — after he was wounded and left for dead — the gypsy-bred Merripen will do anything to protect Win, even hide his true feelings and break her heart. However, nothing can stand in the way of true love . . .

Books by Lisa Kleypas
Published by The House of Ulverscroft:

SUGAR DADDY
BLUE-EYED DEVIL
MINE TILL MIDNIGHT

LISA KLEYPAS

SEDUCE ME
AT SUNRISE

Complete and Unabridged

CHARNWOOD
Leicester

First published in Great Britain in 2008 by
Piatkus Books
An imprint of
Little, Brown Book Group, London

First Charnwood Edition
published 2010
by arrangement with
Little, Brown Book Group
An Hachette Livre UK Company, London

British Library CIP Data

Kleypas, Lisa.
    Seduce me at sunrise.
    1. London (England)- -History- -1800 – 1950- -Fiction.
    2. Love stories. 3. Large type books.
    I. Title
    813.5′4–dc22

    ISBN 978–1–44480–005–0   LP

Published by
F. A. Thorpe (Publishing)
Anstey, Leicestershire

Set by Words & Graphics Ltd.
Anstey, Leicestershire
Printed and bound in Great Britain by
T. J. International Ltd., Padstow, Cornwall

This book is printed on acid-free paper

To Sheila Clover English, a beautiful, kind woman who has so many gifts and talents. Thank you for turning my words into little works of video art, and even more for being a wonderful friend.

1

London, 1848
Winter

Win had always thought Kev Merripen was beautiful, in the way that an austere landscape or a wintry day could be beautiful. He was a large, striking man, uncompromising in every angle. The exotic boldness of his features was a perfect setting for eyes so dark that the irises were barely distinguishable from the pupil. His hair was thick and as black as a raven's wing, his brows strong and straight. And his wide mouth was set with a perpetually brooding curve that Win found irresistible.

Merripen. Her love, but never her lover. They had known each other since childhood, when he had been taken in by her family. Although the Hathaways had always treated him as one of their own, Merripen had acted in the capacity of a servant. A protector. An outsider.

He came to Win's bedroom and stood at the threshold to watch as she packed a valise with a few personal articles from the top of her dresser. A hairbrush, a rack of pins, a handful of handkerchiefs that her sister Poppy had embroidered for her. As Win tucked the objects into the leather bag, she was intensely aware of Merripen's motionless form. She knew what lurked beneath his stillness, because she felt the

1

same undertow of yearning.

The thought of leaving him was breaking her heart. And yet there was no choice. She had been an invalid ever since she'd had scarlet fever two years earlier. She was thin and frail and given to fainting spells and fatigue. Weak lungs, all the doctors had said. Nothing to do but succumb. A lifetime of bed rest followed by an early death.

Win would not accept such a fate.

She longed to get well, to enjoy the things that most people took for granted. To dance, laugh, walk through the countryside. She wanted the freedom to love . . . to marry . . . to have her own family someday.

With her health in such a poor state, there was no possibility of doing any of those things. But that was about to change. She was departing this day for a French clinic, where a dynamic young doctor, Julian Harrow, had achieved remarkable results for patients just like herself. His treatments were unorthodox, controversial, but Win didn't care. She would have done anything to be cured. Because until that day came, she could never have Merripen.

'Don't go,' he said, so softly that she almost didn't hear him.

Win struggled to remain outwardly calm, even as a hot-and-cold chill went down her spine.

'Please close the door,' she managed to say. They needed privacy for the conversation they were about to have.

Merripen didn't move. Color had risen in his swarthy face, and his black eyes glittered with a ferocity that wasn't at all like him. He was all Rom at this moment, his emotions closer to the surface than he ever usually allowed.

She went to close the door herself, while he moved away from her as if any contact between them would result in fatal harm.

'Why don't you want me to go, Kev?' she asked gently.

'You won't be safe there.'

'I'll be perfectly safe,' she said. 'I have faith in Dr. Harrow. His treatments sound sensible to me, and he's had a high success rate — '

'He's had as many failures as successes. There are better doctors here in London. You should try them first.'

'I think my best chances lie with Dr. Harrow.' Win smiled into Merripen's hard black eyes, understanding the things he couldn't say. 'I'll come back to you. I promise.'

He ignored that. Any attempt she made to bring their feelings to light was always met with rock-hard resistance. He would never admit he cared for her, or treat her as anything other than a fragile invalid who needed his protection. A butterfly under glass.

While he went on with his private pursuits.

Despite Merripen's discretion in personal matters, Win was certain there had been more than a few women who had given him their bodies, and used him for their own pleasure. Something bleak and angry rose from the depths of her soul at the thought of Merripen lying with someone else. It would shock everyone who knew her, had they understood the power of her

3

desire for him. It would probably shock Merripen most of all.

Seeing his expressionless face, Win thought, *Very well, Kev. If this is what you want, I'll be stoic. We'll have a pleasant, bloodless good-bye.*

Later she would suffer in private, knowing it would be an eternity until she saw him again. But that was better than living like this, forever together and yet apart, her illness always between them.

'Well,' she said briskly, 'I'll be off soon. And there's no need to worry, Kev. Leo will take care of me during the trip to France, and — '

'Your brother can't even take care of himself,' Merripen said harshly. 'You're not going. You'll stay here, where I can — '

He bit off the words.

But Win had heard a note of something like fury, or anguish, buried in his deep voice.

This was getting interesting.

Her heart began to thump. 'There . . . ' She had to pause to catch her breath. 'There's only one thing that could stop me from leaving.'

He shot her an alert glance. 'What is it?'

It took her a long moment to summon the courage to speak. 'Tell me you love me. Tell me, and I'll stay.'

The black eyes widened. The sound of his indrawn breath cut through the air like the downward arc of an ax stroke. He was silent, frozen.

A curious mixture of amusement and despair surged through Win as she waited for his reply.

'I . . . care for everyone in your family . . . '

'No. You know that's not what I'm asking for.'

Win moved toward him and lifted her pale hands to his chest, resting her palms on a surface of tough, unyielding muscle. She felt the response that jolted through him. 'Please,' she said, hating the desperate edge in her own voice, 'I wouldn't care if I died tomorrow, if I could just hear it once — '

'*Don't*,' he growled, backing away.

Casting aside all caution, Win followed. She reached out to grasp the loose folds of his shirt. 'Tell me. Let's finally bring the truth out into the open — '

'Hush; you'll make yourself ill.'

It infuriated Win that he was right. She could feel the familiar weakness, the dizziness that came along with her pounding heart and laboring lungs. She cursed her failing body. 'I love you,' she said wretchedly. 'And if I were well, no power on earth could keep me away from you. If I were well, I would take you into my bed, and I would show you as much passion as any woman could — '

'No.' His hand lifted to her mouth as if to muffle her, then snatched back as he felt the warmth of her lips.

'If I'm not afraid to admit it, why should you be?' Her pleasure at being near him, touching him, was a kind of madness. Recklessly she molded herself against him. He tried to push her away without hurting her, but she clung with all her remaining strength. 'What if this were the last moment you ever had with me? Wouldn't you have been sorry not to tell me how you felt? Wouldn't you — '

Merripen covered her mouth with his, desperate for a way to make her quiet. They both gasped and went still, absorbing the feel of it. Each strike of his breath on her cheek was a shock of heat. His arms went around her, wrapping her in his vast strength, holding her against the hardness of his body. And then everything ignited, and they were both lost in a furor of need.

She could taste the sweetness of apples on his breath, the bitter hint of coffee, but most of all the rich essence of him. Wanting more, craving him, she pressed upward. He took the innocent offering with a low, savage sound.

She felt the touch of his tongue. Opening to him, she drew him deeper, hesitantly using her own tongue in a slide of silk-on-silk, and he shivered and gasped and held her more tightly. A new weakness flooded her, her senses starving for his hands and mouth and body . . . his powerful weight over and between and inside her . . . Oh, she wanted him, wanted . . .

Merripen kissed her with savage hunger, his mouth moving over hers with rough, luscious strokes. Her nerves blazed with pleasure, and she squirmed and clutched at him, wanting him closer.

Even through the layers of her skirts, she felt the way he urged his hips against hers, the tight subtle rhythm. Instinctively she reached down to feel him, to soothe him, and her trembling fingers encountered the hard shape of his arousal.

He buried an agonized groan in her mouth.

For one scalding moment he reached down and gripped her hand tightly over himself. Her eyes flew open as she felt the pulsing charge, the heat and tension that seemed ready to explode. 'Kev ... the bed ...,' she whispered, going crimson from head to toe. She had wanted him so desperately, for so long, and now it was finally going to happen. 'Take me — '

Merripen cursed and shoved her away from him, turning to the side. He was gasping uncontrollably.

Win moved toward him. 'Kev — '

'*Stay back*,' he said with such force that she jumped in fright.

For at least a minute, there was no sound or movement save the angry friction of their breaths.

Merripen was the first to speak. His voice was weighted with rage and disgust, though whether it was directed against her or himself was impossible to fathom. 'That will never happen again.'

'Because you're afraid you might hurt me?'

'Because I don't want you that way.'

She stiffened with indignation, and gave a disbelieving laugh. 'You responded to me just now. I felt it.'

His color deepened. 'That would have happened with any woman.'

'You ... you're trying to make me believe that you have no particular feeling for me?'

'Nothing other than a desire to protect one of your family.'

She knew it was a lie; she *knew* it. But his callous rejection made leaving a bit easier. 'I ...'

It was difficult to speak. 'How noble of you.' Her attempt at an ironic tone was ruined by her breathlessness. Stupid weak lungs.

'You're overwrought,' Merripen said, moving toward her. 'You need to rest — '

'I'm *fine*,' Win said fiercely, going to the washstand, gripping it to steady herself. When her balance was secured, she poured a splash of water onto a linen cloth, and applied it to her flushed cheeks. Glancing into the looking glass, she made her face into its usual serene mask. Somehow she made her voice calm. 'I will have all of you or nothing,' she said. 'You know the words that will make me stay. If you won't say them, then leave.'

The air in the room was heavy with emotion. Win's nerves screamed in protest as the silence drew out. She stared into the looking glass, able to see only the broad shape of his shoulder and arm. And then he moved, and the door opened and closed.

Win continued to dab at her face with the cool cloth, using it to blot a few stray teardrops. Setting the cloth aside, she noticed that her palm, the one she had used to grip the intimate shape of him, still retained the memory of his flesh. And her lips still tingled from the sweet, hard kisses, and her chest was filled with the ache of desperate love.

'Well,' she said to her flushed reflection, 'now you're motivated.' And she laughed shakily until she had to wipe away more tears.

★   ★   ★

As Cam Rohan supervised the loading of the carriage that would soon depart for the London docks, he couldn't help wondering if he was making a mistake. He had promised his new wife that he would take care of her family. But less than two months after he'd married Amelia, he was sending one of her sisters to France.

'We can wait,' he had told Amelia only last night, holding her against his shoulder, stroking her rich brown hair as it lay in a river over his chest. 'If you wish to keep Win with you a little longer, we can send her to the clinic in the spring.'

'No, she must go as soon as possible. Dr. Harrow made it clear that too much time has already been wasted. Win's best hope of improvement is to start the course of treatment at once.'

Cam had smiled at Amelia's pragmatic tone. His wife excelled at hiding her emotions, maintaining such a sturdy façade that few people perceived how vulnerable she was underneath. Cam was the only one with whom she would let down her guard.

'We must be sensible,' Amelia had added.

Cam had rolled her to her back and stared down at her small, lovely face in the lamplight. Such round blue eyes, dark as the heart of midnight. 'Yes,' he allowed softly. 'But it's not always easy to be sensible, is it?'

She shook her head, her eyes turning liquid.

He stroked her cheek with his fingertips. 'Poor hummingbird,' he whispered. 'You've gone through so many changes in the past months

— not the least of which was marrying me. And now I'm sending your sister away.'

'To a clinic, to make her well,' Amelia had said. 'I know it's best for her. It's only that . . . I'll miss her. Win is the dearest, gentlest one in the family. The peacemaker. We'll all probably murder each other in her absence.' She gave him a little scowl. 'Don't tell anyone I was crying, or I shall be *very* cross with you.'

'No, *monisha*,' he had soothed, cuddling her closer as she sniffled. 'All your secrets are safe with me. You know that.'

And he had kissed away her tears and removed her nightgown slowly, and made love to her even more slowly. 'Little love,' he had whispered as she trembled beneath him. 'Let me make you feel better . . . ' And as he took careful possession of her body, he told her in the old language that she pleased him in all ways, that he loved to be inside her, that he would never leave her. Although Amelia hadn't understood the foreign words, the sound of them had excited her, her hands working on his back like cat paws, her hips pressing upward into his weight. He had pleasured her, and taken his own pleasure, until his wife had fallen into a sated sleep.

For a long while afterward Cam had held her nestled against him, with the trusting weight of her head on his shoulder. He was responsible for Amelia now, and for her entire family.

The Hathaways were a group of misfits that included four sisters, a brother, and Merripen, who was a Rom like Cam. No one seemed to know much about Merripen aside from the fact that he had been taken in by the Hathaway family as a boy, after being wounded and left for dead in a Gypsy hunt. He was something more than a servant, but not quite part of the family.

There was no predicting how Merripen would fare in Win's absence, but Cam had a feeling it wasn't going to be pleasant. They couldn't have been more opposite, the pale blond invalid and the huge Rom. One so refined and otherworldly, the other brown and rough-hewn and barely civilized. But the connection was there, like the path of a hawk that always returned to the same forest, following the invisible map that was etched in its very nature.

When the carriage was properly loaded and the luggage was secured with leather straps, Cam went into the hotel suite where the family was staying. They had gathered in the receiving room to say their good-byes.

Merripen was conspicuously absent.

They crowded the small room, the sisters and their brother, Leo, who was going to France as Win's companion and escort.

'There, now,' Leo said gruffly, patting the back of the youngest, Beatrix, who had just turned sixteen. 'No need to make a scene.'

She hugged him tightly. 'You'll be lonely, so far from home. Won't you take one of my pets to keep you company?'

'No, darling. I'll have to content myself with whatever human companionship I can find on board.' He turned to Poppy, a ruddy-haired beauty of eighteen. 'Good-bye, Sis. Enjoy your first season in London. Try not to accept the first fellow who proposes to you.'

Poppy moved forward to embrace him. 'Dear Leo,' she said, her voice muffled against his shoulder, 'do try to behave while you're in France.'

'No one behaves in France,' Leo told her. 'That's why everyone likes it so much.' He turned to Amelia. It was only then that his self-assured façade began to disintegrate. He drew an unsteady breath. Of all the Hathaway siblings, Leo and Amelia had argued the most frequently, and the most bitterly. And yet she was undoubtedly his favorite. They had been through a great deal together, taking care of the younger siblings after their parents had died. Amelia had watched Leo turn from a promising young architect into a wreck of a man. Inheriting a viscouncy hadn't helped one bit. In fact, the newly acquired title and status had only hastened Leo's dissolution. That hadn't stopped Amelia from fighting for him, trying to save him, every step of the way. Which had annoyed him considerably.

Amelia went to him and laid her head against his chest. 'Leo,' she said with a sniffle. 'If you let anything happen to Win, I will kill you.'

He stroked her hair gently. 'You've threatened to kill me for years, and nothing ever comes of it.'

'I've been w-waiting for the right reason.'

Smiling, Leo pried her head from his chest and kissed her forehead. 'I'll bring her back safe and well.'

'And yourself?'

'And myself.'

Amelia smoothed his coat, her lip trembling. 'Then you had better stop leading the life of a drunken wastrel,' she said.

Leo grinned. 'But I've always believed in cultivating one's natural talents to the fullest.' He lowered his head so she could kiss his cheek. 'You're a fine one to talk about how to conduct oneself,' he said. 'You, who just married a man you barely know.'

'It was the best thing I ever did,' Amelia said.

'Since he's paying for my trip to France, I suppose I can't disagree.' Leo reached out to shake Cam's hand. After a rocky beginning, the two men had come to like each other in a short time. 'Good-bye, *phral*,' Leo said, using the Romany word that Cam had taught him for 'brother.' 'I have no doubt you'll do an excellent job taking care of the family. You've already gotten rid of me, which is a promising beginning.'

'You'll return to a rebuilt home and a thriving estate, my lord.'

Leo gave a low laugh. 'I can't wait to see what you will accomplish. You know, not just any peer would entrust all his affairs to a pair of Gypsies.'

'I would say with certainty,' Cam replied, 'that you're the only one.'

★ ★ ★

After Win had bid farewell to her sisters, Leo settled her into the carriage and sat beside her. There was a soft lurch as the team pulled forward, and they headed to the London docks.

Leo studied Win's profile. As usual, she showed little emotion, her fine-boned face serene and composed. But he saw the flags of color burning on the pale crests of her cheeks, and the way her fingers clenched and tugged at the embroidered handkerchief in her lap. It had not escaped him that Merripen hadn't been there to say good-bye. Leo wondered if he and Win had exchanged harsh words.

Sighing, Leo reached out and put his arm around his sister's thin, breakable frame. She stiffened but did not pull away. After a moment, the handkerchief came up, and he saw that she was blotting her eyes. She was afraid, and ill, and miserable.

And he was all she had.

God help her.

He made an attempt at humor. 'You didn't let Beatrix give you one of her pets, did you? I'm warning you, if you're carrying a hedgehog or a rat, it goes overboard as soon as we're on the ship.'

Win shook her head and blew her nose.

'You know,' Leo said conversationally, still holding her, 'you're the least amusing of all the sisters. I can't think how I ended up going to France with you.'

'Believe me,' came her watery reply, 'I wouldn't be this boring if I had any say in the matter. When I get well I intend to behave very badly indeed.'

'Well, that's something to look forward to.' He rested his cheek on her soft blond hair.

'Leo,' she asked after a moment, 'why did you volunteer to go to the clinic with me? Is it because you want to get well, too?'

Leo was both touched and annoyed by the innocent question. Win, like everyone else in the family, considered his excessive drinking an illness that might be cured by a period of abstinence and healthful surroundings. But his drinking was merely a symptom of the real illness — a grief so persistent that at times it threatened to stop his heart from beating.

There was no cure for losing Laura.

'No,' he said to Win. 'I have no aspirations to get well. I merely want to continue my debauchery with new scenery.' He was rewarded by a small chuckle. 'Win . . . did you and Merripen quarrel? Is that why he wasn't there to see you off?' At her prolonged silence, Leo rolled his eyes. 'If you insist on being close-mouthed, Sis, it's going to be a long journey indeed.'

'Yes, we quarreled.'

'About what? Harrow's clinic?'

'Not really. That was part of it, but . . . ' Win shrugged uncomfortably. 'It's too complicated. It would take forever to explain.'

'We're about to cross an ocean and half of France. Believe me, we have time.'

★ ★ ★

After the carriage had departed, Cam went to the mews behind the hotel, a tidy building with horse stalls and a carriage house on the ground floor, and servants' accommodations above. As

15

he had expected, Merripen was grooming the horses. The hotel mews were run on a part-livery system, which meant some of the stabling chores had to be assumed by the horse owners. At the moment Merripen was taking care of Cam's black gelding, a three-year-old named Pooka.

Merripen's movements were light, quick, and methodical as he ran a brush over the horse's shining flanks.

Cam watched him for a moment, appreciating the Rom's deftness. The story that Gypsies were exceptionally good with horses was no myth. A Rom considered the horse to be a comrade, an animal of poetry and heroic instincts. And Pooka accepted Merripen's presence with a calm deference he showed to few people.

'What do you want?' Merripen asked without looking at him.

Cam approached the open stall leisurely, smiling as Pooka lowered his head and nudged his chest. 'No, boy . . . no sugar lumps.' He patted the muscular neck. His shirtsleeves were rolled up to his elbows, exposing the tattoo of a black flying horse on his forearm. Cam had no memory of when he'd gotten the tattoo . . . It had been there forever, for reasons his grandmother would never explain.

The symbol was an Irish nightmare steed called a *pooka*, an alternately malevolent and benevolent horse who spoke in a human voice and flew at night on widespread wings. According to legend, the *pooka* would come to an unsuspecting human's door at midnight, and take him on a ride that would leave him forever changed.

Cam had never seen a similar mark on anyone else.

Until Merripen.

Through a quirk of fate, Merripen had recently been injured in a house fire. And as his wound was being treated, the Hathaways had discovered the tattoo on Merripen's shoulder.

That had raised more than a few questions in Cam's mind.

He saw Merripen glance at the tattoo on his arm. 'What do you make of a Rom wearing an Irish design?' Cam asked.

'There are Roma in Ireland. Nothing unusual.'

'There's something unusual about this tattoo,' Cam said evenly. 'I've never seen another like it, until you. And since it came as a surprise to the Hathaways, you've evidently taken great care to keep it hidden. Why is that, my *phral*?'

'Don't call me that.'

'You've been part of the Hathaway family since childhood,' Cam said. 'And I've married into it. That makes us brothers, doesn't it?'

A disdainful glance was his only reply.

Cam found perverse amusement in being friendly to a Rom who so clearly despised him. He understood exactly what had engendered Merripen's hostility. The addition of a new male to a family tribe, or *vitsa*, was never an easy situation, and usually his place would be low in the hierarchy. For Cam, a stranger, to come in and act as the head of the family was nearly unendurable. It didn't help that Cam was *poshram*, a half-breed born of a Romany mother and an Irish *gadjo* father. And if there was

17

anything that could make matters even worse, Cam was wealthy, which was shameful in the eyes of the Rom.

'Why have you always kept it hidden?' Cam persisted.

Merripen paused in his brushing and gave Cam a cold, dark glance. 'I was told it was the mark of a curse. That on the day I discovered what it meant, and what it was for, I or someone close to me, was fated to die.'

Cam showed no outward reaction, but he felt a few prickles of unease at the back of his neck.

'Who are you, Merripen?' he asked softly.

The big Rom went back to work. 'No one.'

'You were part of a tribe once. You must have had family.'

'I don't remember any father. My mother died when I was born.'

'So did mine. I was raised by my grand-mother.'

The brush halted in midstroke. Neither of them moved. The stable became deadly quiet, except for the snuffling and shifting of horses. 'I was raised by my uncle. To be one of the *asharibe*.'

'Ah.' Cam kept any hint of pity from his expression, but privately he thought, *You poor bastard*.

No wonder Merripen fought so well. Some Gypsy tribes took their strongest boys and turned them into bare-knuckle fighters, pitting them against each other at fairs and pubs and gatherings, for onlookers to make bets on. Some of the boys were disfigured or even killed. And the ones who survived were hardened fighters down to the bootstraps, and designated as warriors of the tribe.

'Well, that explains your sweet temperament,' Cam said. 'Was that why you chose to stay with the Hathaways after they took you in? Because you no longer wanted to live as an *asharibe*?'

'Yes.'

'You're lying, *phral*,' Cam said, watching him closely. 'You stayed for another reason.' And Cam knew from the Rom's visible flush that he'd hit upon the truth.

Quietly, Cam added, 'You stayed for her.'

2

Twelve years earlier

There was no goodness in him. No softness. He had been raised to sleep on hard ground, to eat plain food and drink cold water, and to fight other boys on command. If he ever refused to fight, he was beaten by his uncle, the *rom baro*, the big male of the tribe. There was no mother to plead for him, no father to intervene in the *rom baro's* harsh punishments. No one ever touched him except in violence. He existed only to fight, to steal, to do things against the *gadje*.

Most Gypsies did not hate the pale, doughy Englishmen who lived in tidy houses and carried pocket watches and read books by the hearth. They only distrusted them. But Kev's tribe despised *gadje*, mostly because the *rom baro* did. And whatever the leader's whims, beliefs, and inclinations were, you followed them.

Eventually, because the *rom baro's* tribe had inflicted such mischief and misery whenever they set up camp, the *gadjos* had decided to scourge them from the land.

The Englishmen had come on horses, carrying weapons. There had been gunshots, clubbings, sleeping Romas attacked in their beds, women and children screaming and crying. The camp had been scattered and everyone had been driven off, the *vardo* wagons set on fire, many of the horses stolen by the *gadjos*.

Kev had tried to fight them, to defend the *vitsa*, but he had been struck on the head with the heavy butt of a gun. Another had stabbed him in the back with a bayonet. The tribe had left him for dead. Alone in the night, he had lain half-conscious by the river, listening to the rush of dark water, feeling the chill of hard, wet earth beneath him, dimly aware of his own blood seeping in warm runlets from his body. He had waited without fear for the great wheel to roll into darkness. He had no reason or desire to live.

But just as Night yielded to the approach of her sister Morning, Kev found himself gathered up and carried away in a small rustic cart. A *gadjo* had found him, and had bid a local boy to help carry the dying Rom into his house.

It was the first time Kev had ever been beneath the ceiling of anything other than a *vardo*. He found himself torn between curiosity at his foreign surroundings and rage at the indignity at having to die indoors under the care of a *gadjo*. But Kev was too weak, too much in pain, to lift a finger in his own defense.

The room he occupied was not much bigger than a horse stall, holding only a bed and a chair. There were cushions, pillows, framed needlework on the walls, a lamp with beaded fringe. Had he not been so ill, he would have gone mad in the overstuffed little room.

The *gadjo* who had brought him there . . . Hathaway . . . was a tall, slender man with pale yellow hair. His gentle manner, his diffidence, made Kev hostile. Why had Hathaway saved him? What could he want from a Romany boy? Kev refused to talk to the *gadjo* and wouldn't take medicine. He rejected any overture of kindness. He owed this Hathaway nothing. He hadn't wanted to be saved, hadn't wanted to live. So he lay there flinching and silent whenever the man changed the bandage on his back.

There was only one time Kev spoke, and that was when Hathaway had asked about the tattoo.

'What is this mark for?'

'It's a curse,' Kev said through gritted teeth. 'Don't speak of it to anyone, or the curse will fall on you, too.'

'I see.' The man's voice was kind. 'I will keep your secret. But I'll tell you that as a rationalist, I don't believe in such superstitions. A curse has only as much power as the subject gives it.'

Stupid gadjo, Kev thought. Everyone knew that to deny a curse was to bring *very* bad luck on oneself.

It was a noisy household, full of children. Kev could hear them beyond the closed door of the room he had been put in. But there was something else . . . a faint, sweet presence nearby. He felt it hovering, outside the room, just out of his reach. And he yearned for it, hungered for relief from the darkness and fever and pain.

Amid the clamor of children bickering, laughing, singing, he heard a murmur that raised every hair on his body. A girl's voice. Lovely, soothing. He wanted her to come to him. He willed it as he lay there, his wounds mending with torturous slowness. *Come to me . . .*

But she never appeared. The only ones who entered the room were Hathaway and his wife, a pleasant but wary woman who regarded Kev as if he were a wild animal that had found its way into her civilized home. And he behaved like one, snapping and snarling whenever they came near him. As soon as he could move under his own power, he washed himself with the basin of warm water they left in his room. He would not eat in front of them but waited until they had left a tray by the bed. His entire will was devoted to healing enough to be able to escape.

On one or two occasions the children came to look at him, peeking around the edge of the partially open door. There were two little girls named Poppy and Beatrix, who giggled and squealed with happy fright when he growled at them. There was another, older daughter, Amelia, who glanced at him with the same skeptical assessment the mother had. And there was a tall blue-eyed boy, Leo, who looked not much older than Kev himself.

'I want to make it clear,' the boy had said from the doorway, his voice quiet, 'that no one intends to do you any harm. As soon as you are able to leave, you are free to do so.' He had stared at Kev's sullen, feverish face for a moment before adding, 'My father is a kind man. A Samaritan. But I'm not. So don't even think of injuring or insulting any of the Hathaways, or you'll answer to me.'

Kev respected that. Enough to give Leo a slight nod. Of course, if Kev were well, he could have bested the boy easily, sent him to the ground bleeding and broken. But Kev had begun to accept that this odd little family really didn't mean him harm. Nor did they want anything from him. They had merely provided care and shelter as if he were a stray dog. They seemed to expect nothing in return.

That didn't lessen his contempt for them and their ridiculously soft, comfortable world. He hated them all, nearly as much as he hated himself. He was a fighter, a thief, steeped in violence and deceit. Couldn't they see that? They seemed to have no comprehension of the danger they had brought into their own home.

After a week, Kev's fever had eased and his wound had mended enough to allow him to move. He had to leave before something terrible happened, before he did something. So Kev woke early one morning and dressed with painstaking slowness in the clothes they had given him, which had belonged to Leo.

It hurt to move, but Kev ignored the fierce pounding in his head and the jabbing fire in his back. He filled his coat pockets with a knife and fork from his food tray, a candle stub, a sliver of soap. The first light of dawn shone through the little window above the bed. The family would be awake soon. He started for the door, felt dizzy, and half-collapsed onto the mattress. Gasping, he tried to collect his strength.

There was a tap at the door, and it opened. His lips parted to snarl at the visitor.

'May I come in?' he heard a girl ask softly.

The curse died on Kev's lips. His senses were

24

overwhelmed. He closed his eyes, breathing, waiting.

It's you. You're here.

At last.

'You've been alone for so long,' she said, approaching him, 'I thought you might want some company. I'm Winnifred.'

Kev drew in the scent and sound of her, his heart pounding. Carefully he eased to his back, ignoring the pain that shot through him. He opened his eyes.

He had never thought any *gadji* could compare to Romany girls. But this one was remarkable, an otherworldly creature as pale as moonlight, her hair silver-blond, her features formed with tender gravity. She looked warm and innocent and soft. Everything he wasn't. His entire being responded so acutely to her that he reached out and seized her with a quiet grunt.

She gasped a little but held still. Kev knew it wasn't right to touch her. He didn't know how to be gentle. He would hurt her without even trying. And yet she relaxed in his hold, and stared at him with those steady blue eyes.

Why wasn't she frightened of him? He was actually frightened *for* her, because he knew what he was capable of.

He hadn't been aware of pulling her closer. All he knew was that now part of her weight was resting on him as he lay on the bed, and his fingertips had curled into the pliant flesh of her upper arms.

'Let go,' she told him gently.

He didn't want to. Ever. He wanted to keep

her against him, and pull her braided hair down and comb his fingers through the pale silk. He wanted to carry her off to the ends of the earth.

'If I do,' he said gruffly, 'will you stay?'

The delicate lips curved. Sweet, delicious smile. 'Silly boy. Of course I'll stay. I've come to visit you.'

Slowly his fingers loosened. He thought she would run away, but she remained. 'Lie back,' she told him. 'Why are you dressed so early?' Her eyes widened. 'Oh. You mustn't leave. Not until you're well.'

She needn't have worried. Kev's plans to escape had disappeared the second he had seen her. He eased back against the pillows, watching intently as she sat on the chair. She was wearing a pink dress. The edges of it, at the neck and wrists, were trimmed with little ruffles.

'What is your name?' she asked.

Kev hated talking. *Hated* making conversation with anyone. But he was willing to do anything to keep her with him. 'Merripen.'

'Is that your first name?'

He shook his head.

Winnifred tilted her head to the side. 'Won't you tell it to me?'

He couldn't. A Rom could only share his true name with others in the Rom.

'At least give me the first letter,' she coaxed.

Kev stared at her, perplexed.

'I don't know many Gypsy names,' she said. 'Is it Luca? Marko? Stefan?'

It occurred to Kev that she was trying to play a game with him. Teasing him. He didn't know

26

how to respond. Usually if someone tried to tease him, he responded by sinking his fist into the offender's face.

'Someday you will tell me,' she said with a little grin. She made a move as if to rise from the chair, and Kev's hand shot out to grip her arm. Surprise flickered across her face.

'You said you would stay,' he said roughly.

Her free hand came to the one clamped around her wrist. 'I will. Be at ease, Merripen. I'm only going to fetch some bread and tea for us. Let me go. I'll come right back.' Her palm was light and warm as it rubbed over his hand. 'I'll stay in here all day, if you wish.'

'They won't let you.'

'Oh yes, they will.' She coaxed his hand to loosen, gently prying at his fingers. 'Don't be so anxious. My goodness. I thought Gypsies were supposed to be merry.'

She almost made him smile.

'I've had a bad week,' he told her gravely.

She was still busy trying to detach his fingers from her arm. 'Yes, I can see that. How did you come to be hurt?'

'*Gadjos* attacked my tribe. They may come for me here.' He stared at her hungrily but forced himself to let go of her. 'I'm not safe. I should go.'

'No one would dare take you away from us. My father is a very respected man in the village. A scholar.' Seeing Merripen's doubtful expression, she added, 'The pen is mightier than the sword, you know.'

That sounded like something a *gadjo* would say. It made no sense at all. 'The men who attacked

27

my *vitsa* last week were not armed with pens.'

'You poor thing,' she said compassionately. 'I'm sorry. Your wounds must hurt after all this moving about. I'll get you some tonic.'

Kev had never been the object of sympathy before. He didn't like it. His pride bristled. 'I won't take it. *Gadjo* medicine doesn't work. If you bring it, I'll only throw it on the — '

'All right. Don't excite yourself. I'm sure it's not good for you.' She went to the door, and a thrill of desperation shook Kev's frame. He was certain she would not come back. And he wanted her near him so badly. Had he the strength, he would have leaped from the bed and seized her again. But that wasn't possible.

So he fixed her with a sullen stare and muttered, 'Go, then. Devil take you.'

Winnifred paused at the doorway and glanced over her shoulder with a quizzical grin. 'How contrary and cross you are. I will come back with bread and tea and a book, and I will stay as long as it takes to get a smile from you.'

'I never smile,' he told her.

Much to his surprise, Win did return. She spent the better part of a day reading to him, some dull and wordy story that made him drowsy with contentment. No music, no rustling of trees in the forest, no bird-songs had ever pleased him as much as her soft voice. Occasionally another family member came to the doorway, but Kev couldn't bring himself to snap at any of them. He was full of ease for the first time he could ever remember. He couldn't seem to hate anyone when he was so close to happiness.

The next day the Hathaways brought him to the main room in the cottage, a parlor filled with worn furniture. Every available surface was covered with sketches, needlework, and piles of books. One couldn't move without knocking something over.

While Kev half-reclined on the sofa, the smaller girls played on the carpet nearby, trying to teach tricks to Beatrix's pet squirrel. Leo and his father played chess in the corner. Amelia and her mother cooked in the kitchen. And Win sat close to Kev and worked on his hair.

'You have the mane of a wild beast,' she told him, using her fingers to pull apart snarls, then combing the tangled black strands with great care. 'Hold still. I'm trying to make you look more civi — oh, do stop flinching. Your head can't possibly be that sensitive.'

Kev wasn't flinching because of the tangles, or the comb. It was that he had never been touched for so long by anyone in his life. He was mortified, inwardly alarmed . . . but as he glanced warily around the room, it seemed no one minded or cared about what Win was doing.

He settled back with slitted eyes. The comb tugged a little too hard, and Win murmured an apology and rubbed the smarting spot with her fingertips. So gently. It made his throat tight and his eyes sting. Deeply disquieted, bewildered, Kev swallowed back the feeling. He stayed tense but passive beneath her touch. He could hardly breathe for the pleasure she gave him.

Next came a cloth draped around his neck, and the scissors.

'I'm very good at this,' Win said, pushing his head forward and combing the locks at the back of his neck. 'And your hair wants cutting. There's enough wool on your head to stuff a mattress.'

'Beware, lad,' Mr. Hathaway said cheerfully. 'Recollect what happened to Samson.'

Kev's head lifted. 'What?'

Win pushed it back down. 'Samson's hair was his source of strength,' she said. 'After Delilah cut it, he turned weak and was captured by the Philistines.'

'Haven't you read the Bible?' Poppy asked.

'No,' Kev said. He held still as the scissors bit carefully through the thick waves at his nape.

'Then you're a heathen?'

'Yes.'

'Are you the kind that eats people?' Beatrix asked with great interest.

Win answered before Kev could say anything. 'No, Beatrix. One may be a heathen without being a cannibal.'

'But Gypsies do eat hedgehogs,' Beatrix said. 'And that's just as bad as eating people. Because hedgehogs do have feelings, you know.' She paused as a heavy lock of black hair fell to the floor. 'Oooooh, how pretty!' the little girl exclaimed. 'May I have it, Win?'

'No,' Merripen said gruffly, his head still bent.

'Why ever not?' Beatrix asked.

'Someone could use it to make a bad-luck charm. Or a love spell.'

'Oh, I wouldn't do that,' Beatrix said earnestly. 'I just want to line a nest with it.'

'Never mind, darling,' Win said serenely. 'If it

30

makes our friend uncomfortable, your pets will have to make do with some other nesting material.' The scissors snipped through another heavy black swath. 'Are all Gypsies as superstitious as you?' she asked Kev.

'No. Most are worse.'

Her light laugh tickled his ear, her warm breath bringing gooseflesh to the surface. 'Which would you hate more, Merripen . . . the bad luck, or the love spell?'

'The love spell,' he said without hesitation.

For some reason the entire family laughed. Merripen glowered at all of them but found no mockery in their collective gaze, only friendly amusement.

Kev was quiet, listening to them chatter while Win cut layers in his hair. It was the oddest conversation he'd ever witnessed, the girls interacting freely with their brother and father. They all moved from one subject to another, debating ideas that didn't apply to them, situations that didn't affect them. There was no point to any of it, but they seemed to enjoy themselves tremendously.

He had never known people like this existed. He had no idea how they had survived this long.

★ ★ ★

The Hathaways were an unworldly lot, eccentric and cheerful and preoccupied with books and art and music. They lived in a ramshackle cottage, but instead of repairing door frames or holes in the ceiling, they pruned roses and wrote poetry.

31

If a chair leg broke off, they merely wedged a stack of books beneath it. Their priorities were a mystery to him. And he was mystified still further when, after his wounds had healed sufficiently, they invited him to make a room for himself in the stable loft.

'You may stay as long as you wish,' Mr. Hathaway had told him, 'though I expect that someday you'll want to strike out in search of your tribe.'

But Kev no longer had a tribe. They had left him for dead. This was his stopping place.

He began to take care of the things the Hathaways had paid no attention to, such as repairing the holes in the ceiling and the decaying joints beneath the chimney stack. Despite his terror of heights, he did new coat work on the thatched roof. He took care of the horse and the cow, and tended the kitchen garden, and even mended the family's shoes. Soon Mrs. Hathaway trusted him to take money to the village to buy food and other necessities.

There was only one time that his presence at the Hathaway cottage seemed in jeopardy, and that was when he had been caught fighting some village toughs.

Mrs. Hathaway was alarmed by the sight of him, battered and bloody-nosed, and had demanded to know how it had happened. 'I sent you to fetch a round from the cheesemaker, and you come home empty-handed, and in such a condition,' she cried. 'What violence did you do, and why?'

Kev hadn't explained, only stood grim-faced

at the door as she berated him.

'I won't tolerate brutality in this household. If you can't bring yourself to explain what happened, then collect your things and leave.'

But before Kev could move or speak, Win had entered the house. 'No, Mother,' she had said calmly. 'I know what happened — my friend Laura just told me. Her brother was there. Merripen was defending our family. Two other boys were shouting insults about the Hathaways, and Merripen thrashed them for it.'

'Insults of what nature?' Mrs. Hathaway asked, bewildered.

Kev stared hard at the floor, his fists clenched.

Win didn't flinch from the truth. 'They're criticizing our family,' she said, 'because we're harboring a Rom. Some of the villagers don't like it. They're afraid Merripen might steal from them, or place curses on people, or other such nonsense. They blame us for taking him in.'

In the silence that followed, Kev trembled with undirected rage. And at the same time, he was overwhelmed with defeat. He was a liability to the family. He could never live among the *gadje* without conflict.

'I will go,' he said. It was the best thing he could do for them.

'Where?' Win asked, a surprising edge to her voice, as if the notion of his leaving had annoyed her. 'You belong here. You have nowhere else to go.'

'I'm a Rom,' he said simply. He belonged nowhere and everywhere.

'You will not leave,' Mrs. Hathaway astonished

him by saying. 'Certainly not because of some village ruffians. What would it teach my children, to let such ignorance and despicable behavior prevail? No, you will stay. It is only right. But you must not fight, Merripen. Ignore them, and they will eventually lose interest in taunting us.'

A stupid *gadjo* sentiment. Ignoring never worked. The fastest way to silence a bully's taunts was to beat him to a bloody pulp.

A new voice entered the conversation. 'If he stays,' Leo remarked, coming into the kitchen, 'he will most certainly have to fight, Mother.'

Like Kev, Leo looked much the worse for wear, with a blackened eye and a split lip. He gave a crooked grin at his mother's and sister's exclamations. Still smiling, he glanced at Kev. 'I thrashed one or two of the fellows you overlooked,' he said.

'Oh dear,' Mrs. Hathaway said sorrowfully, taking her son's hand, which was bruised and bleeding from a gash where he must have caught someone's tooth with his knuckle. 'These are hands meant for holding books. Not fighting.'

'I like to think I can manage both,' Leo said dryly. His expression turned serious as he gazed at Kev. 'I'll be damned if anyone will tell me who may live in my home. As long as you wish to stay, Merripen, I'll defend you like a brother.'

'I don't want to make trouble for you,' Kev muttered.

'No trouble,' Leo replied, gingerly flexing his hand. 'After all, some principles are worth standing up for.'

3

Principles. Ideals. The harsh realities of Kev's former life had never allowed for such things. But constant exposure to the Hathaways had changed him, elevating his thoughts to considerations beyond mere survival. Certainly he would never be a scholar or a gentleman. He spent years, however, listening to the Hathaways' animated discussions about Shakespeare, Galileo, Flemish art versus Venetian, democracy and monarchy and theocracy, and every imaginable subject. He had learned to read, and even acquired some Latin and a few words of French. He had changed into someone his former tribe would never have recognized.

Kev never came to think of Mr. and Mrs. Hathaway as parents, although he would have done anything for them. He had no desire to form attachments to people. That would have required more trust and intimacy than he could summon. But he did care for all the Hathaway brood, even Leo. And then there was Win, for whom Kev would have died a thousand times over.

He would never degrade Win with his touch, or dare to assume a place in her life other than as a protector. She was too fine, too rare. As she grew into womanhood, every man in the county was enthralled by her beauty.

Outsiders tended to view Win as an ice

maiden, neat and unruffled and cerebral. But outsiders knew nothing of the sly wit and warmth that lurked beneath her perfect surface. Outsiders hadn't seen Win teaching Poppy the steps to a quadrille until they had both collapsed to the floor in giggles. Or frog-hunting with Beatrix, her apron filled with leaping amphibians. Or the droll way she read a Dickens novel with an array of voices and sounds, until the entire family howled at her cleverness.

Kev loved her. Not in the way that novelists and poets described. Nothing so tame. He loved her beyond earth, heaven, or hell. Every moment out of her company was agony; every moment with her was the only peace he had ever known. Every touch of her hands left an imprint that ate down to his soul. He would have killed himself before admitting it to anyone. The truth was buried deep in his heart.

Kev did not know if Win loved him in return. All he knew was that he didn't want her to.

★   ★   ★

'There,' Win said one day after they had rambled through dry meadows and settled to rest in their favorite place. 'You're almost doing it.'

'Almost doing what?' Kev asked lazily. They reclined by a clump of trees bordering a winterbourne, a stream that ran dry in the summer months. The grass was littered with purple rampion and white meadowsweet, the latter spreading an almondlike fragrance through the warm, fetid air.

'Smiling.' She lifted on her elbows beside him, her fingers brushing his lips.

Kev stopped breathing.

A pipit rose from a nearby tree on taut wings, drawing out a long note as he descended.

Intent on her task, Win shaped the corners of Kev's mouth upward and tried to hold them there.

Aroused and amused, Kev let out a smothered laugh and brushed her hand away.

'You should smile more often,' Win said, still staring down at him. 'You're very handsome when you do.'

She was more dazzling than the sun, her hair like cream silk, her lips a tender shade of pink. At first her gaze seemed like nothing more than friendly inquiry, but as it held on his, he realized she was trying to read his secrets.

He wanted to pull her down with him and cover her body with his. It had been four years since he had come to live with the Hathaways. Now he was finding it more and more difficult to control his feelings for Win.

'What are you thinking when you look at me like that?' she asked softly.

'I can't say.'

'Why not?'

Kev felt the smile hovering on his lips again, this time edged with wryness. 'It would frighten you.'

'Merripen,' she said decisively, 'nothing you could ever do or say would frighten me.' She frowned. 'Are you *ever* going to tell me your first name?'

'No.'

'You will. I'll make you.' She pretended to beat against his chest with her fists.

Kev caught her slim wrists in his hands, restraining her easily. His body followed the motion, rolling to trap her beneath him. It was wrong, but he couldn't stop himself. And as he pinned her with his weight, felt her wriggle instinctively to accommodate him, he was almost paralyzed by the primal pleasure of it. He expected her to struggle, to fight him, but instead she went passive in his hold, smiling up at him.

Dimly Kev remembered one of the mythology stories the Hathaways were so fond of . . . the Greek one about Hades, the god of the under-world, kidnapping the maiden Persephone in a flowery field and dragging her down through an opening in the earth. Down to his dark, private world where he could possess her. Although the Hathaway daughters had all been indignant about Persephone's fate, Kev's sympathies had privately been on Hades' side. Romany culture tended to romanticize the idea of kidnapping a woman for one's bride, even mimicking it during their court-ship rituals.

'I don't see why eating a mere half-dozen pomegranate seeds should have condemned Persephone to stay with Hades part of every year,' Poppy had said in outrage. 'No one told her the rules. It wasn't fair. I'm certain she would never have touched a thing, had she known what would happen.'

'And it wasn't a very filling snack,' Beatrix had added, perturbed. 'If I'd been there, I would have asked for a pudding or a jam pasty, at least.'

'Perhaps she wasn't altogether unhappy, having to stay,' Win had suggested, her eyes twinkling. 'After all, Hades did make her his queen. And the story says he possessed 'the riches of the earth.''

'A rich husband,' Amelia had said, 'doesn't change the fact that Persephone's main residence is in an undesirable location with no view whatsoever. Just think of the difficulties in leasing it out during the off-months.'

They had all agreed that Hades was a complete villain.

But Kev had understood exactly why the underworld god had stolen Persephone for his bride. He had wanted a little bit of sunshine, of warmth, for himself, down in the cheerless gloom of his dark palace.

'So your tribe members who left you for dead . . . ,' Win said, bringing Kev's thoughts back to the present, ' . . . *they're* allowed to know your name, but I'm not?'

'That's right.' Kev watched the brindling of sun and leaf shadows on her face. He wondered how it would feel to press his lips to that soft light-tricked skin.

A delectable notch appeared between Win's tawny brows. 'Why? Why can't I know?'

'Because you're a *gadji*.' His tone was more tender than he had meant it to be.

'Your *gadji*.'

At this foray into dangerous territory, Kev felt his heart contract painfully. She wasn't his, nor could she ever be. Except in his heart.

He rolled off her, rising to his feet. 'It's time to go back,' he said curtly. He reached down for her, gripped her small extended hand, and hauled her upward. She didn't check the momentum but instead let herself fall naturally against him. Her skirts fluttered around his legs, and the slim feminine shape of her body pressed all along his front. Desperately he searched for the strength, the will, to push her away.

'Will you ever try to find them, Merripen?' she asked. 'Will you ever go away from me?'

Never, he thought in a flash of ardent need. But instead he said, 'I don't know.'

'If you did, I would follow you. And I would bring you back home.'

'I doubt the man you marry would allow that.'

Win smiled as if the statement were ridiculous. She eased herself away and let go of his hand. They began the walk back to Hampshire House in silence. 'Tobar?' she suggested after a moment. 'Garridan? Palo?'

'No.'

'Rye?'

'No.'

'Cooper? . . . Stanley? . . . '

'No.'

★ ★ ★

To the pride of the entire Hathaway family, Leo was accepted at the Academie des Beaux-Arts in Paris, where he studied art and architecture for two years. So promising was Leo's talent that part of his tuition was assumed by the renowned

London architect Rowland Temple, who said that Leo could repay him by working as his draughtsman upon returning.

Few would have argued that Leo had matured into a steady and good-natured young man, with a keen wit and a ready laugh. And in light of his talent and ambition, there was the promise of even more attainment. Upon his return to England, Leo took up residence in London to fulfill his obligation to Temple, but he also came frequently to visit his family at Primrose Place. And to court a pretty, dark-haired village girl named Laura Dillard.

During Leo's absence, Kev had done his best to take care of the Hathaways. And Mr. Hathaway had tried on more than one occasion to help Kev plan a future for himself. Such conversations turned out to be an exercise in frustration for them both.

'You are being wasted,' Mr. Hathaway had told Kev, looking mildly troubled.

Kev had snorted at that, but Hathaway had persisted.

'We must consider your future. And before you say a word, let me state that I am aware of the Rom's preference to live in the present. But you have changed, Merripen. You have advanced too far to neglect what has taken root in you.'

'Do you want me to leave?' Kev asked quietly.

'Heavens, no. Not at all. As I have told you before, you may stay with us as long as you wish. But I feel it my duty to make you aware that in staying here, you are sacrificing many opportunities for self-improvement. You should go out into the world, as Leo has. Take an apprenticeship, learn a trade, perhaps enlist in the military — '

'What would I get from that?' Kev had asked.

'To start with, the ability to earn more than the pittance I'm able to give you.'

'I don't need money.'

'But as things stand, you haven't the means to marry, to buy your own plot of land, to — '

'I don't want to marry. And I can't own land. No one can.'

'In the eyes of the British government, Merripen, a man most certainly can own land, and a house upon it.'

'The tent shall stand when the palace shall fall,' Kev had replied prosaically.

Hathaway had let out an exasperated chuckle. 'I would rather argue with a hundred scholars,' he had told Kev, 'than with one Gypsy. Very well, we will let the matter rest for now. But bear in mind, Merripen . . . life is more than following the impulses of primitive feeling. A man must make his mark on the world.'

'Why?' Kev asked in genuine bewilderment, but Hathaway had already gone to join his wife in the rose garden.

* * *

Approximately a year after Leo had returned from Paris, tragedy struck the Hathaway family. Until then none of them had ever known true sorrow, fear, or grief. They had lived in what had seemed to be a magically protected family circle. But Mr. Hathaway complained of odd, sharp

42

pains in his chest one evening, leading his wife to conclude that he was suffering dyspepsia after a particularly rich supper. He went to bed early, quiet and gray-faced. No more was heard from their room until daybreak, when Mrs. Hathaway came out weeping and told the stunned family that their father was dead.

And that was only the beginning of the Hathaways' misfortune. It seemed the family had fallen under a curse, in which the full measure of their former happiness had been converted to sorrow. 'Trouble comes in threes' was one of the sayings Merripen remembered from his childhood, and to his bitter regret, it proved to be true.

Mrs. Hathaway was so overcome by grief that she took to her bed after her husband's funeral, and suffered such melancholy that she could scarcely be persuaded to eat or drink. None of her children's attempts to bring her back to her usual self were effective. In a startlingly short time, she had wasted away to almost nothing.

'Is it possible to die of a broken heart?' Leo asked somberly one evening, after the doctor had left with the pronouncement that he could discern no physical cause of their mother's decline.

'She should want to live for Poppy and Beatrix, at least,' Amelia said, keeping her voice low. At that moment, Poppy was putting Beatrix to bed in another room. 'They're still too young to be without a mother. No matter how long I had to live with a broken heart, I would force myself to do it, if only to take care of them.'

'But you have a core of steel,' Win said, patting her older sister's back. 'You are your own source of strength. I'm afraid Mother has always drawn hers from Father.' She glanced at Merripen with despairing blue eyes. 'Merripen, what would the Rom prescribe for melancholy? Anything, no matter how outlandish, that might help her? How would your people view this?'

Kev shook his head, switching his gaze to the hearth. 'They would leave her alone. The Rom have a fear of excessive grief.'

'Why?'

'It tempts the dead to come back and haunt the living.'

All four were silent then, listening to the hiss and snap of the small fire.

'She wants to be with Father,' Win said eventually. Her tone was pensive. 'Wherever he has gone. Her heart is broken. I wish it weren't. I would exchange my life, my heart, for hers, if such a trade were possible. I wish — ' She broke off with a quick breath as Kev's hand closed over her arm.

He had not been aware of reaching out for her, but her words had provoked him irrationally. 'Don't say that,' he muttered. He was not so far removed from his Romany past that he had forgotten the power of words to tempt fate.

'Why not?' she whispered.

Because it wasn't hers to give.

Your heart is mine, he thought savagely. *It belongs to me.*

And though he hadn't said the words aloud, it seemed somehow that Win had heard them. Her eyes widened, darkened, and a flush born of strong emotion rose in her face. And right there, in the presence of her brother and sister, she lowered her head and pressed her cheek to the back of Kev's hand.

Kev longed to comfort her, envelop her with kisses, surround her with his strength. Instead he released her arm carefully and risked a wary glance at Amelia and Leo. The former had picked up a few pieces of kindling from the hearthside basket, and was occupying herself by feeding them to the fire. The latter was watching Win intently.

Less than six months after her husband's death, Mrs. Hathaway was laid to rest beside him. And before the siblings could begin to accept that they had been orphaned with such cruel swiftness, the third tragedy occurred.

★ ★ ★

'Merripen.' Win stood at the front threshold of the cottage, hesitating to come in. There was such a queer look on her face that Kev rose to his feet at once.

He was bone-weary and dirty, having just come in from working all day at a neighbor's house, building a gate and fence around their yard. To set the fence posts, Kev had dug holes in ground that had already been permeated with the frost of approaching winter. He had just sat down at the table with Amelia, who was attempting to clean spots from one of Poppy's dresses with a quill dipped in spirit of turpentine. The scent of the chemical burned in Kev's nostrils as he drew in a quick breath. He knew from Win's expression that something was very wrong.

'I've been with Laura and Leo today,' Win said. 'Laura took ill earlier . . . She said her throat hurt, and her head, and so we took her home at once and her family sent for the doctor. He said it was scarlet fever.'

'Oh God,' Amelia breathed, the color draining from her face. The three of them were silent with shared horror.

There was no other fever that burned so violently or spread so quickly. It provoked a brilliant red rash from the skin, imparting a fine, gritty texture like the glass paper used to smooth pieces of wood. And it burned and ravaged its way through the body until the organs failed. The disease lingered in the expired air, in locks of hair, on the skin itself. The only way to protect others was to isolate the patient.

'Was he certain?' Kev asked in a controlled voice.

'Yes, he said the signs are unmistakable. And he said — '

Win broke off as Kev strode toward her. 'No, Merripen!' And she held up a slim white hand with such desperate authority that it stopped him in his tracks. 'No one must come near me. Leo is at Laura's house. He won't leave her. They said it was all right for him to stay, and . . . you must gather up Poppy and Beatrix, and Amelia, too, and take them to our cousins in Hedgerley. They won't like it, but they'll take them in and — '

'I'm not going anywhere,' Amelia said, her manner calm even though she was trembling slightly. 'If you have the fever, you'll need me to take care of you.'

'But if you should catch it — '

'I had a very mild bout of it when I was a young child. That means I'm probably safe from it now.'

'What about Leo?'

'I'm afraid he didn't have it. Which may put him in danger.' Amelia glanced at Kev. 'Merripen, did you ever — '

'I don't know.'

'Then you should stay away with the children until this is over. Will go you collect them? They went out to play at the winterbourne. I'll pack their things.'

Kev found it nearly impossible to leave Win when she might be ill. But there was no choice. Someone had to take her sisters to a safe place.

Before an hour had passed, Kev had found Beatrix and Poppy, loaded the bewildered girls into the family carriage, and taken them on the half-day journey to Hedgerley. By the time he had settled them with their cousins and returned to the cottage, it was well past midnight.

Amelia was in the parlor, wearing her nightclothes and dressing robe, her hair trailing down her back in a long braid. She sat before the fire, her shoulders hunched inward.

She looked up with surprise as Kev entered the house. 'You shouldn't be here. The danger — '

'How is she?' Kev interrupted. 'Any sign of fever yet?'

'Chills. Pains. No rise in temperature, as far as I can tell. Perhaps that's a good sign. Perhaps that means she'll only have it lightly.'

'Any word from the Dillards? From Leo?'

Amelia shook her head. 'Win said he meant to sleep in the parlor, and go to her whenever they would allow it. It isn't at all proper, but if Laura . . . well, if she doesn't live through this . . . ' Amelia's voice thickened, and she paused to swallow back tears. 'I suppose if it comes to that, they wouldn't want to deprive Laura of her last moments with the man she loves.'

Kev sat nearby and silently sorted through platitudes he'd heard *gadje* say to one another. Things about endurance, and accepting the Almighty's will, and about worlds far better than this one. He couldn't bring himself to repeat any of it to Amelia. Her grief was too honest, her love for her family too real.

'It's too much,' he heard Amelia whisper after a while. 'I can't bear losing anyone else. I'm so afraid for Win. I'm afraid for Leo.' She rubbed her forehead. 'I sound like the rankest coward, don't I?'

Kev shook his head. 'You would be a fool not to be afraid.'

That elicited a small, dry chuckle. 'I am definitely not a fool, then.'

★　★　★

By morning Win was flushed and feverish, her legs moving restlessly beneath the covers. Kev went to a window and drew open the curtain, admitting the weak light of dawn.

She awakened as he approached the bed, her blue eyes wide in her red-burnished face. 'No,' she croaked, trying to shrink away from him. 'You're not supposed to be here. Don't come near me; you'll catch it. *Please* go — '

'Quiet,' Kev said, sitting on the edge of the mattress. He caught Win as she tried to roll away, and settled his hand on her forehead. He felt the burning pulse beneath her fragile skin, the veins lit with raging fever.

As Win struggled to push him away, Kev was alarmed by how feeble she had grown. Already.

'Don't,' she sobbed, writhing. Weak tears slid from her eyes. 'Please don't touch me. I don't want you here. I don't want you to get sick. Oh, *please* go . . . '

Kev pulled her up against him, her body living flame beneath the thin layer of her nightgown, the pale silk of her hair streaming over both of them. And he cradled her head in one of his hands, the powerful battered hand of a bare-knuckle fighter. 'You're mad,' he said in a low voice, 'if you think I would leave you now. I'll see you safe and well no matter what it takes.'

'I won't live through this,' she whispered.

Kev was shocked by the words, and even more by his own reaction to them.

'I'm going to die,' she said, 'and I won't take you with me.'

Kev gripped her more closely, letting her fitful breaths blow against his face. No matter how she writhed, he wouldn't let go. He breathed the air from her, taking it deep into his own lungs.

49

'*Stop*,' she cried, trying desperately to twist away from him. The exertion caused her flush to darken. 'This is madness . . . Oh, you stubborn wretch, let me go!'

'Never.' Kev smoothed her wild, fine hair, the strands darkening where her tears had tracked. 'Easy,' he murmured. 'Don't exhaust yourself. Rest.'

Win's struggles slowed as she recognized the futility of resisting him. 'You're so strong,' she said faintly, the words born not of praise, but damnation. 'You're so strong . . . '

'Yes,' Kev said, gently using a corner of the bed linens to dry her face. 'I'm a brute, and you've always known it, haven't you?'

'Yes,' she whispered.

'And you're going to do as I say.' He cradled her against his chest and gave her some water.

She took a few painful sips. 'Can't,' she managed, turning her face away.

'More,' he insisted, bringing the cup back to her lips.

'Let me sleep, please — '

'After you drink more.'

Kev wouldn't relent until she obeyed with a moan. Settling her back into the pillows, he let her drowse for a few minutes, then returned with some toast softened in broth. He bullied her into taking a few spoonfuls.

By that time Amelia had awakened, and she came into Win's room. A quick double blink was Amelia's only reaction to the sight of Win leaning back against Kev's arm while he fed her.

'Get rid of him,' Win told her sister hoarsely,

her head resting on Kev's shoulder. 'He's torturing me.'

'Well, we've always known he was a fiend,' Amelia said in a reasonable tone, coming to stand at the bedside. 'How dare you, Merripen? . . . Coming into an unsuspecting girl's room and feeding her toast.'

'The rash has started,' Kev said, noting the roughness that was rising up Win's throat and cheeks. Her silken skin had turned sandy and red. He felt Amelia's hand touch his back, clenching in a loose fold of his shirt as if she needed to hold on to him for balance.

But Amelia's voice was light and steady. 'I'll mix a solution of soda-water. That should soothe the rawness, dear.'

Kev felt a surge of admiration for Amelia. No matter what disasters came her way, she was willing to meet all challenges. Of all the Hathaways, she had shown the toughest mettle so far. And yet Win would have to be stronger and even more obstinate, if she was to survive the days to come.

'While you bathe her,' he told Amelia, 'I'll fetch the doctor.'

Not that he had any faith in a *gadjo* doctor, but it might give the sisters peace of mind. Kev also wanted to see how Leo and Laura were faring.

After relinquishing Win to Amelia's care, Kev went to the Dillards' home. But the maid who answered the door told him that Leo wasn't available.

'He's in there with Miss Laura,' the maid said

brokenly, blotting her face with a rag. 'She knows no one; she is near insensible. She is failing fast, sir.'

Kev felt the traction of his short pared nails against the tough skin of his palms. Win was less robust than Laura Dillard, less sturdy in form and constitution. If Laura was sinking so fast, it hardly seemed possible that Win would be able to withstand the same fever.

His next thoughts were of Leo, who was not a brother by blood but certainly a tribesman. Leo loved Laura Dillard with an intensity that would not allow him to accept her death rationally, if at all. Kev was more than a little concerned for him. 'What is Mr. Hathaway's condition?' Kev asked. 'Does he show any sign of illness?'

'No, sir. I don't think so. I don't know.'

But from the way her watery gaze slid away from his, Kev understood that Leo was not well. He wanted to take Leo away from the death watch, *now*, and put him to bed to preserve his strength for the days to come. But it would be cruel to deny Leo the last hours with the woman he loved.

'When she passes,' Kev said bluntly, 'send him home. But don't let him go alone. Have someone accompany him all the way to the doorstep of the Hathaway cottage. Do you understand?'

'Yes, sir.'

Two days later, Leo came home.

'Laura's dead,' he said, and collapsed in a delirium of fever and grief.

4

The scarlet fever that had swept the village was a particularly virulent strain, the worst effects falling on the very young and the old. There were not enough doctors to tend the ailing, and no one outside Primrose Place dared to come. After visiting the cottage to examine the two patients, the exhausted doctor had prescribed hot vinegar poultices for the throat. He had also left a tonic containing tincture of aconite. It seemed to have no effect on either Win or Leo.

'We're not doing enough,' Amelia said on the fourth day. Neither she nor Kev had had sufficient sleep, both of them taking turns caring for the ailing brother and sister. Amelia came into the kitchen, where Kev was boiling water for tea. 'The only thing we've accomplished so far is to make their decline more comfortable. There must be something that can stop the fever. I won't let this happen.' She stood rigid and trembling, stacking word upon word as if trying to shore up her defenses.

And she looked so vulnerable that Kev was moved to compassion. He was not comfortable with touching other people, or being touched, but a brotherly feeling caused him to step toward her.

'No,' Amelia said quickly, as she realized he had been about to reach out to her. Taking a step back, she gave a strong shake of her head. 'I

. . . I'm not the kind of woman who can lean on anyone. I would fall to pieces.'

Kev understood. For people like her, and himself, closeness meant too much.

'What is to be done?' Amelia whispered, wrapping her arms around herself.

Kev rubbed his weary eyes. 'Have you heard of a plant called deadly nightshade?'

'No.' Amelia was only familiar with herbs used for cooking.

'It only blooms at night. When the sun comes up, the flowers die. There was a *drabengro*, a 'man of poison' in my tribe. Sometimes he sent me to get the plants that were difficult to find. He told me deadly nightshade was the most powerful herb he knew of. It could kill a man, but it could also bring someone back from the brink of death.'

'Did you ever see it work?'

Kev nodded, giving her a sidelong glance as he rubbed the taut muscles at the back of his neck. 'I saw it cure fever,' he muttered. And he waited.

'Get some,' Amelia finally said, her voice unsteady. 'It may prove to be fatal. But they're both sure to die without it.'

★ ★ ★

Kev boiled the plants, which he had found in the corner of the village graveyard, down to thin black syrup. Amelia stood beside him as he strained the deadly broth and poured it into a small eggcup.

'Leo first,' Amelia said resolutely, though her

expression was doubt-ridden. 'He's worse off than Win.'

They went to Leo's bedside. It was astonishing how quickly a man could deteriorate from scarlet fever, how emaciated their strapping brother had become. Leo's formerly handsome face was unrecognizable, turgid and swollen and discolored. His last coherent words had been the day before, when he had begged Kev to let him die. His wish would soon be granted. From all appearances a coma was only hours, if not minutes, away.

Amelia went directly to a window and opened it, letting the cold air sweep away the taint of vinegar.

Leo moaned and stirred feebly, unable to resist as Kev forced his mouth open, lifted a spoon, and poured four or five drops of the tincture onto his dry, fissured tongue.

Amelia went to sit beside her brother, smoothing his dull hair, kissing his brow.

'If it was going to . . . to have an adverse effect,' she said, when Kev knew she meant 'if it was going to kill him,' ' . . . how long would it take?'

'Five minutes to an hour.' Kev saw the way Amelia's hand shook as she continued to smooth Leo's hair.

It seemed the longest hour of Kev's life as they sat and watched Leo, who moved and muttered as if he was in the middle of a nightmare.

'Poor boy,' Amelia murmured, running a cool rag over his face.

When they were certain that no convulsions

were forthcoming, Kev retrieved the eggcup and stood.

'You're going to give it to Win now?' Amelia asked, still looking down at her brother.

'Yes.'

'Do you need help?'

Kev shook his head. 'Stay with Leo.'

Kev went to Win's room. She was still and quiet on the bed. She no longer recognized him, her mind and body consumed in the red heat of fever. As he lifted her and let her head fall back on his arm, she writhed in protest.

'Win,' he said softly. 'Love, be still.' Her eyes slitted open at the sound of his voice. 'I'm here,' he whispered. He picked up a spoon and dipped it into the cup. 'Open your mouth, little *gadji*. Do it for me.' But she refused. She turned her face, and her lips moved in a soundless whisper.

'What is it?' he murmured, easing her head back. 'Win. You must take this medicine.'

She whispered again.

Comprehending the scratchy words, Kev stared at her in disbelief. 'You'll take it if I tell you my name?'

She struggled to produce enough saliva to speak. 'Yes.'

His throat got tighter and tighter, and the corners of his eyes burned. 'It's Kev,' he managed to say. 'My name is Kev.'

She let him put the spoon between her lips then, and the inky poison trickled down her throat.

Her body relaxed against him. As he continued to hold her, the fragile body felt as light and hot as flame in his arms.

I will follow you, he thought, *whatever your fate is*.

Win was the only thing on earth he had ever wanted. She would not leave without him.

Kev bent over her, and touched the dry, hot lips with his own.

A kiss she could not feel and would never remember.

He tasted the poison as he let his mouth linger on hers. Lifting his head, he glanced at the bedside table where he had set the remainder of the deadly nightshade. There was more than enough left to kill a healthy man.

It seemed as if the only thing that kept Win's spirit from leaving her body was the confinement of Kev's arms. So he held her and rocked her. He thought briefly of praying. But he would not acknowledge any being, supernatural or mortal, who threatened to take her from him.

The world had become this quiet shadowed room, the slender body in his arms, the breath that filtered softly in and out of her lungs. He followed that rhythm with his own breath, his own heartbeat. Leaning back against the bed, he fell into a dark trance as he waited for their shared fate.

Unaware of how much time passed, he rested with her until a movement in the doorway and a glow of light awakened him.

'Merripen.' Amelia's husky voice. She held a candle at the threshold.

Kev felt blindly for Win's cheek, laid his hand along the side of her face, and felt a thrill of

57

panic as his fingers met cool skin. He felt for the pulse in her throat.

'Leo's fever has broken,' Amelia said. Kev could barely hear her over the blood rush in his ears. 'He's going to be well.'

A weak but steady throb lay beneath Kev's searching fingertips. Win's heartbeat . . . the pulse that sustained his universe.

5

London, 1849

The addition of Cam Rohan to the Hathaway family had set the table for a new company. It was puzzling, how one person could change everything. Not to mention infuriating.

But then, everything was infuriating to Kev now. Win had gone to France, and there was no reason for him to be pleasant or even civil. Her absence had put him in the prowling fury of a wild creature deprived of its mate. He was always aware of his need for her, and the unendurable knowledge that she was somewhere far away and he couldn't reach her.

Kev had forgotten how this felt, this black hatred of the world and all its occupants. It was an unwelcome reminder of his boyhood, when he'd known nothing but violence and misery. And yet the Hathaways all seemed to expect him to behave as usual, to take part in the family routine, to pretend the Earth had gone on spinning.

The only thing that kept him sane was the knowledge of what *she* would want him to do. She would want him to take care of her sisters. And refrain from killing her new brother-in-law.

Kev could hardly stand the bastard.

The rest of them adored him. Cam Rohan had come and swept Amelia, a determined spinster, completely off her feet. Seduced her, as a matter of fact, which Kev still hadn't forgiven him for. But Amelia was entirely happy with her husband, even though he was half Rom.

None of them had ever met anyone quite like Rohan, whose origins were as mysterious as Kev's own. For most of his life, Rohan had worked at a gentlemen's gaming club, Jenner's, eventually becoming a factotum and then owning a small interest in the highly lucrative business. Burdened with a growing fortune, he had invested it as badly as possible to spare himself the supreme embarrassment of being a Gypsy with money. It hadn't worked. The money kept coming, every foolish investment returning miraculous dividends. Rohan sheepishly called it his good-luck curse.

But as it turned out, Rohan's curse was useful, since taking care of the Hathaways was an expensive proposition. Their family estate in Hampshire, which Leo had inherited last year along with his title, had burned down recently and was being rebuilt. And Poppy needed clothes for her London season, and Beatrix wanted to go to finishing school. On top of that, there were Win's clinic bills. As Rohan had pointed out to Kev, he was in a position to do a great deal for the Hathaways and that should be reason enough for Kev to tolerate him.

Therefore, Kev tolerated him.
Barely.

★ ★ ★

'Good morning,' Rohan said cheerfully, coming into the dining area of the family's suite at the Rutledge Hotel. They were already halfway through breakfast. Unlike the rest of them, Rohan was not an early riser, having spent most of his life in a gambling club where there was activity at all hours of the night. *A town Gypsy*, Kev thought with contempt.

Freshly washed and dressed in *gadjo* clothes, Rohan was exotically handsome, with dark hair worn a shade too long and a diamond stud sparkling in one ear. He was lean and supple, with an easy way of moving. Before taking the chair next to Amelia, he leaned down to kiss her head, an open display of affection that caused her to color. There had been a time in the not-too-distant past when Amelia would have disapproved of such demonstrations. Now she merely blushed and looked bemused.

Kev scowled down at his half-finished plate.

'Are you still sleepy?' he heard Amelia ask Rohan.

'At this rate, I won't be fully awake until noon.'

'You should try some coffee.'

'No, thank you. I can't abide the stuff.'

Beatrix spoke then. 'Merripen drinks lots of coffee. He *loves* it.'

'Of course he does,' Rohan said. 'It's dark and bitter.' He grinned as Kev gave him a warning glance. 'How are you faring this morning, *phral*?'

'Don't call me that.' Although Kev didn't raise his voice, there was a savage note in it that gave everyone pause.

After a moment, Amelia spoke to Rohan in a deliberately light tone. 'We're going to the

61

dressmaker's today, Poppy and Beatrix and I. We'll probably be gone till supper.' While Amelia went on to describe the gowns and hats and fripperies they would need, Kev felt Beatrix's small hand creep over his.

'It's all right,' Beatrix whispered. 'I miss them, too.'

At sixteen, the youngest Hathaway sibling was at that vulnerable age between childhood and adulthood. A sweet-natured little scamp, she was as inquisitive as one of the many pets she had accumulated. Since Amelia's marriage to Rohan, Beatrix had been begging to go to finishing school. Kev suspected she had read one too many novels featuring heroines who acquired airs and graces at 'academies for young ladies.' He was doubtful that finishing school would turn out well for the free-spirited Beatrix.

Letting go of his hand, Beatrix turned her attention back to the conversation, which had progressed to the subject of Rohan's latest investment.

It had become something of a game to Rohan to find an investment opportunity that wouldn't succeed. The last time he had tried it, he had bought a London rubber manufactory that was failing badly. As soon as Cam purchased it, however, the company had acquired patent rights for vulcanization and had invented something called the rubber band. And now people were buying millions of the things.

' . . . this one is sure to be a disaster,' Cam was saying. 'There is a pair of brothers, both of them blacksmiths, who have come up with a design for a man-powered vehicle. They call it a volocycle. Two wheels set on a tubular steel frame, propelled by pedals you push with your feet.'

'Only two wheels?' Poppy asked, perplexed. 'How could one ride it without falling over?'

'The driver would have to balance his center of mass over the wheels.'

'How would one turn the vehicle?'

'More importantly,' Amelia said in a dry tone, 'how would one *stop* it?'

'By the application of one's body to the ground?' Poppy suggested.

Cam laughed. 'Probably. We'll put it into production, of course. Westcliff says he's never seen a more disastrous investment. The volocycle looks uncomfortable as the devil, and requires balance far beyond the abilities of the average man. It won't be affordable, or practical. After all, no sane man would choose to pedal along the street on a two-wheeled contraption in lieu of riding a horse.'

'It sounds quite fun, though,' Beatrix said wistfully.

'It's not an invention a girl could try,' Poppy pointed out.

'Why not?'

'Our skirts would get in the way.'

'Why must we wear skirts?' Beatrix asked. 'I think trousers would be ever so much more comfortable.'

Amelia looked appalled and amused. 'These are observations best kept in the family, dear.' Picking up a glass of water, she raised it in Rohan's direction. 'Well, then. Here's to your first failure.' She raised an eyebrow. 'I hope you're not risking the entire family fortune before we reach the dressmaker's?'

He grinned at her. 'Not the entire fortune. Shop with confidence, *monisha*.'

When breakfast was concluded, the women left the dining table, while Rohan and Kev stood politely.

Lowering himself back into the chair, Rohan watched as Kev began to leave. 'Where are you going?' Rohan asked lazily. 'Meeting with your tailor? Going to discuss the latest political events at the local coffeehouse?'

'If your goal is to annoy me,' Kev informed him, 'there's no need to make an effort. You annoy me just by breathing.'

'Forgive me. I would try to refrain from the habit, but I've become rather fond of it.' Rohan gestured to a chair. 'Join me, Merripen. We need to discuss a few things.'

Kev complied with a glower.

'You're a man of few words, aren't you?' Rohan observed.

'Better than to fill the air with empty chatter.'

'I agree. I'll go straight to the point, then. While Leo . . . Lord Ramsay . . . is in Europe, his entire estate, his financial affairs, and three of his sisters have been placed in the care of a pair of Roma. It's not what I'd call an ideal situation. If Leo were in any condition to stay, I would have kept him here and sent Poppy to France with Win.'

But Leo was not in good condition, as they both knew. He had been a broken man, a wastrel, ever since the death of Laura Dillard. And although he was finally coming to terms with his grief, his path to healing, in both body and spirit, would not be short.

'Do you actually believe,' Kev asked, his voice riddled with contempt, 'that Leo will check himself in as a patient at a health clinic?'

'No. But he'll stay close by to keep an eye on Win. And it's a remote setting where opportunities for trouble are limited. He did well in France before, when he was studying architecture. Perhaps living there again will help to recall him to himself.'

'Or,' Kev said darkly, 'he'll disappear to Paris and drown himself in drink and prostitutes.'

Rohan shrugged. 'Leo's future is in his own hands. I'm more concerned about what we're facing here. Amelia is determined that Poppy should have a season in London, and that Beatrix should go to finishing school. At the same time, the rebuilding of the manor in Hampshire has to continue. The ruins need to be cleared and the grounds — '

'I know what has to be done.'

'Then you will manage the project? You'll work with the architect, the builders, the masons and carpenters, and so forth?'

Kev glared at him with rank antagonism. 'I won't be gotten rid of. And I'll be damned if I work for you, or answer to you — '

'Wait.' Rohan's hands lifted in a staying gesture, a scattering of gold rings gleaming richly on his dark fingers. 'Wait. For God's sake, I'm not trying to get rid of you. I'm proposing a partnership. Frankly, I'm no more thrilled by the prospect than you are. But there is much to be accomplished. And we have more to gain by working together than being at cross-purposes.'

Idly picking up a table knife, Kev ran his fingers along the blunt edge and the intricate gilded handle. 'You want me to go to Hampshire and oversee the work crews while you stay in London with the women?'

'Come and go as you please. I'll be traveling back and forth to Hampshire every now and again to look over things.' Rohan gave him an astute glance. 'You have nothing keeping you in London, do you?'

Kev shook his head.

'Then it's settled?' Rohan pressed.

Although Kev hated to admit it, the plan was not without appeal. He hated London, the grime and clamor and crowded buildings, the smog and noise. He longed to return to the country. And the thought of rebuilding the manor, exhausting himself with hard work . . . It would do him some good. Besides, he knew what the Ramsay estate needed better than anyone. Rohan might know every street, square, and rookery in London, but he wasn't at all familiar with country life. It only made sense for Kev to take charge of the Ramsay estate.

'I'll want to make improvements to the land as well,' Kev said, setting down the knife. 'There are field gates and fences that need repair. Ditches and drainage channels to be dug. And the tenant farmers are still using flails and reap-hooks because there is no threshing machine. The estate should have its own bakehouse to save the tenants from having to go to the village for their bread. Also — '

'Whatever you decide,' Rohan said hastily, having the typical Londoner's complete lack of interest in farming. 'Attracting more tenants will benefit the estate, of course.'

'I know you've already commissioned an architect and builder. But from now on, I'll be the one they come to with questions. I'll need access to the Ramsay accounts. And I'm going to pick the land crews and manage them without interference.'

Rohan's brows lifted at Kev's authoritative manner. 'Well. This is a side of you I haven't seen before, *chal*.'

'Do you agree to my terms?'

'Yes.' Rohan extended his hand. 'Shall we shake on it?'

Kev stood, ignoring the overture. 'Not necessary.'

Rohan's white teeth flashed in a grin. 'Merripen, would it be so terrible to attempt a friendship with me?'

'We'll never be friends. At best, we're enemies with a common purpose.'

Rohan continued to smile. 'I suppose the end result is the same.' He waited until Kev had reached the door before saying casually, 'By the way, I'm going to pursue the matter of the tattoos. If there is a connection between the two of us, I want to find out what it is.'

'You'll do so without my cooperation,' Kev said stonily.

'Why not? Aren't you curious?'

'Not in the least.'

Rohan's hazel eyes were filled with speculation. 'You have no ties to the past or the Rom, and no knowledge of why a unique design was inked into your arm in early childhood. What are you afraid of finding out?'

'You've had the same tattoo for just as long,' Kev shot back. 'You have no more idea about what it's for than I do. Why take such an interest in it now?'

'I . . . ' Absently Rohan rubbed his arm over his shirtsleeve, where the tattoo was located. 'I always assumed it was done at some whim of my grandmother's. She would never explain why I had the mark, or what it meant.'

'Did she know?'

'I believe so.' Rohan's mouth quirked. 'She seemed to know everything. She was a powerful herbalist, and a believer in the Biti Foki.'

'Fairy people?' Kev asked with a disdainful curl of his lips.

Rohan smiled. 'Oh yes. She assured me she was on personal terms with many of them.' The trace of amusement faded. 'When I was about ten years old, my grandmother sent me away from the tribe. She said I was in danger. My cousin Noah brought me to London and helped me to find work at the gambling club as a list-maker's runner. I've never seen any of my tribe since then.' Rohan paused, his face becoming shadowed. 'I was banished from the Rom without ever knowing why. And I had no reason to assume the tattoo had anything to do with it. Until I met you. We have two things in common, *phral*: we're outcasts, and we bear the mark of an Irish nightmare horse. And I think that finding out where it came from may help us both.'

★   ★   ★

In the following months Kev prepared the Ramsay estate for reconstruction. A mild and halfhearted winter had fallen over the village of Stony Cross and its environs, where the Ramsay estate was located. Beige grasses were crisped with frost, and stones rested hard-frozen by the banks of the Avon and Itchen rivers. Catkins emerged on willows, soft and tender as a lamb's tail, while dogwood sent up red winter stems to splinter the pale gray landscape.

The crews employed by John Dashiell, the contractor who would rebuild the Ramsay manor, were hardworking and efficient. The first two months were spent clearing the remains of the house, carting off charred wood and broken rock and rubble. A small gatehouse on the approach road was repaired and refurbished for the Hathaways' convenience.

Once the ground began to soften in March, the rebuilding of the manor would start in earnest. Kev was certain the crews had been warned in advance that the project was being supervised by a Rom, for they offered no objection to his presence or his authority. Dashiell, being a self-made and pragmatic man, didn't seem to care if his clients were English,

69

Romany, or any other nationality, so long as his payment schedule was met.

Near the end of February, Kev made the twelve-hour journey from Stony Cross to London. He had received word from Amelia that Beatrix had quit finishing school. Even though Amelia had added that all was well, Kev wanted to make certain for himself. The two months' separation was the longest he had ever spent away from the Hathaway sisters, and he was surprised by how intensely he had missed them.

It seemed the feeling was mutual. As soon as Kev arrived at their suite at the Rutledge Hotel, Amelia, Poppy, and Beatrix all pounced on him with unseemly enthusiasm. He tolerated their shrieks and kisses with gruff indulgence, secretly pleased by the warmth of their welcome.

Following them into the family parlor, Kev sat with Amelia on an overstuffed settee, while Cam Rohan and Poppy occupied nearby chairs. Beatrix perched on a footstool at Kev's feet. The women looked well, Kev thought . . . all three stylishly dressed and groomed, their dark hair arranged in pinned-up curls, except for Beatrix, who had plaits.

Amelia in particular seemed happy, laughing easily, radiating a contentment that could only come from a good marriage. Poppy was emerging as a beauty, with her fine features and her rich auburn-toned hair . . . a warmer, more approachable version of Win's delicate blond perfection. Beatrix, however, was subdued and thin. To anyone who didn't know her, Beatrix would appear to be a normal, cheerful girl. But

Kev saw the subtle signs of tension and strain on her face.

'What happened at school?' Kev asked with his customary bluntness.

Beatrix unburdened herself eagerly. 'Oh, Merripen, it was all my fault. School is horrid. I *abhor* it. I did make a friend or two, and I was sorry to leave them. But I didn't get on with my teachers. I was always saying the wrong thing in class, asking the wrong questions — '

'It appeared,' Amelia said wryly, 'that the Hathaway method of learning and debating wasn't welcome in school.'

'And I got into some rows,' Beatrix continued, 'because some of the girls said their parents told them not to associate with me because we have Gypsies in the family, and for all they knew I might be part Gypsy, too. And I said I wasn't, but even if I were it was no cause for shame, and I called them snobs, and then there was a lot of scratching and hair-pulling.'

Kev swore under his breath. He exchanged glances with Rohan, who looked grim. Their presence in the family was a liability to the Hathaway sisters . . . and yet there was no remedy for that.

'And then,' Beatrix said, 'my problem came back.'

Everyone was silent. Kev reached out and settled his hand on her head, his fingers curving over the shape of her skull. '*Chavi*,' he murmured, a Romany endearment for a young girl. Since he rarely used the old language, Beatrix gave him a round-eyed look of surprise.

Beatrix's problem had first appeared after Mr. Hathaway's death. It recurred every now and then in times of anxiety or distress. She had a compulsion to steal things, usually small things like pencil stubs or bookmarks, or the odd piece of flatware. Sometimes she didn't even remember taking an object. Later she would suffer intense remorse, and go to extraordinary lengths to return the things she had filched.

Kev removed his hand from her head and looked down at her. 'What did you take, little ferret?' he asked gently.

She looked chagrined. 'Hair ribbons, combs, books . . . small things. And then I tried to put everything back, but I couldn't remember where it all went. So there was a great rumpus, and I came forward to confess, and I was asked to leave the school. And now I'll never be a lady.'

'Yes, you will,' Amelia said at once. 'We're going to hire a governess, which is what we should have done in the beginning.'

Beatrix regarded her doubtfully. 'I don't think I would want any governess who would work for our family.'

'Oh, we're not as bad as all that — ,' Amelia began.

'Yes, we are,' Poppy informed her. 'We're odd, Amelia. I've always told you that. We were odd even before you brought Mr. Rohan into the family.' Casting a quick glance at Cam, she said, 'No offense meant, Mr. Rohan.'

His eyes glinted with amusement. 'None taken.'

Poppy turned to Kev. 'No matter how difficult

it is to find a proper governess, we *must* have one. I need help. My season has been nothing short of disaster, Merripen.'

'It's only been two months,' Kev said. 'How can it be a disaster?'

'I'm a wallflower.'

'You can't be.'

'I'm *lower* than a wallflower,' she told him. 'No man wants anything to do with me.'

Kev looked at Rohan and Amelia incredulously. A beautiful, intelligent girl like Poppy should have been overrun with suitors. 'What is the matter with these *gadjos?*' Kev asked in amazement.

'They're all idiots,' Rohan said. 'They never waste an opportunity to prove it.'

Glancing back at Poppy, Kev cut to the chase. 'Is it because there are Gypsies in the family? Is that why you're not sought after?'

'Well, it doesn't exactly help,' Poppy admitted. 'But the greater problem is that I have no social graces. I'm constantly making faux pas. And I'm dreadful at small talk. You're supposed to go lightly from topic to topic like a butterfly. It's not easy to do, and there's no point to it. And the young men who do bring themselves to approach me find an excuse to flee after five minutes. Because they flirt and say the silliest things, and I have no idea how to respond.'

'I wouldn't want any of them for her, anyway,' Amelia said crisply. 'You should see them, Merripen. A more useless flock of preening peacocks could not be found.'

'I believe it would be called a muster of

peacocks,' Poppy said. 'Not a flock.'

'Call them a knot of toads instead,' Beatrix said.

'A colony of penguins,' Amelia joined in.

'A rumpus of baboons,' Poppy said, laughing.

Kev smiled slightly, but he was still preoccupied. Poppy had always dreamed of a London season. For it to turn out this way must be a crushing disappointment. 'Have you been invited to the right events?' he asked. 'The dances . . . the dinner things . . . '

'Balls and soirees,' Poppy supplied. 'Yes, thanks to the patronage of Lord Westcliff and Lord St. Vincent, we've received invitations. But merely getting past the door doesn't make one desirable, Merripen. It only affords one the opportunity to prop up the wall while everyone else dances.'

Kev frowned at Amelia and Rohan. 'What are you going to do about this?'

'We're going to withdraw Poppy from the season,' Amelia said, 'and tell everyone that on second thought, she's still too young to be out in society.'

'No one will believe that,' Beatrix said. 'After all, Poppy's almost *nineteen*.'

'There's no need to make me sound like a warty old crone, Bea,' Poppy said indignantly.

' — and in the meantime,' Amelia continued with great patience, 'we'll find a governess who will teach both Poppy and Beatrix how to behave.'

'She had better be good,' Beatrix said, pulling a grunting black-and-white guinea pig from her pocket and snuggling it under her chin. 'We have a lot to overcome. Don't we, Mr. Nibbles?'

★　★　★

Later, Amelia took Kev aside. She reached into the pocket of her gown and extracted a small, white square. She gave it to him, her gaze searching his face. 'Win wrote other letters to the family, and of course you shall read those as well. But this was addressed solely to you.'

Unable to speak, Kev closed his fingers around the bit of parchment sealed with wax.

He went to his hotel room, which was separate from the rest of the family's at his request. Sitting at a small table, he broke the seal with scrupulous care.

There was Win's familiar writing, the pen strokes small and precise.

Dear Kev,

I hope this letter finds you in full health and vigor. I cannot imagine you in any other state, actually. Every morning I awaken in this place, which seems another world entirely, and I am surprised anew to find myself so far away from my family. And from you.

The journey across the channel was trying, the land route to the clinic even more so. As you know, I am not a good traveler, but Leo saw me safely here. He is now residing a short distance away as a paying guest at a small château, and so far he has come to visit every other day . . .

75

Win's letter went on to describe the clinic, which was quiet and austere. The patients suffered from a variety of ailments, but most especially those of the lung and pulmonary system.

Instead of dosing them with narcotic drugs and keeping them inside, as most doctors prescribed, Dr. Harrow put them all on a program of exercise, cold baths, health tonics, and a simple abstemious diet. Compelling the patients to exercise was a controversial treatment, but according to Dr. Harrow, motion was the prevailing instinct of all animal life.

The patients started every day with a morning walk outside, rain or shine, followed by an hour in the gymnasium for activities such as ladder-climbing or lifting dumbbells. So far Win could hardly manage any exercises without becoming severely out of breath, but she thought she could detect a small improvement in her abilities. Everyone at the clinic was required to practice breathing on a new device called a spirometer, an apparatus for measuring the volume of air inspired and expired by the lungs.

There was more about the clinic and the patients, which Kev skimmed over quickly. And then he reached the last paragraphs.

Since my illness I have had the strength to do very little except to love [Win had written], *but that I have done, and I still do, in full measure. I am sorry for the way I shocked you the morning I left, but I do not regret the sentiments I expressed.*

I am running after you, and life, in desperate pursuit. My dream is that someday you will both turn and let me catch you. That dream carries me through every night. I long to tell you so many things, but I am not free yet.

I hope to be well enough someday to shock you again, with far more pleasing results.

I have enclosed a hundred kisses in this letter. You must count them out carefully and not lose any.

Yours,
Winnifred

Flattening the slip of paper on the table, Kev smoothed it and ran his fingertips along the delicate lines of script. He read it twice more.

He let his hand close over the parchment, crushing it tightly, and he hurled it into the hearth, where a small fire was burning.

And he watched the parchment light and smolder, until the whiteness had darkened into ash and every last word from Win had disappeared.

6

London, 1851
Spring

At long last, Win had come home.

The clipper from Calais was docked, the hold packed with luxury goods, and bags of letters and parcels to be delivered by the Royal Mail. It was a medium-sized ship with seven spacious staterooms for the passengers, each lined with Gothic arched panels and painted a glossy shade of Florence white.

Win stood on the deck and watched the crew employing the ground tackle to moor the ship. Only then would the passengers be allowed to disembark.

Once, the excitement that gripped her would have made it impossible to breathe. But Win was returning to London a different woman. She wondered how her family would react to the changes in her. And of course they had changed as well: Amelia and Cam had been married for two years now, and Poppy and Beatrix were now out in society.

And Merripen . . . but Win's mind shied from thoughts of him, which were too stirring to dwell on in anything other than a private setting.

She gazed at her surroundings, the forest of ship masts, the endless acres of quay and jetty, the immense warehouses for tobacco, wool, wine, and other items of commerce. There was movement everywhere, sailors, passengers, provision agents, laborers, vehicles, and livestock. A profusion of odors thickened the air: goats and horses, spices, ocean salt, tar, dry rot. And above all hung the stench of chimney smoke and coal vapor, darkening as the night pressed close over the city.

Win longed to be in Hampshire, where the spring meadows would be green and thick with primroses and wildflowers and the hedgerows were in bloom. According to Amelia, the restoration of the Ramsay estate was not yet complete, but the manor was habitable now. It seemed the work had gone with miraculous speed under Merripen's direction.

The gangplank was lowered from the vessel and secured. As Win watched the first few passengers descend to the dock, she saw her brother's tall, almost lanky form leading the way.

France had been good for both of them. Whereas Win had gained some much-needed weight, Leo had lost his dissipated bloat. He had spent so much time out-of-doors, walking, painting, swimming, that his dark brown hair had lightened a few shades and his skin had soaked up sun. His eyes, a striking pale shade of blue, were startling in his tanned face.

Win knew that her brother would never again be the gallant, unguarded boy he had been before Laura Dillard's death. But he was no longer a suicidal wreck, which would no doubt be a great relief to the rest of the family.

In a relatively short time, Leo bounded back up the gangplank. He came to Win with a wry grin, clamping his top hat more firmly on his head.

'Is anyone waiting for us?' Win asked eagerly.

'No.'

Worry creased her forehead. 'They didn't receive my letter, then.' She and Leo had sent word that they would be arriving a few days earlier than expected, owing to a change in the clipper line's schedule.

'Your letter is probably stuck at the bottom of a Royal Mail satchel somewhere,' Leo said. 'Don't worry, Win. We'll go to the Rutledge by hackney. It isn't far.'

'But it will be a shock to the family for us to arrive before we're expected.'

'Our family likes to be shocked,' he said. 'Or at least, they're accustomed to it.'

'They'll also be surprised that Dr. Harrow has come back with us.'

'I'm sure they won't mind his presence at all,' Leo replied. One corner of his mouth twitched in private amusement. 'Well . . . most of them won't.'

★　★　★

Evening had fallen by the time they reached the Rutledge Hotel. Leo arranged for rooms and managed the luggage, while Win and Dr. Harrow waited in a corner of the spacious lobby.

'I'll allow you to reunite with your family in private,' Harrow said. 'My manservant and I will go to our rooms and unpack.'

'You are welcome to come with us,' Win said,

80

but she was secretly relieved when he shook his head.

'I won't intrude. Your reunion should be private.'

'But we will see you in the morning?' Win asked.

'Yes.' He stood looking down at her, a slight smile on his lips.

Dr. Julian Harrow was an elegant man, supernally composed, effortlessly charming. He was dark-haired and gray-eyed and possessed a square-jawed attractiveness that had caused nearly all of his female patients to fall a little bit in love with him. One of the women at the clinic had remarked dryly that Harrow's personal magnetism not only affected men, women, and children but also extended to armoires, assorted chairs, and the nearby goldfish in a bowl.

As Leo had put it: 'Harrow doesn't look at all like a doctor. He looks like a woman's fantasy of a doctor. I suspect half his practice consists of love-struck females who prolong their illness merely to continue being treated by him.'

'I assure you,' Win had said, laughing, 'I am neither love struck, nor am I the least bit inclined to prolong my illness.'

But she had to admit, it was difficult not to feel *something* for a man who was attractive, attentive, and had also cured her of a debilitating condition. And Win thought Julian might possibly have feelings for her in return. During the past year, especially, when Win's health had rebounded into full vitality, Julian had begun to treat her as something more than a mere patient.

They had gone on long walks through the impossibly romantic scenery of Provence, and he had flirted with her, and made her laugh. His attentions had soothed her wounded spirit after Merripen had so callously ignored her.

Eventually Win had accepted that the feelings she had for Merripen were not reciprocated. She had even cried on Leo's shoulder. Her brother had pointed out that she had seen very little of the world and knew next to nothing about men.

'Don't you think it's possible your attachment to Merripen was a result of proximity as much as anything else?' Leo had asked gently. 'Let's look at the situation honestly, Win. You have nothing in common with him. You're a lovely, sensitive, literate woman, and he's . . . Merripen. He likes to chop wood for entertainment. And apparently it falls to me to point out the indelicate truth that some couples are well-suited in the bedroom but not anywhere else.'

Win had been shocked out of her tears by his bluntness. 'Leo Hathaway, are you suggesting — '

'Lord Ramsay now, thank you,' he had teased.

'*Lord Ramsay*, are you suggesting that my feelings for Merripen are carnal in nature?'

'They're certainly not intellectual,' Leo had said, and grinned as she punched him in the shoulder.

After much reflection, however, Win had had to admit that Leo had a point. Of course, Merripen was far more intelligent, and educated, than her brother gave him credit for. As far as she remembered, Merripen had challenged Leo in many a philosophical discussion and had memorized more Greek and Latin than anyone else in the family except her father. But Merripen had only learned those things to fit in with the Hathaways, not because he had any real interest in obtaining an education.

Merripen was a man of nature; he craved the feel of earth and sky. He would never be more than half-tame. And he and Win were as different as fish from fowl.

Julian took her hand in his long, elegant one. His fingers were smooth and well tended, tapered at the tips. 'Winnifred,' he said gently, 'now that we're away from the clinic, life won't be quite so well regulated. You must safeguard your health. Make certain you rest tonight, no matter how tempting it is to stay up all hours.'

'Yes, Doctor,' Win said, smiling up at him. She felt a surge of affection for him, remembering the first time she had managed to climb the exercise ladder in the clinic. Julian had been behind her every step, his encouragements soft in her ear, his chest firm against her back. *A little higher, Winnifred. I won't let you fall.* He hadn't done any of the work for her. Only kept her safe as she climbed.

★   ★   ★

'I'm a bit nervous,' Win admitted as Leo escorted her to the Hathaways' suite on the hotel's second floor.

'Why?'

'I'm not sure. Perhaps because we've all changed.'

'The essential things haven't changed.' Leo gripped her elbow firmly. 'You're still the delightful girl you were. And I'm still a scoundrel with a taste for spirits and lightskirts.'

'Leo,' she said, darting a quick frown at him. 'You're not planning to go back to your old ways, are you?'

'I will avoid temptation,' he replied, 'unless it happens to fall directly in my path.' He stopped her at the middle landing. 'Do you want to pause for a moment?'

'Not at all.' Win continued enthusiastically upward.

'I love stair climbing. I love doing anything I couldn't do before. And from now on I'm going to live by the motto 'Life is to be lived to the fullest.''

Leo grinned. 'You should know that I've said that on many occasions in the past, and it always got me in trouble.'

Win glanced at her surroundings with pleasure. After living in the austere surroundings of Harrow's clinic for so long, she would enjoy a taste of luxury.

Elegant, modern, and supremely comfortable, the Rutledge was owned by the mysterious Harry Rutledge, about whom there were so many rumors that no one could even say definitively whether he was British or American. All that was known for certain was that he had lived for a time in America and had come to England to create a hotel that combined the opulence of Europe with the best of American innovations.

The Rutledge was the first hotel to design every single bedroom en suite with its own private bathroom. And there were delights such as food service lifts, built-in cupboards in the bedrooms, private meeting rooms with atrium glass ceilings, and gardens designed as outdoor rooms. The hotel also featured a dining room that was said to be the most beautiful in England, with so many chandeliers that the ceiling had required extra reinforcements during construction.

They reached the door of the Hathaways' suite, and Leo knocked gently.

There were a few movements within. The door opened to reveal a young fair-haired maid. The maid's gaze swept over the both of them. 'May I help you, sir?' she asked Leo.

'We've come to see Mr. and Mrs. Rohan.'

'Beg pardon, sir, but they have just retired for the evening.'

The hour was quite late, Win thought, deflated. 'We should go our rooms and let them rest,' she told Leo. 'We'll come back in the morning.'

Leo stared at the housemaid with a slight smile, and asked in a soft, low voice, 'What is your name, child?'

Her brown eyes widened, and a blush crept up her cheeks. 'Abigail, sir.'

'Abigail,' he repeated. 'Tell Mrs. Rohan that her sister is here and wishes to see her.'

'Yes, sir.' The maid giggled and left them at the door.

Win gave her brother a wry glance as he

helped to remove her cloak. 'Your way with women never fails to astonish me.'

'Most women have a tragic attraction to rakes,' he said regretfully. 'I really shouldn't use it against them.'

Someone came into the receiving room. He saw Amelia's familiar form, clad in a blue dressing robe, accompanied by Cam Rohan, who was handsomely disheveled in an open-necked shirt and trousers.

Her blue eyes as round as saucers, Amelia stopped at the sight of her brother and sister. A white hand fluttered to Amelia's throat. 'Is it really you?' she asked unsteadily.

Win tried to smile, but it was impossible when her lips were trembling with emotion. She tried to imagine how she must appear to Amelia, who had seen her last as a frail invalid. 'I'm home,' she said, a slight break in her voice.

'Oh, Win! I dreamed — I so hoped — ' Amelia stopped and rushed forward, and their arms went around each other, fast and tight.

Win closed her eyes and sighed, feeling that at last she had come home. *My sister.* She basked in the soft comfort of Amelia's arms.

'You're so beautiful,' Amelia said, drawing back to cup Win's wet cheeks with her hands. 'So healthy and strong. Oh, look at this goddess. Cam, just look at her!'

'You look well,' Rohan told Win, his eyes glowing. 'Better than I've ever seen you, little sister.' Carefully he embraced her and kissed her forehead. 'Welcome back.'

'Where are Poppy and Beatrix?' Win asked,

clinging to Amelia's hand.

'They're abed, but I'll go wake them.'

'No, let them sleep,' Win said quickly. 'We shan't stay for long — we're both exhausted — but I had to see you before retiring for the night.'

Amelia's gaze went to Leo, who had hung back near the door. Win heard the quiet intake of her sister's breath as she saw the changes in him.

'There's my old Leo,' Amelia said softly.

Win was surprised to see a flicker of something in Leo's sardonic expression — a sort of boyish vulnerability, as if he was embarrassed by his own pleasure in the reunion. 'Now you'll weep for a different cause,' he told Amelia. 'Because as you see, I've come back as well.'

She flew to him, and was swallowed in a strong embrace. 'The French wouldn't have you?' she asked, her voice muffled against his chest.

'On the contrary, they adored me. But there's no entertainment in staying where one is wanted.'

'That's too bad,' Amelia said, standing on her toes to kiss his cheek. 'Because you're *very* much wanted here.'

Smiling, Leo reached out to shake Rohan's hand. 'I look forward to seeing the improvements you wrote about. It seems the estate is thriving.'

'You can ask Merripen on the morrow,' Rohan replied easily. 'He knows every inch of the place, and the name of every servant and tenant. And he has much to say on the subject, so be forewarned that any conversation about the estate will be a lengthy one.'

'On the morrow,' Leo repeated, giving Win a quick glance. 'He's in London then?'

'Here at the Rutledge. He's in town to visit a placement agency to hire more servants.'

'I have much to thank Merripen for,' Leo said with uncharacteristic sincerity, 'and you as well, Rohan. The devil knows why you've undertaken so much for my sake.'

'It was for the family's sake, as well.'

As the two men talked, Amelia drew Win to a settee near the hearth. 'Your face is fuller,' Amelia said, openly cataloging the changes in her sister. 'Your eyes are brighter, and your figure is altogether splendid.'

'No more corsets,' Win said with a grin. 'Dr. Harrow says they compress the lungs, force the spine and head into an unnatural attitude, and weaken the back muscles.'

'Scandalous!' Amelia exclaimed, her eyes sparkling. 'No corset even on formal occasions?'

'He allows that I might wear one very rarely, but only loosely laced.'

'What else does Dr. Harrow say?' Amelia was clearly entertained. 'Any opinions on stockings and garters?'

'You may hear it from the source himself,' Win said. 'Leo and I have brought Dr. Harrow back with us.'

'Lovely. Does he have business here?'

'Not that I know of.'

'I suppose since he's from London, he has relations and friends to meet?'

'Yes, that's part of it, but — ' Win felt herself

88

flush a little. 'Julian has expressed a personal interest in spending time with me away from the setting of the clinic.'

Amelia's lips parted in surprise. 'Julian,' she repeated. 'Does he mean to *court* you, Win?'

'I'm not sure. I'm not at all experienced in these matters. But I think so.'

'Do you like him?'

Win nodded without hesitation. 'Quite a lot.'

'Then I'm certain to like him as well. And I will be glad of the chance to thank him personally for what he has done.'

They grinned at each other, basking in the delight of being reunited. But after a moment Win thought of Merripen, and her pulse began to throb with uncomfortable force, and nerves jumped everywhere in her body.

'How is he, Amelia?' she finally brought herself to whisper.

There was no need for Amelia to ask who 'he' was. 'Merripen has changed,' she said cautiously, 'nearly as much as you and Leo. Cam says what Merripen has accomplished with the estate is no less than astounding. It requires a broad array of skills to direct builders, craftsmen, and grounds-men, and also to repair the tenant farms. And Merripen has done it all. When necessary, he'll strip off his coat and lend his own back to a task. He's earned the respect of the workers — they never dare to question his authority.'

'I'm not surprised, of course,' Win said, while a bittersweet feeling came over her. 'He has always been a very capable man. But when you say he has changed, what do you mean?'

'He has become rather . . . hard.'

'Hard-hearted? Stubborn?'

'Yes, and remote. He seems to take no satisfaction in his success, nor does he exhibit any real pleasure in life. Oh, he has learned a great deal, and he wields authority effectively, and he dresses better to befit his new position. But oddly, he seems less civilized than ever. I think . . . ' An uncomfortable pause. 'Perhaps it may help him to see you again. You were always a good influence.'

Win eased her hands away and glowered down at her own lap. 'I doubt that. I doubt I have any influence on Merripen whatsoever. He has made his lack of interest very clear.'

'Lack of interest?' Amelia repeated, and gave a strange little laugh. 'No, Win, I wouldn't say that at all. Any mention of you earns his closest attention.'

'One may judge a man's feelings by his actions.' Win sighed and rubbed her weary eyes. 'At first I was hurt by the way he ignored my letters. Then I was angry. Now I merely feel foolish.'

'Why, dear?' Amelia asked, her blue eyes filled with concern.

For loving, and having that love tossed back in her face. For wasting an ocean's worth of tears on a big, hard-hearted brute.

And for still wanting to see him despite all that.

Win shook her head. The talk of Merripen had made her agitated and melancholy. 'I'm weary after the long journey, Amelia,' she said with a half smile. 'Would you mind if I — '

'No, no, go at once,' her sister said, drawing Win up from the settee and putting a protective arm around her. 'Leo, do take Win to her room. You're both exhausted. We'll have time for talking tomorrow.'

'Ah, that lovely tone of command,' Leo reminisced. 'I'd hoped that by now you would have rid her of the habit of barking out orders like a drill sergeant, Rohan.'

'I enjoy all her habits,' Rohan replied, smiling at his wife.

'What room is Merripen in?' Win whispered to Amelia.

'Third floor, number twenty-one,' Amelia whispered back. 'But you mustn't go tonight, dear.'

'Of course.' Win smiled at her. 'The only thing I intend to do tonight is go to bed without delay.'

7

Third floor, number twenty-one. Win pulled the hood of her cloak farther over her head, concealing her face as she walked along the quiet hallway.

She had to find Merripen, of course. She had come too far. She had crossed miles of earth, an ocean, and come to think of it, she had climbed the equivalent of a thousand ladders in the clinic gymnasium, all to reach him. Now that they were in the same *building*, she was hardly going to end her journey prematurely.

The hotel hallways were bracketed at each end with colonnaded light wells to admit the sun in the daytime hours. Win could hear strains of music from deep within the hotel. There must be a private party in the ballroom, or an event in the famous dining room. Harry Rutledge was called the hotelier to royalty, welcoming the famous, the powerful, and the fashionable to his establishment.

Glancing at the gilded numbers on each door, Win finally found 21. Her stomach plunged, and every muscle clenched with anxiety. She felt a light sweat break out on her forehead. Fumbling a little with her gloves, she managed to pull them off and tuck them into the pockets of her cloak.

A tremulous knock at the door with her knuckles. And she waited in frozen stillness, head downbent, hardly able to breathe for nerves. She gripped her arms around herself beneath the concealing cloak.

She was not certain how much time passed, only that it seemed an eternity before the door was unlocked and opened.

Before she could bring herself to look up, she heard Merripen's voice. She had forgotten how deep and dark it was, how it seemed to reach down to the center of her.

'I didn't send for a woman tonight.'

That last word forestalled Win's reply.

'Tonight' implied that there had been other nights when he had indeed sent for a woman. And although Win was unworldly, she certainly understood what happened when a woman was sent for and received by a man at a hotel.

Her brain swarmed with thoughts. She had no right to object if Merripen wanted a woman to service him. She did not own him. They had made no promises or agreements. He did not owe her fidelity.

But she couldn't help wondering . . . How many women? How many nights?

'No matter,' he said brusquely. 'I can use you. Come in.' A large hand reached out and gripped Win's shoulder, hauling her past the threshold without giving her the opportunity to object.

I can use you?

Anger and consternation tumbled through her. She had no idea what to do or say. Somehow it didn't seem appropriate simply to throw back her hood and cry, *Surprise!*

Merripen had mistaken her for a prostitute, and now the reunion she had dreamed of for so long was turning into a farce.

'I assume you were told that I'm a Rom,' he said.

Her face still concealed by the hood, Win nodded.

'And that doesn't matter to you?'

Win managed a single shake of her head.

There was a soft, humorless laugh that didn't sound at all like Merripen. 'Of course not. As long as the money is good.'

He left her momentarily, striding to the window to close the heavy velvet curtains against the smoke-hazed lights of London. A single lamp strained to illuminate the dimness of the room.

Win glanced at him quickly. It was Merripen . . . but as Amelia had said, he was altered. He had lost weight, perhaps a stone. He was huge, lean, almost rawboned. The neck of his shirt hung open, revealing the brown, hairless chest, the gleaming curve of powerful muscle. She thought at first it was a trick of the light, the immense bulwark of his shoulders and upper arms. Good Lord, how strong he'd become.

But none of that intrigued or startled her as much as his face. He was still as handsome as the devil, with those black eyes and that wicked mouth, the austere angles of nose and jaw, the high planes of his cheekbones. There were new lines, however, deep, bitter grooves that ran from nose to mouth, and the trace of a permanent frown between his thick brows. And most disturbing of all, a hint of cruelty in his expression. He looked capable of things that *her* Merripen never could have done.

Kev, she thought in despair and wonder, *what's happened to you?*

He came to her. Win had forgotten the fluid way he moved, the breathtaking vitality that seemed to charge the air. Hastily she lowered her head.

Merripen reached out for her, and felt her flinch. He must have also detected the tremors that ran through her frame, for he said in a pitiless tone, 'You're new at this.'

She managed a hoarse whisper: 'Yes.'

'I won't hurt you.' Merripen guided her to a nearby table. As she stood facing away from him, he reached around to the fastenings of her cloak. The heavy garment fell away, revealing her straight blond hair, which was falling from its combs. She heard his breath catch. A moment of stillness. Win closed her eyes as Merripen's hands skimmed her sides. Her body was fuller, more curved, strong in the places where she had once been frail. She wore no corset, in spite of the fact that a decent woman always wore a corset. There was only one conclusion a man could have drawn from that.

As he leaned over to lay her cloak at the side of the table, Win felt the unyielding surface of his body brush against hers. The scent of him, clean and rich and male, unlocked a flood of memories. He smelled like the outdoors, like dry leaves and clean rain-soaked earth. He smelled like Merripen.

She didn't want to be so undone by him. And yet it shouldn't have been a surprise. Something about him had always reached through her composure, down to the vein of purest feeling. This raw exhilaration was terrible and sweet, and no man had ever done this to her except him.

'Don't you want to see my face?' she asked huskily.

A cold, level reply. 'It's of no concern to me if you're plain or fair.' But his breath hastened as his hands settled on her, one sliding up her spine, urging her to bend forward. And his next words fell on her ears like black velvet.

'Put your hands on the table.'

Win obeyed blindly, trying to understand herself, the sudden sting of tears, the excitement that throbbed all through her. He stood behind her. His hand continued to move over her back in slow, soothing paths, and she wanted to arch upward like a cat. His touch awakened sensations that had lain dormant for so long. These hands had soothed and cared for her all during her illness; they had pulled her from the very brink of death.

And yet he was not touching her with love, but with impersonal skill. She comprehended that he fully intended to take her, use her, as he had put it. And after an intimate act with a complete stranger, he planned to send her away a stranger still. It was beneath him, the coward. Would he never allow himself to be involved with anyone?

He had closed one hand in her skirts now, easing them upward. Win felt the touch of a cold draft on her ankle, and she couldn't help but imagine what it would be like if she let him go on.

Aroused and panicking, she stared down at

her fists and choked out, 'Is this how you treat women now, Kev?'

Everything stopped. The world halted on its axis.

Her skirt hem dropped, and she was seized in a fierce, hurtful grip and spun around. Caught helplessly, she looked up into his dark face.

Merripen was expressionless, save for the widening of his eyes. As he stared at her, a flush burned across his cheeks and the bridge of his nose.

'*Win*.' Her name was carried on a shaken breath.

She tried to smile at him, to say something, but her mouth was trembling, and she was blinded by pleasure tears. To be with him again . . . it overwhelmed her in every way.

One of his hands came upward. The calloused tip of his thumb smoothed over the gloss of dampness beneath her eye. His hand cradled the side of her face so gently that her lashes fluttered down, and she didn't resist as she felt him bring her closer. His parted lips touched the salty wake of the tear and followed it along her cheek. And then the gentleness evaporated. With a swift, greedy move, he reached for her back, her hips, clutching her hard against him.

His mouth found hers with hot, urgent pressure. He tasted her . . . She reached up to his cheeks and shaped her fingers over the scrape of bristle. A sound came from low in his throat, a masculine growl of pleasure and need. His arms clasped around her in an unbreakable hold, for which she was grateful. Her knees threatened to give way entirely.

Lifting his head, Merripen looked down at her with dazed dark eyes. 'How can you be here?'

'I came back early.' A shiver went through her as his hot breath fanned against her lips. 'I wanted to see you. Wanted you — '

He took her mouth again, no longer gentle. He sank his tongue into her, aggressively searching. Both his hands came up to her head, angling it to make her mouth fully accessible. She reached around him, gripping the powerful stretch of his back, the hard muscles that went on and on.

Merripen groaned as he felt her hands on him. He groped at the combs in her hair, tugged them out, and tangled his fingers in the long silken locks. Pulling her head back, he sought the fragile skin of her throat and dragged his mouth along it as if he wanted to consume her. His hunger escalated and drove his breath faster and his pulse harder, until Win realized he was close to losing all control.

He scooped her up with shocking ease. He carried her to the bed and lowered her swiftly to the mattress. His lips found hers, ravaging deep and sweet, draining her with hot, seeking kisses.

He lowered over her, his solid weight pinning her in place. Win felt him grip the front of her traveling gown, pulling so hard she thought the fabric might tear. The thick cloth resisted his efforts, although a few of the buttons at the back of her gown strained and popped. 'Wait . . . wait . . . ,' she whispered, afraid he would rip her gown to shreds. He was too caught up in his savage desire to hear anything.

As Merripen cupped the soft shape of her

breast over the gown, the tip ached and hardened. His head bent. To Win's astonishment, she felt him biting against the cloth until her nipple was caught in the light clamp of his teeth. A whimper escaped her, and her hips jerked upward reflexively.

Merripen crawled over her. His face was misted with sweat, his nostrils flared from the force of his breathing. The front of her skirts had ridden up between them. He tugged them higher and impelled himself between her thighs until she felt the thick ridge of him between the layers of her drawers and his trousers. Her eyes flew open. She stared up into the black fire of his gaze. He moved against her, letting her feel every inch of what he wanted to put inside her, and she moaned and opened to him.

He made a primitive sound as he rubbed over her again, caressing her with unspeakable intimacy. She wanted him to stop, and at the same time she wanted him never to stop. 'Kev.' Her voice was shaking. 'Kev — '

But his mouth covered hers, penetrating deeply, while his hips moved in slow strokes. Shaken and impassioned, she lifted against that demanding hardness. Each wicked thrust caused sensations to spread, heat unfolding.

Win writhed helplessly, unable to speak with his mouth possessing hers. More heat, more delicious friction. Something was happening, her muscles tightening, her senses opening in readiness for . . . for what? She was going to faint if he didn't stop. Her hands groped at his shoulders, pushing at him, but he ignored the feeble shove. Reaching beneath her, he cupped her squirming bottom and pulled her higher, right against the pumping, sliding pressure. A suspended moment of exquisite tension, so sharp that she gave an uneasy whimper.

Suddenly he flung himself away from her, going to the opposite side of the room. Bracing his hands against the wall, he hung his head and panted, and shivered like a wet dog.

Dazed and trembling, Win moved slowly, restoring her clothing. She felt desperate and painfully empty, needing something she had no name for. When she was covered again, she left the bed on unsteady legs.

She approached Merripen cautiously. It was obvious he was aroused. Painfully so. She wanted to touch him again. Most of all she wanted him to put his arms around her and tell her how overjoyed he was to have her back.

But he spoke before she reached him. And his tone was not encouraging. 'If you touch me,' he said in a guttural voice, 'I'm going to drag you back to that bed. And I won't be responsible for what happens next.'

Win stopped, plaiting her fingers.

Eventually Merripen recovered his breath. And he gave her a glance that should have immolated her on the spot.

'Next time,' he said flatly, 'some advance warning of your arrival might be a good idea.'

'I did send advance notice.' Win was amazed that she could even speak. 'It must have been lost.' She paused. 'That was a f-far warmer welcome than I expected, considering the way you've ignored me for the past two years.'

'I haven't ignored you.'

Win took quick refuge in sarcasm. 'You wrote to me once in two years.'

Merripen turned and rested his back against the wall. 'You didn't need letters from me.'

'I needed any small sign of affection! And you gave me none.' She stared at him incredulously as he remained silent. 'For heaven's sake, Kev, aren't you even going to say that you're glad I'm well again?'

'I'm glad you're well again.'

'Then why are you behaving this way?'

'Because nothing else has changed.'

'*You've* changed,' she shot back. 'I don't know you anymore.'

'That's as it should be.'

'Kev,' she said in bewilderment, 'why are you behaving this way? I went away to get well. *Surely* you can't blame me for that.'

'I blame you for nothing. But the devil knows what you could want from me now.'

I want you to love me, she wanted to cry out. She had traveled so far, and yet there was more distance between them than ever. 'I can tell you what I *don't* want, Kev, and that is to be estranged from you.'

Merripen's expression was stony and unfeeling. 'We're not estranged.' He picked up her cloak and handed it to her. 'Put this on. I'll take you to your room.'

Win pulled the garment around herself, stealing discreet glances at Merripen, who was all brooding energy and suppressed power as he

101

tucked his shirt into his trousers. The X of the braces over his back highlighted his magnificent build.

'You needn't walk with me to my room,' she said in a subdued voice. 'I can find my way back without — '

'You're to go nowhere in this hotel alone. It's not safe.'

'You're right,' she said sullenly. 'I would hate to be accosted by someone.'

The shot hit its mark. Merripen's mouth hardened and he gave her a dangerous glance as he shrugged into his coat.

How much he reminded her just now of the rough, wrathful boy he had been when he had first come to the Hathaways.

'Kev,' she said softly, 'can't we resume our friendship?'

'I'm still your friend.'

'But nothing more?'

'No.'

Win couldn't help glancing at the bed, at the rumpled counterpane that covered it, and a new surge of heat went through her.

Merripen went still as he followed the direction of her gaze. 'That shouldn't have happened,' he said roughly. 'I shouldn't have — ' He stopped and swallowed audibly. 'I haven't . . . had a woman in a while. You were in the wrong place at the wrong time.'

Win had never been so mortified. 'You're saying you would have reacted that way with any woman?'

'Yes.'

'I don't believe you!'

'Believe what you like.' Merripen went to the door and opened it to glance in both directions along the hallway. 'Come here.'

'I want to stay. I need to talk with you.'

'Not alone. Not at this hour.' He paused. 'I told you to come here.'

This last was said with a quiet authority that made her bristle. But she obeyed.

As Win reached him, Merripen pulled the hood of her cloak up to conceal her face. Ascertaining that the hallway was still clear, he guided her outside the room and closed the door.

They were silent as they went to the staircase at the end of the hallway. Win was acutely conscious of his hand resting lightly on her back. Reaching the top step, she was surprised when he stopped her.

'Take my arm.'

She realized he intended to help her down the stairs, as he had always done when she was ill. Stairs had been a particular trial for her. The entire family had been terrified that she would faint while going up or down the steps, and perhaps break her neck. Merripen had often carried her rather than let her take the risk.

'No, thank you,' she said. 'I'm able to do it on my own now.'

'Take it,' he repeated, reaching for her hand.

Win snatched it back, while her chest tightened with annoyance. 'I don't want your help. I'm no longer an invalid. Though it seems you preferred me that way.'

Although she couldn't see his face, she heard his sharply indrawn breath. She felt ashamed at the petty accusation, even as she wondered if there wasn't a grain of truth in it.

Merripen didn't reply, however. If she had hurt him, he bore it stoically. They descended the stairs separately, in silence.

Win was utterly confused. She had pictured this night a hundred different ways. Every possible way but this. She led the way to her door and reached in her pocket for the key.

Merripen took the key from her and opened the door. 'Go and light the lamp.'

Conscious of his large, dark form waiting at the threshold, Win went to the bedside table. Carefully she lifted the glass globe of the lamp, lit the wick, and replaced the glass.

After inserting the key into the other side of the door, Merripen said, 'Lock it behind me.'

Turning to look at him, Win felt a miserable laugh knotting in her throat. 'This is where we left off, isn't it? Me, throwing myself at you. You, turning me away. I thought I understood before. I wasn't well enough for the kind of relationship I wanted with you. But now I don't understand. Because there's nothing to stop us from finding out if . . . if we are meant to . . . ' Distressed and mortified, she couldn't find words for what she wanted. 'Unless I was mistaken in how you once felt for me? Did you ever desire me, Kev?'

'No.' His voice was barely audible. 'It was only friendship. And pity.'

Win felt her face go very white. Her eyes and nose prickled. A hot tear leaked down her cheek.

'Liar,' she said, and turned away.

The door closed gently.

* * *

Kev never remembered walking back to his room, only that he eventually found himself standing beside his bed. Groaning a curse, he sank to his knees and gripped huge handfuls of the counterpane and buried his face in it.

He was in hell.

Holy Christ, how Win devastated him. He had starved for her for so long, dreamed of her so many nights, and woken to so many bitter mornings without her that at first he hadn't believed she was real.

He thought of Win's lovely face, and the softness of her mouth against his, and the way she had arched beneath his hands. She had felt different, her body supple and strong. But her spirit was the same, radiant with the endearing sweetness and honesty that had always pierced straight to his heart. It had taken all his strength not to go to his knees before her.

Win had asked for friendship. Impossible. How could he could separate any part of the unwieldy tangle of his feelings, and hand over such a small piece? And she knew better than to ask. Even in the Hathaways' eccentric world, some things were forbidden.

Kev had nothing to offer Win except degradation. Even Cam Rohan had been able to provide Amelia with his considerable wealth. But Kev had no worldly possessions, no grace of character, no education, no advantageous connections, nothing that the *gadje* valued. He had been isolated and maltreated even by the people of his own tribe for reasons he had never understood. But on some elemental level, he knew that he must have deserved it. Something about him had destined him for a life of violence. And no rational being would say there was any benefit for Win Hathaway to love a man who was, essentially, a brute.

If she was well enough to marry someday, it would be to a gentleman.

To a gentle man.

8

In the morning, Leo met the governess.

Poppy and Beatrix had both written to him about having acquired a governess a year earlier. Her name was Miss Marks, and they both liked her, although their descriptions didn't exactly convey *why* they should like such a creature. Apparently she was slight and quiet and stern. She was helping not only the sisters but the entire family learn to acquit itself in society.

Leo thought this social instruction was probably a good thing. For everyone else, not himself.

When it came to polite behavior, society tended to be far more exacting of women than men. And if a man had a title and held his liquor reasonably well, he could do or say nearly anything he liked, and still be invited everywhere.

Through a quirk of fate Leo had inherited a viscouncy, which had taken care of the first part of the equation. And now after the long stay in France, he had limited his drinking to a glass of wine or two at supper. Which meant he was relatively certain of being received at any dull and respectable event in London that he had no desire to attend.

He only hoped that the formidable Miss Marks would try to correct him. It might be amusing to set her back on her heels.

Leo knew next to nothing about governesses,

save for the drab creatures in novels, who tended to fall in love with the lord of the manor, always with bad results. However, Miss Marks was entirely safe from him. For a change, he had no interest in seducing anyone. His former dissipated pursuits had lost their power to enthrall him.

On one of Leo's ambles around Provence to visit some Gallo-Roman architectural remains, he had encountered one of his old professors from the Ecole des Beaux-Arts. The chance meeting had resulted in a renewed acquaintanceship. In the months to come, Leo had spent many an afternoon sketching, reading, and studying in the professor's atelier, or workshop. Leo had arrived at some conclusions that he intended to put to the test now that he was back in England.

As he strolled nonchalantly along the long hallway that led to the Hathaway suite, he heard rapid footsteps. Someone was running toward him from the other direction. Moving to the side, Leo waited with his hands tucked in his trouser pockets.

'Come here, you little fiend!' he heard a woman snarl. 'You oversized rat! When I get my hands on you, I'll rip out your innards!'

The bloodthirsty tone was unladylike. Appalling. Leo was vastly entertained. The footsteps drew closer . . . but there was only one set of them. Who on earth could she be chasing?

It quickly became clear that she was not pursuing a 'who' but a 'what.' The furry, slithery body of a ferret came loping along the hallway with a frilly object clamped in his mouth. Most hotel guests would no doubt be disconcerted by the sight of a small carnivorous mammal streaking toward them. However, Leo had lived for years with Beatrix's creatures: mice appearing in his pockets, baby rabbits in his shoes, hedgehogs wandering casually past the dining table. Smiling, he watched the ferret hurry past him.

The woman came soon after, a mass of rustling gray skirts as she ran full bore after the creature. But if there was one thing ladies' clothing was not designed to do, it was to facilitate ease of movement. Weighted by layers and layers of fabric, she stumbled and fell a few yards away from Leo. A pair of spectacles went flying to the side.

Leo was at her side in an instant, crouching on the floor as he sorted through the hissing tangle of limbs and skirts. 'Are you hurt? I feel certain there's a woman in here somewhere . . . Ah, there you are. Easy, now. Let me — '

'*Don't touch me*,' she snapped, batting at him with her fists.

'I'm not touching you. That is, I'm only touching you with the — *ow*, damn it — with the intention of helping.' Her hat, a little scrap of wool felt with cheap corded trim, had fallen over her face. Leo managed to push it back to the top of her head, narrowly missing a sharp blow to his jaw. '*Christ*. Would you stop flailing for a moment?'

Struggling to a sitting position, she glared at him.

Leo crawled to retrieve the spectacles and returned to hand them to her. She snatched them from him without a word of thanks.

She was a lean, anxious-looking woman. A young woman with narrowed eyes, from which bad temper flashed out. Her light brown hair was pulled back with a gallows-rope tightness that made Leo wince just to see it. One would have hoped for some compensating feature — a soft pair of lips, perhaps, or a pretty bosom. But no, there was only a stern mouth, a flat chest, and gaunt cheeks. If Leo were compelled to spend any time with her — which, thankfully, he wasn't — he would have started by feeding her.

'If you want to help,' she said coldly, hooking the spectacles around her ears, 'retrieve that blasted ferret for me. Perhaps I've tired him enough that you may be able to run him to ground.'

Still crouching on the floor, Leo glanced at the ferret, which had paused ten yards away and was watching them both with bright, beady eyes. 'What is his name?'

'Dodger.'

Leo gave a low whistle and a few clicks of his tongue. 'Come here, Dodger. You've caused enough trouble for the morning. Though I can't fault your taste in . . . ladies' garters? Is that what you're holding?'

The woman watched, stupefied, as the ferret's long, slender body wriggled toward Leo. Chattering busily, Dodger crawled onto Leo's thigh. 'Good fellow,' Leo said, stroking the sleek fur.

'How did you do that?' the woman asked in annoyance.

'I have a way with animals. They tend to acknowledge me as one of their own.' Leo gently pried a frilly bit of lace and ribbon from the long front teeth. It was definitely a garter, deliciously feminine and impractical. He gave the woman a mocking smile as he handed it to her. 'No doubt this is yours.'

He hadn't really thought that, of course. He had assumed the garter belonged to someone else. It was impossible to fathom this stern female wearing something so frivolous. But as he saw a blush spreading across the young woman's cheeks, he realized it actually *was* hers. Intriguing.

He gestured with the ferret hanging relaxed in his hand and said, 'I take it this animal doesn't belong to you?'

'No, to one of my charges.'

'Are you by chance a governess?'

'That is no concern of yours.'

'Because if you are, then one of your charges is most definitely Miss Beatrix Hathaway.'

She scowled. 'How do you know that?'

'My sister is the only person I know of who would bring a garter-stealing ferret to the Rutledge Hotel.'

'Your *sister*?'

He smiled into her astonished face. 'Lord Ramsay, at your service. And you are Miss Marks, the governess?'

'Yes,' she muttered, ignoring the hand he reached down for her. She rose to her feet unassisted.

Leo felt an irresistible urge to provoke her. 'How gratifying. I've always wanted a family governess to harass.'

The comment seemed to incense her beyond all expectation. 'I am aware of your reputation as a skirt-chaser, my lord. I find no cause for humor in it.'

Leo didn't think she found cause for humor in much of anything. 'My reputation has lasted in spite of a two-year absence?' he asked, affecting a tone of pleased surprise.

'You're *proud* of it?'

'Well, of course. It's easy to have a good reputation — you merely have to do nothing. But earning a bad reputation . . . well, that takes some effort.'

A contemptuous stare burned through the spectacle lenses. 'I despise you,' she announced. Turning on her heel, she walked away from him.

Leo followed, carrying the ferret. 'We've only just met. You can't despise me until you really get to know me.'

She ignored him as he followed her to the Hathaway suite. She ignored him as he knocked at the door, and she ignored him as they were welcomed inside by the maid.

There was some kind of commotion going on in the suite, which shouldn't have been a surprise considering it was his family's suite. The air was filled with cursing, exclamations, and grunts of physical combat.

'Leo?' Beatrix appeared from the main receiving room and hurried over to them.

'Beatrix, darling!' Leo was amazed by the

112

difference the past two and a half years had made in his youngest sister. 'How you've grown — '

'Yes, never mind that,' she said impatiently, snatching the ferret from him. 'Go in there and help Mr. Rohan!'

'Help him with what?'

'He's trying to stop Merripen from killing Dr. Harrow.'

'Already?' Leo asked blankly, and rushed into the receiving room.

9

After attempting to sleep on a bed that had turned into a torture rack, Kev had awoken with a heavy heart. And other, more urgent discomforts.

He'd been plagued with stimulating dreams in which Win's naked body had been writhing against him, beneath him. All the desires he kept at bay in the daylight hours had expressed themselves in those dreams . . . He had been holding Win, thrusting inside her, and taking her cries into his mouth . . . kissing her from head to toe and back again. And in those same dreams she had behaved in a most un-Win-like manner, delicately feasting on him with a wanton mouth, exploring him with inquisitive little hands.

Washing in frigid water had helped his condition marginally, but Kev was still aware of the heat burning far too close to the surface.

He was going to have to face Win today and converse with her in front of everyone, as if everything were ordinary. He was going to have to look at her and not think about the softness between her thighs, and how she had cradled him as he had thrust against her, and how he had felt her warmth even through the layers of their clothes. And how he had lied to her and made her cry.

Feeling wretched and explosive, Kev dressed in the town clothes that the family insisted he wear when in London. 'You know how much value *gadje* place on appearance,' Rohan had told him, dragging him to Savile Row. 'You have to look respectable, or it will reflect badly on your sisters to be seen with you.'

Rohan's former employer, Lord St. Vincent, had recommended a shop that specialized in bespoke tailoring. *You won't get anything decent in made-to-measure,* St. Vincent had said, flicking an assessing glance over Kev. *No pattern would fit him.*

Kev had submitted to the indignity of having measurements taken, being draped with countless fabrics, and going for endless fittings. Rohan and the Hathaway sisters had all seemed pleased with the results, but Kev couldn't see any difference between his new attire and the old. Clothes were clothes, something that covered the body to protect it from the elements.

Scowling, Kev donned a white pleated shirt and black cravat, a vest with a notched collar, and narrow-legged trousers. He pulled on a wool town coat with front flap pockets and a split at the back. (Despite his disdain for *gadjo* clothing, he had to admit it was a fine, comfortable coat.)

As was his habit, Kev went to the Hathaway suite for breakfast. He kept his face expressionless, even though his gut was twisting and his pulse was rampaging. All at the thought of seeing Win. But he would manage the situation adeptly. He would be calm and quiet, and Win would be her usual composed self, and they would get past this first unholy awkward meeting.

All his intentions, however, vanished as he

entered the suite, went to the receiving room, and saw Win on the floor. In her underclothes.

She was lying prostrate on her stomach, trying to push upward, while a man leaned over her. Touching her.

The sight exploded inside Kev.

With a bloodthirsty roar, he reached Win in a flash, snatching her up in possessive arms.

'Wait,' she gasped. 'What are you — oh, *don't*! Let me expl — *no*!'

He deposited her unceremoniously on a sofa behind him, and turned to face the other man. The only thought in Kev's mind was swift and effective dismemberment, starting by ripping the bastard's head off.

Prudently the man had rushed behind a heavy chair, placing it between them. 'You must be Merripen,' he said. 'And I'm — '

'A dead man,' Kev growled, starting for him.

'He's my doctor!' Win cried. 'He's Dr. Harrow, and — Merripen, don't you dare hurt him!'

Ignoring her, Kev went forward about two strides before he felt a leg hook around his, sending him hurtling to the floor. It was Cam Rohan, who pounced on him, knelt on his arms, and gripped the back of his neck.

'Merripen, you *idiot*,' Rohan said, struggling to keep him down, 'he's the damned doctor. What do you think you're doing?'

'Killing . . . him . . . ,' Kev grunted, lurching upward despite Rohan's restraining weight.

'Bloody hell!' Rohan exclaimed. 'Leo, help me hold him! *Now*.'

Leo rushed over to help. It took both of them to keep Merripen down.

'I love our family gatherings,' he heard Leo say. 'Merripen, what the devil is your problem?'

'Win is in her underclothes, and that man — '

'These are not my underclothes,' came Win's exasperated voice. 'This is an exercise costume!'

Merripen twisted to look in her direction. Since Rohan and Leo were still pinning him down, he couldn't look all the way up. But he saw that Win was clad in loose-fitting drawers and a bodice with bare arms. 'I know underclothes when I see them,' he snapped.

'These are Turkish trousers, and a perfectly respectable bodice. Every woman at the clinic wears this same costume. Exercising is necessary for my health, and I am certainly not going to do it in a gown and cors — '

'He was touching you!' Kev interrupted harshly.

'He was making certain that I had the correct form.'

The doctor approached with caution. There was a flicker of humor in his alert gray eyes. 'It's a Hindu exercise, actually. It's part of a strength-training system I've developed. All my patients have incorporated it into their daily schedules. Please believe that my attentions to Miss Hathaway were entirely respectful.' He paused and asked wryly, 'Am I safe now?'

Leo and Cam, still struggling with Kev, both answered simultaneously, 'No.'

By this time, Poppy, Beatrix, and Miss Marks had hurried into the room.

'Merripen,' Poppy said, 'Dr. Harrow wasn't hurting Win a bit, and — '

'He's really very nice, Merripen,' Beatrix chimed in. 'Even my animals like him.'

'Easy,' Rohan said quietly to Kev, speaking in Romany so that no one else could understand. 'This is no good for anyone.'

Kev went still. 'He was touching her,' he replied in the old language, even though he hated using it.

And he knew Rohan understood that a Rom found it difficult, even impossible, to tolerate any other man putting a hand on his woman, for any reason.

'She's not yours, *phral*,' Rohan said in Romany, not without sympathy.

Slowly Kev forced himself to relax.

'May I get off him now?' Leo asked. 'There's only one kind of exertion I enjoy before breakfast. And this is not it.'

Rohan allowed Kev to stand but kept one arm twisted behind his back.

Win went to stand beside Harrow. The sight of her wearing so little, being so near another man, caused muscles to twitch all over Kev's body. He could see the shape of her hips and legs. The entire family had gone insane, letting her dress that way in front of an outsider and acting as though it were appropriate. *Turkish trousers* . . . as if giving them such a name made them anything but underdrawers.

'I insist that you apologize,' Win said. 'You've been very rude to my guest, Merripen.'

Her guest? Kev stared at her in outrage.

'No need,' Harrow said hastily. 'I know how it must have appeared.'

Win glared at Kev. 'He has made me well again, and *this* is the way you repay him?' she demanded.

'You made yourself well,' Harrow said. 'It was a result of your own efforts, Miss Hathaway.'

Win's expression softened as she glanced at the doctor. 'Thank you.' But when she looked back at Kev, the frown returned. 'Are you going to apologize, Merripen?'

Rohan twisted his arm a bit more tightly. 'Do it, damn you,' Rohan muttered. 'For the sake of the family.'

Glaring at the doctor, Kev spoke in Romany. '*Ka xlia ma pe tute.*' (I'm going to shit on you.)

'Which means,' Rohan said hastily, ' ''Please forgive the misunderstanding; let's part as friends.'' '

'*Te malavel les i menkiva,*' Kev added for good measure. (May you die of a malignant wasting disease.)

'Roughly translated,' Rohan said, 'that means, 'May your garden be filled with fine, fat hedgehogs.' Which, I may add, is considered quite a blessing among the Rom.'

Harrow looked skeptical. But he murmured, 'I accept your apology. No harm done.'

'Excuse us,' Rohan said pleasantly, still twisting Kev's arm. 'Go on with breakfast, please . . . We have some errands to accomplish. Please tell Amelia when she rises that I'll return at approximately midday.' And he steered Kev from the room, with Leo at their heels.

As soon as they were out of the suite and in

119

the hallway, Rohan released Kev's arm and turned to face him.

Raking his hand through his hair, Rohan asked with mild exasperation, 'What did you hope to get out of killing Win's doctor?'

'Enjoyment.'

'No doubt you would have. Win didn't seem to be enjoying it, however.'

'Why is Harrow here?' Kev asked fiercely.

'I can answer that one,' Leo said, leaning a shoulder against the wall with casual ease. 'Harrow wants to become better acquainted with the Hathaways. Because he and my sister are . . . close.'

Kev abruptly felt a sickening weight in his stomach, as if he'd swallowed a handful of river stones. 'What do you mean?' he asked, even though he knew. No man could be exposed to Win and not fall in love with her.

'Harrow is a widower,' Leo said. 'A decent enough fellow. More attached to his clinic and patients than anything else. But he's a sophisticated man, widely traveled, and wealthy as the devil. And he's a collector of beautiful objects. A connoisseur of fine things.'

Neither of the other men missed the implication. Win would indeed be an exquisite addition to a collection of fine things.

It was difficult to ask the next question, but Kev forced himself to. 'Does Win care for him?'

'I don't believe Win knows how much of what she feels for him is gratitude, and how much is true affection.' Leo gave Kev a pointed glance. 'And there are still a few unresolved questions she has to answer for herself.'

'I'll talk to her.'

'I wouldn't, if I were you. Not until she cools a bit. She's rather incensed with you.'

'Why?' Kev asked, wondering if she had confided to her brother about the events of the previous night.

'Why?' Leo's mouth twisted. 'There's such a dazzling array of choices, I find myself in a quandary about which one to start with. Putting the subject of this morning aside, what about the fact that you never wrote to her?'

'I did,' Kev said indignantly.

'One letter,' Leo allowed. 'The farm report. She showed it to me, actually. How could one forget the soaring prose you wrote about fertilizing the field near the east gate? I'll tell you, the part about sheep dung nearly brought a tear to my eye, it was so sentimental and — '

'What did she expect me to write about?' Kev demanded.

'Don't bother to explain, my lord,' Cam interceded as Leo opened his mouth. 'It's not the way of the Rom to put our private thoughts on paper.'

'It's not the way of the Rom to run an estate and manage crews of workmen and tenant farmers, either,' Leo replied. 'But he's done that, hasn't he?' Leo smiled sardonically at Kev's sullen expression. 'In all likelihood, Merripen, you'd make a far better lord of the manor than I will. Look at you . . . Are you dressed like a Rom? Do you spend your days lounging by the campfire, or are you poring over estate account

121

books? Do you sleep outside on the hard ground, or inside on a nice feather bed? Do you even speak like a Rom anymore? No, you've lost your accent. You sound like — '

'What is your point?' Kev interrupted curtly.

'Only that you've made compromises right and left since you came to this family. You've done whatever you had to, to be close to Win. So don't be a bloody hypocrite and turn all Rom now that you finally have a chance to — ' Leo stopped and lifted his eyes heavenward. 'Good Lord. This is too much even for me. And I thought I was inured to drama.' He gave Rohan a sour look. 'You talk to him. I'm going to have my tea.'

He went back into the suite, leaving them in the hallway.

'I didn't write about sheep dung,' Kev muttered. 'It was another kind of fertilizer.'

Rohan tried unsuccessfully to smother a grin. 'Be that as it may, *phral*, the word 'fertilizer' should probably be left out of a letter to a lady.'

'Don't call me that.'

Rohan started down the hallway. 'Come with me. There actually is an errand I want you for.'

'Not interested.'

'It's dangerous,' Rohan coaxed. 'You might get to hit someone. Maybe even start a brawl. Ah . . . I knew that would convince you.'

* * *

One of the qualities Kev found most annoying about Cam Rohan was his persistence in trying

122

to find out about the tattoos. He had pursued the mystery for two years.

Despite the multitude of responsibilities he shouldered, Rohan never missed an opportunity to delve further into the matter. He had searched diligently for his own tribe, asking for information from every passing *vardo* and going to every Romany camp. But it seemed as if Rohan's tribe had disappeared from the face of the earth, or at least had gone to the other side of it. He would probably never find them — there was no limit to how far a tribe might travel, and no guarantee they would ever return to England.

Rohan had searched marriage records, birth and death records, to find any mention of his mother, Sonya, or himself. Nothing so far. He had also consulted heraldic experts and Irish historians to find out the possible significance of the *pooka* symbol. All they had been able to do was dredge up the familiar legends of the nightmare horse: that he spoke in a human voice, that he appeared at midnight and called for you to come with him, and you could never refuse. And when you went with him, if you survived the ride, you were changed forever when you returned.

Cam had also not been able to find a meaningful connection between the Rohan and Merripen names, which were common among the Rom. Therefore Rohan's latest approach was to search for Kev's tribe, or anyone who knew about it.

Kev was understandably hostile about this plan, which Rohan revealed to him as they walked to the hotel mews.

'They left me for dead,' Kev said. 'And you want me to help you find them? If I see any of them, especially the *rom baro*, I'll kill him with my bare hands.'

'Fine,' Rohan returned equably. '*After* they tell us about the tattoo.'

'All they'll say is what I've already told you — it's the mark of a curse. And if you ever find out what it means — '

'Yes, yes, I know. We're doomed. But if I'm wearing a curse on my arm, Merripen, I want to know about it.'

Kev gave him a glance that should have felled him on the spot. He stopped at a corner of the stables, where hoof picks, clippers, and files were neatly organized on shelves. 'I'm not going. You'll have to look for my tribe without me.'

'I need you,' Rohan countered. 'For one thing, the place we're headed to is *kekkeno mushes puv*.'

Kev stared at him in disbelief. *Kekkeno mushes puv*, translated as 'no-man's-land,' was a squalid plain located on the Surrey side of the Thames. The open muddy ground was crowded with ragged Gypsy tents, a few dilapidated *vardos*, feral dogs, and nearly feral Roma. But that wasn't the real danger. There was another, non-Gypsy group called the Chorodies, descendants of rogues and outcasts, mainly Saxon in origin. The Chorodies were truly vile, dirty, and ferocious, without customs or manners. Going anywhere near them was virtually asking to be attacked or robbed. It was hard to imagine a more dangerous place in London except for a few Eastside rookeries.

'Why do you think anyone from my tribe could be in such a place?' Kev asked, more than a little shocked by the idea. Surely, even under the *rom baro*'s leadership, they wouldn't have sunk so low.

'Not long ago I met a *chal* from the Bosvil tribe. He said his youngest sister, Shuri, was married long ago to your *rom baro*.' Rohan stared at Merripen intently. 'It seems the story of what happened to you has been told all through Romanija.'

'I don't see why,' Kev muttered, feeling suffocated. 'It's not important.'

Rohan shrugged casually, his gaze trained on Kev's face. 'The Rom take care of their own. No tribe would ever leave an injured or dying boy behind, no matter what the circumstances. And apparently it brought a curse on the *rom baro's* tribe . . . Their luck turned very bad, and most of them came to ruin. There's justice for you.'

'I never cared about justice.' Kev was vaguely surprised by the rustiness of his own voice.

Rohan spoke with quiet understanding. 'It's a strange life, isn't it? . . . A Rom with no tribe. No matter how hard you look, you can never find a home. Because to us, home is not a building or a tent or *vardo* . . . home is a family.'

Kev had a difficult time meeting Rohan's gaze. The words cut too close to his heart. In all the time he had known Rohan, Kev had never felt a kinship with him until now. But Kev could no longer ignore the fact that they had too damn much in common. They were two outsiders with pasts full of unanswered questions. And each of them had been drawn to the Hathaways, and had found a home with them.

'I'll go with you, damn it,' Kev said gruffly. 'But only because I know what Amelia would do to me if I let something happen to you.'

10

Somewhere in England, spring had covered the ground with green velvet and coaxed flowers from the hedgerows. Somewhere the sky was blue and the air was sweet. But not in no-man's-land, where smoke from millions of chimney pipes had soured the complexion of the city with a yellow fog that daylight could barely penetrate. There was little but mud and misery in this barren place. It was located approximately a quarter mile from the river and bordered by a hill and a railway.

Kev was grim and silent as he and Rohan led their horses through the Romany camp. Tents were loosely scattered, with men sitting at the entrances and whittling pegs or making baskets. Kev heard a few boys shouting at one another. As he rounded a tent, he saw a small group gathered around a fight. Men angrily shouted instructions and threats to the boys as if they were animals in a pit.

Stopping at the sight, Kev stared at the boys while images from his own childhood flashed through his mind. Pain, violence, fear . . . the wrath of the *rom baro,* who would beat Kev further if he lost. And if he won, sending another boy bloodied and broken to the ground, there would be no reward. Only the crushing guilt of harming someone who had done no wrong to him.

What is this? the *rom baro* had roared,

discovering Kev huddled in a corner, crying, after he had beaten a boy who had begged him to stop. *You pathetic, sniveling dog. I'll give you one of these* — His booted foot had landed in Kev's side, bruising a rib — *for every tear you shed. What kind of idiot would cry for winning? Crying after doing the only thing you're good for? I'll drive the softness out of you, big bawling infant* — He hadn't stopped kicking Kev until he was unconscious.

The next time Kev had beaten someone, he had felt no guilt. He had felt nothing.

Kev wasn't aware that he'd frozen in his tracks, or that he was breathing heavily, until Rohan spoke to him softly.

'Come, *phral.*'

Tearing his gaze away from the boys, Kev saw the compassion and sanity in the other man's eyes. The dark memories receded. Kev gave a short nod and followed.

Rohan stopped at two or three tents, asking the whereabouts of a woman named Shuri. The responses were grudging. As expected, the Roma regarded Rohan and Kev with obvious suspicion and curiosity. The Roma's dialect was difficult to interpret, a medley of deep Romany and what was called 'tinker patois,' a slang used by urban Gypsies.

Kev and Rohan were directed to one of the smaller tents, where an older boy sat by the entrance on an overturned pail. He carved buttons with a small knife.

'We're looking for Shuri,' Kev said in the old language.

The boy glanced over his shoulder into the tent. '*Mami*,' he called. 'There are two men to see you. Roma dressed like *gadjos*.'

A singular-looking woman came to the entrance. She was not quite five feet tall, but her torso and head were broad, her complexion dark and wrinkled, her eyes lustrous and black. Kev recognized her immediately. It was indeed Shuri, who had only been about sixteen when she had married the *rom baro*. Kev had left the tribe not long after that.

The years had not been kind to her. Shuri had once been a striking beauty, but a life of hardship had aged her prematurely. Although she and Kev were nearly the same age, the difference between them could have been twenty years instead of two.

She stared at Kev without much interest. Then her eyes widened, and her gnarled hands moved in a gesture commonly used to protect oneself against evil spirits.

'Kev,' she breathed.

'Hello, Shuri,' he said with difficulty, and followed it with a greeting he hadn't said since childhood. '*Droboy tume Romale*.'

'Are you a spirit?' she asked him.

Rohan looked at him alertly. 'Kev?' he repeated. 'Is that your tribal name?'

Kev ignored him. 'I'm not a spirit, Shuri.' He gave her a reassuring smile. 'If I were, I wouldn't have grown any older, would I?'

She shook her head, her eyes slitting in a leery squint. 'If it's really you, show me the mark.'

'May I do it inside?'

After a long hesitation, Shuri nodded reluctantly, waving both Kev and Rohan into the tent.

Cam paused at the entrance and spoke to the boy. 'Make certain the horses aren't stolen,' he said, 'and I'll give you a half crown.' He wasn't certain whether the horses would be more in danger from the Chorodies or the Roma.

'Yes, *kako*,' the boy said, using a respectful form of address for a much older male.

Smiling ruefully, Cam followed Merripen into the tent.

The structure was made of rods stuck into the ground and bent at the top, with other supporting rods fastened to it with string. The whole of it was covered with coarse brown cloth that had been pinned together over the ribs of the structure. There were no chairs or tables. To a Rom, the ground served perfectly well for both purposes. But there was an abundant pile of pots and trenchers in the corner, and a light pallet covered with cloth. The interior of the tent was heated by a small coke fire glowing in a three-legged pan.

At Shuri's direction, Cam sat cross-legged by the fire pan. He stifled a grin as Shuri insisted on seeing Merripen's tattoo, which provoked a long-suffering glance from him. Being a modest and private man, Merripen was probably cringing inside at having to undress in front of them. But he set his jaw and tugged off his coat, and unbuttoned his vest.

Rather than remove his shirt entirely, Merripen unfastened it and let it fall to reveal his upper back and shoulders, the muscled slopes gleaming like copper. The tattoo was still a mildly startling sight to Cam, who had never seen it on anyone but himself.

Muttering in deep Romany, using a few words that sounded like Sanskrit, Shuri moved behind Kev to look at the tattoo. Merripen's head lowered, and he breathed quietly.

Cam's amusement faded as he saw Merripen's face, detached save for a slight frown. For Cam it would have been a joy and a relief to encounter someone from his past. For Merripen, the experience was pure misery. But he bore it with a stoic endurance that touched Cam. And Cam discovered that he didn't like to see Merripen being made so vulnerable.

After glancing at the mark of the nightmare horse, Shuri moved away from Merripen and motioned for him to dress himself. 'Who is this man?' she asked, nodding in Cam's direction.

'One of my *kumpania*,' Merripen muttered. *Kumpania* was a word used to describe a clan, a group united though not necessarily by family ties. Pulling his clothes back on, Merripen asked brusquely, 'What happened to the tribe, Shuri? Where is the *rom baro*?'

'In the ground,' the woman said, with a pointed lack of respect for her husband. 'And the tribe is scattered. After the tribe saw what he did to you, Kev . . . making us leave you for dead . . . it all went bad after that. No one wanted to follow him. The *gadjos* finally hanged him, when he was caught making *wafodu luvvu*.'

'What is that?' Cam asked, unable to follow her accent.

'Counterfeit money,' Merripen said.

'Before that,' Shuri continued, 'the *rom baro* had tried to make some of the young boys into *asharibe*, to earn coins at fairs and in the London streets. But none of them could fight like you, and their parents would only let the *rom baro* go so far with them.' Her shrewd dark eyes turned in Cam's direction. 'The *rom baro* called Kev his fighting dog,' she said. 'But the dogs were treated better than he was.'

'Shuri — ,' Merripen muttered, scowling. 'He doesn't need to know — '

'My husband wanted Kev to die,' she continued, 'but even the *rom baro* wouldn't dare to kill him outright. So he starved the boy and put him in too many fights, and gave him no bandages or salve for his wounds. He was never given a blanket, only a bed of straw. We used to sneak food and medicine to him when the *rom baro* wasn't looking. But there was no one to defend him, poor boy.' Her gaze turned chiding as she spoke to Merripen directly. 'And it wasn't easy to help you, when you would do nothing but snarl and snap. Never a word of thanks, not even a smile.'

Merripen was silent, his face averted as he finished fastening the last of his waistcoat buttons.

Cam found himself thinking it was a good thing the *rom baro* was already dead. Because he was feeling a powerful urge to hunt the bastard down and kill him. And Cam didn't like Shuri's criticism of Merripen. Not that Merripen had ever been a model of charm . . . but after he had been raised in such a merciless environment, it was a bloody miracle that he was able to live like a normal man.

The Hathaways had done more than save Merripen's life. They had saved his soul as well.

'Why did your husband bear Merripen such hatred?' Cam asked softly.

'The *rom baro* hated all things *gadjo*. He used to say that if any of the tribe ever went with one of the *gadje*, he would kill them.'

Merripen looked at her sharply. 'But I'm Romany.'

'You're *poshram*, Kev. Half *gadjo*.' She smiled at his open astonishment. 'You never suspected? You have the look of a *gadjo*, you know. That narrow nose. The shape of your jaw.'

Merripen shook his head, speechless at the revelation.

'Holy hell,' Cam whispered.

'Your mother married a *gadjo*, Kev,' Shuri continued. 'The tattoo you bear is the mark of his family. But your father left her, as *gadjos* tend to do. And after we thought you died, the *rom baro* said, 'Now there's only one.''

'Only one what?' Cam managed to ask.

'Brother.' Shuri moved to stir the contents of the fire pan, sending a brighter glow through the tent. 'Kev had a younger brother.'

Emotion flooded Cam. He felt a dazzling change in all his awareness, a new inflection in every thought. After he had spent all his life believing himself to be alone, here was someone who shared his blood. A true brother. Cam stared at Merripen, watching the realization dawn in the coffee-dark eyes. Cam didn't think the news would be as welcome to Merripen as it was to him, but he didn't give a damn.

'The grandmother took care of both children for a while,' Shuri continued. 'But then the grandmother had cause to think the *gadjos* might come and take them. Perhaps even kill them. So she kept one boy, while Kev was sent to our tribe into the care of his Uncle Pov, the *rom baro*. I'm sure the grandmother didn't suspect how the *rom baro* would abuse him, or she never would have done it.'

Shuri glanced at Merripen. 'She probably thought that since Pov was a strong man, he would do a good job of protecting you. But he thought of you as an abomination, being half — ' She stopped with a gasp as Cam shoved up his coat and shirtsleeve, and showed his forearm to her. The *pooka* tattoo stood out in dark, inky relief against his skin.

'I'm his brother,' Cam said, his voice slightly hoarse.

Shuri's gaze moved from one man's face to the other. 'Yes, I see,' she eventually murmured. 'Not a close likeness, but it is there.' A curious smile touched her lips. '*Devlesa avilan*. It is God who brought you together.'

Whatever Merripen's opinion was of who or what had brought them together, he didn't share it. Instead he asked tersely, 'Do you know our father's name?'

Shuri looked regretful. 'The *rom baro* never mentioned it. I'm sorry.'

'No, you've helped quite a lot,' Cam said. 'Do you know anything about why the *gadjos* might have wanted to — '

'*Mami*,' came the boy's voice from outside. 'Chorodies are coming.'

'They want the horses,' Merripen said, rising swiftly to his feet. He pressed a few coins into Shuri's hand. 'Luck and good health,' he said.

'*Kushti bok*,' she replied, returning the sentiment.

Cam and Merripen hurried outside the tent. Three Chorodies were approaching. With their matted hair, filthy complexions, rotted mouths, and a stench that preceded them well before their arrival, they seemed more like animals than men. A few curious Roma watched from a safe distance. It was clear there would be no help from that quarter.

'Well,' Cam said beneath his breath, 'this should be entertaining.'

'Chorodies like knives,' Merripen said. 'But they don't know how to use them. Leave this to me.'

'Go right ahead,' Cam said agreeably.

One of the Chorodies spoke in a dialect Cam couldn't understand. But he gestured to Cam's horse, Pooka, who eyed them nervously and shuffled his feet.

'Like hell,' Cam muttered.

Merripen replied to the man with a handful of equally incomprehensible words. As he had predicted, the Chorodie reached behind his back and produced a jagged knife. Merripen appeared relaxed, but his fingers flexed, and Cam saw the way his posture altered in subtle readiness for attack.

The Chorodie lunged forward with a harsh cry, aiming for the mid-to-lower torso. But Merripen turned in a nimble sidestep. With impressive speed and dexterity, he grabbed the attacking arm. He jerked the Chorodie off-balance, using his own momentum against him. Before another heartbeat had passed, Merripen had flipped his opponent to the ground, twisting the bastard's arm in the process. An audible fracture caused all of them, even Cam, to flinch. The Chorodie howled in agony. Prying the knife from the man's limp hand, Merripen tossed it to Cam, who caught it reflexively.

Merripen glanced at the remaining two Chorodies. 'Who's next?' he asked coldly.

Although the words were spoken in English, the creatures appeared to understand his meaning. They fled without a backward glance, leaving their injured companion to drag himself away with loud groans.

'Very nice, *phral*,' Cam said in admiration.

'We're leaving,' Merripen informed him curtly. 'Before more of them come.'

'Let's go to a tavern,' Cam said. 'I need a drink.'

Merripen mounted his bay without a word. For once, it seemed, Merripen and Cam were in agreement.

★   ★   ★

Taverns were often described as the busy man's recreation, the idle man's business, and the melancholy man's sanctuary. The Hell and Bucket, located in the more disreputable environs of London, could also have been called the criminal's covert and the drunkard's haven. It suited Cam and Kev's purposes quite well, being a place that would serve two Roma without blinking an eye. The ale was good quality, twelve-bushel strength, and although the barmaids were surly, they did an adequate job of keeping the tankard full and the floor swept.

Cam and Kev sat at a small table, lit by a turnip that had been carved into a candleholder, with tallow runneling over its purple-tinged sides. Kev drank half a tankard without stopping and set the vessel down. He rarely drank anything except wine, and that in moderation. He didn't like the loss of control that came with drinking.

Cam, however, drained his own tankard. He leaned back in his chair and surveyed Kev with a slight smile. 'I've always been amused by your inability to hold your liquor,' Cam remarked. 'A Rom your size should be able to drink a quarter barrel to the pitching. But now to discover that you're half-Irish as well . . . it's inexcusable, *phral*. We'll have to work on your drinking skills.'

'We're not going to tell this to anyone,' Kev told him grimly.

'About the fact that we're brothers?' Cam seemed to enjoy Kev's visible wince. 'It's not so bad, being half *gadjo*,' he told Kev kindly, and snickered at his expression. 'It certainly explains why both of us have found a stopping place, while most Roma choose to wander forever. It's the Irish in us that — '

'*Not . . . one . . . word*,' Kev said. 'Not even to the family.'

Cam sobered a little. 'I don't keep secrets from my wife.'

'Not even for her safety?'

Cam appeared to think that over, gazing through one of the narrow windows of the tavern. The streets thronged with costermongers, the wheels of their barrows rattling over the cobblestones. Their cries rose thick in the air as they tried to interest customers in bonnet boxes, toys, lucifer matches, umbrellas, and brooms. On the opposite side of the street, a butcher-shop window gleamed crimson and white with freshly cut meat.

'You think our father's family might still want to kill us?' Cam asked.

'It's possible.'

Absently Cam rubbed over his own sleeve, over the place where the *pooka* mark was located. 'You realize that none of this: the tattoos, the secrets, splitting us apart, giving us different names, would have happened unless our father was a man of some worth. Because otherwise, the *gadjos* wouldn't give a damn about a pair of half-breed children. I wonder why he left our mother? I wonder — '

'I don't give a damn.'

'I'm going to do a new search of parish birth records. Perhaps our father — '

'Don't. Let it lie.'

'*Let it lie?*' Cam gave him an incredulous glance. 'Do you actually want to ignore what we found out today? Ignore the kinship between us?'

'Yes.'

Shaking his head slowly, Cam turned one of the gold rings on his fingers. 'After today, Brother, I understand much more about you. The way you — '

'Don't call me that.'

'I imagine being raised like a pit animal doesn't inspire many fond feelings for the human race. I'm sorry that you were the unlucky one, being sent to our uncle. But you can't let that stop you from leading a full life now. From finding out who you are.'

'Finding out who I am won't get me what I want. Nothing will. So there's no point in it.'

'What is it you want?' Cam asked softly.

Clamping his mouth shut, Kev glared at Cam.

'You can't even bring yourself to say it?' Cam prodded. When Kev remained obstinately silent, Cam reached over for his tankard. 'Are you going to finish this?'

'No.'

Cam drank the ale in a few expedient gulps. 'You know,' he remarked wryly, 'it was a lot easier managing a club full of drunkards, gamblers, and assorted criminals than it is to deal with you and the Hathaways.' He set the tankard down and waited a moment before asking quietly, 'Did you suspect anything? Did you think the tie between us might be this close?'

'No.'

'I think I did, deep down. I always knew I wasn't supposed to be alone.'

Kev gave him a dour look. 'This changes nothing. I'm not your family. There is no tie between us.'

'Blood counts for something,' Cam replied affably. 'And since the rest of my tribe has disappeared, you're all I've got, *phral*. Just try and get rid of me.'

139

11

Win descended the main staircase of the hotel while one of the Hathaways' footmen, Charles, followed closely. 'Careful, Miss Hathaway,' he cautioned. 'One slip and you could break your neck on these stairs.'

'Thank you, Charles,' she said without moderating her speed. 'But there's no need to worry.' She was quite adept at stairs, having gone up and down long staircases at the clinic in France as part of her daily exercise. 'I should warn you, Charles, that I will proceed at a vigorous pace.'

'Yes, miss,' he said, sounding disgruntled. Charles was somewhat stout, and not fond of walking. Although he was getting on in years, the Hathaways were loath to dismiss him before he wished to retire.

Win bit back a smile. 'Just to Hyde Park and back, Charles.'

As they neared the entrance to the hotel, Win saw a tall, dark form moving through the lobby. It was Merripen, looking moody and distracted as he walked with his gaze focused downward. She couldn't suppress the flutters of pleasure that went through her at the sight of him, the handsome, bad-tempered beast. He approached the stairs, glancing upward, and his expression changed as he saw her. There was a flash of hunger in his eyes before he managed to extinguish it. But that brief, bright flare caused Win's spirits to lift immeasurably.

After the scene that morning, and Merripen's display of jealous rage, Win had apologized to Julian. The doctor had been amused rather than disconcerted. 'He is exactly as you described,' Julian had said, adding ruefully, ' . . . only more.'

'More' was a fitting word to apply to Merripen, she thought. There was nothing understated about him. At the moment he looked rather like the brooding villain of a sensation novel. The kind who was always vanquished by the fair-haired hero.

The discreet glances Merripen was attracting from a group of ladies in the lobby made it evident that Win was not the only one who found him mesmerizing. The civilized attire suited him. He wore the well-tailored clothes without a trace of self-consciousness, as if he couldn't have cared less whether he was dressed like a gentleman or a dock laborer. And knowing Merripen, he didn't.

Win stopped and waited, smiling, as he came to her. His gaze swept over her, not missing a detail of the simple pink walking gown and matching saque jacket.

'You're dressed now,' Merripen remarked, as if he were surprised that she wasn't parading naked through the lobby.

'This is a walking dress,' she said. 'As you can see, I'm going out for some air.'

'Who's escorting you?' he asked, even though he could see the footman standing a few feet away.

'Charles,' she replied.

'*Only* Charles?' Merripen looked outraged. 'You need more protection than that.'

'We're only walking to Marble Arch,' she said, amused.

'Are you out of your mind, woman? Do you have any idea what could happen to you at Hyde Park? There are pickpockets, cutpurses, confidence tricksters, and gangs, all ready for a nice little pigeon like you to pluck.'

Rather than take offense, Charles said eagerly, 'Perhaps Mr. Merripen has a point, Miss Hathaway. It *is* rather far . . . and one never knows . . .'

'Are you offering to go in his stead?' Win asked Merripen.

As she had expected, he put on a show of grumbling reluctance. 'I suppose so, if the alternative is to see you traipsing through the streets of London and tempting every criminal in sight.' He frowned at Charles. 'You needn't go with us. I'd rather not have to look after you, too.'

'Yes, sir,' came the footman's grateful reply, and he went back up the stairs with considerably more enthusiasm than he had shown while descending them.

Win slipped her hand through Merripen's arm and felt the fierce tension in his muscles. Something had upset him deeply, she realized. Something far more than her exercise costume or the prospective walk to Hyde Park.

They left the hotel, Merripen's long strides easily keeping measure with her brisk ones. Win kept her tone casual and cheerful. 'How cool and bracing the air is today.'

'It's polluted with coal smoke,' he said, steering her around a puddle as if it might cause mortal harm to get her feet wet.

'Actually, I detect a strong scent of smoke from your coat. Not tobacco smoke, either. Where did you and Mr. Rohan go this morning?'

'To a Romany camp.'

'For what reason?' Win persisted. With Merripen, one could not be easily be put off by terseness, or one would never get anything out of him.

'Rohan thought we might find someone there from my tribe.'

'And did you?' she asked softly, knowing the subject was a sensitive one.

A restless shift of the muscle beneath her hand. 'No.'

'Yes, you did. I can tell you're brooding.'

Merripen glanced down at her, and saw how closely she was studying him. He sighed. 'In my tribe, there was a girl named Shuri . . . '

Win felt a pang of jealousy. A girl he had known and never mentioned. Perhaps he had cared for her.

'We found her today in the camp,' Merripen continued. 'She hardly looks the same. She was once very beautiful, but now she appears much older than her years.'

'Oh, that's too bad,' Win said, trying to sound sincere.

'Her husband, the *rom baro*, was my uncle. He was . . . not a good man.'

That was hardly a surprise, considering the condition Merripen had been in when Win had first met him. Wounded, abandoned, and so savage that it was clear he had lived like a wild creature.

Win was filled with compassion and tenderness. She wished they were in some private place where she could coax Merripen to tell her everything. She wished she could embrace him, not as a lover, but as a loving friend. No doubt many people would think it ludicrous that she should feel so protective of such an invulnerable-seeming man. But beneath that hard and impervious façade, Merripen possessed a rare depth of feeling. She knew that about him. She also knew that he would deny it to the death.

'Did Mr. Rohan tell Shuri about his tattoo?' Win asked. 'That it was identical to yours?'

'Yes.'

'And what did Shuri say about it?'

'Nothing.' His reply was a shade too quick.

A pair of street sellers, one bearing bundles of watercress, the other carrying umbrellas, approached them hopefully. But one glower from Merripen caused them to retreat, braving the traffic of carriages, carts, and horses to go to the other side of the street.

Win didn't say anything for a minute or two, just held Merripen's arm as he guided her along with exasperating bossiness, muttering, 'Don't step there,' or, 'Come this way,' or, 'Tread carefully here,' as if stepping on broken or uneven pavement might result in severe injury.

'Kev,' she finally protested, 'I'm not fragile.'

'I know that.'

'Then please don't treat me as if I'll break at the first misstep.'

Merripen grumbled a little, something about the street not being good enough for her. It was too rough. Too dirty.

Win couldn't help chuckling. 'For heaven's sake. If this street was paved with gold and angels were sweeping it, you would still say it was too rough and dirty for me. You must rid yourself of this habit of protecting me.'

'Not while I live.'

Win was quiet, gripping his arm more tightly. The passion buried beneath the rough, simple words filled her with an almost indecent pleasure. So easily, he could reach down to the deepest region of her heart.

'I'd rather not be put on a pedestal,' she finally said.

'You're not on a pedestal. You're — ' But he checked the words, and he shook his head a little, as if he was vaguely surprised he'd said them. Whatever had happened that day, it had shaken his self-control badly.

Win pondered what possible things Shuri might have said. Something about the connection between Cam Rohan and Merripen . . .

'Kev.' Win eased her pace, forcing him to go more slowly as well. 'Even before I left for France, I had the idea that those tattoos were evidence of a close link between you and Mr. Rohan. Being so ill, I had little to do except observe the people in my sphere. I noticed things that no one else had the time to perceive, or

145

think about. And I've always been especially attuned to you.' Taking in his expression with a quick sidelong glance, Win saw that he didn't like that. He didn't want to be understood, or observed. He wanted to stay safe in his iron-clad solitude.

'And when I met Mr. Rohan,' Win continued in a casual tone, as if they were having an ordinary conversation, 'I was struck by many similarities between the two of you. The tilt of his head, that half smile he has . . . the way he gestures with his hands . . . all things I had seen you do. And I thought to myself, *I wouldn't be surprised to learn someday that the two of them are . . . brothers.*'

Merripen stopped completely. He turned to face her, standing right there on the street while other pedestrians were forced to go around them, muttering about how inconsiderate it was for people to block a public footpath. Win looked up into his heathen dark eyes and gave an innocent shrug. And she waited for his response.

'Improbable,' he said gruffly.

'Improbable things happen all the time,' Win said. 'Especially to our family.' She continued to stare at him, reading him. 'It's true, isn't it?' she asked in wonder. 'He's your brother?'

Kev hesitated. His whisper was so soft she could barely hear it. 'Younger brother.'

'I'm glad for you. For both of you.' She smiled up at him steadily, until his mouth took on a wry, answering curve.

'I'm not.'

'Someday you will be.'

After a moment he pulled her arm through his and they began walking again.

'If you and Mr. Rohan are brothers,' Win said, 'then you're half *gadjo*. Just like he is. Are you sorry about that?'

'No, I — ' He paused to mull over the discovery. 'I wasn't as surprised as I should have been. I've always felt I was Romany and . . . something other.'

And Win understood what he didn't say. Unlike Rohan, he wasn't eager to face this entire other identity, this vast part of himself that was so far unrealized. 'Are you going to talk about it with the family?' she asked softly. Knowing Merripen, he would want to keep the information private until he'd sorted through all its implications.

He shook his head. 'There are questions that must be answered first. Including why the *gadjo* who fathered us wanted to kill us.'

'He did? Good heavens, why?'

'My guess is that it was probably some question of inheritance. With *gadjos*, it usually comes down to money.'

'So bitter,' Win said, clinging more tightly to his arm.

'I have reason.'

'You have reason to be happy as well. You have found a brother today. And you found out that you're half-Irish.'

That actually drew a rumble of amusement from him. '*That* should make me happy?'

'The Irish are a remarkable race. And I see it in you: your love of land, your tenacity . . . '

'My love of brawling.'

'Yes. Well, perhaps you should continue to suppress that part.'

'Being part-Irish,' he said, 'I should be a more proficient drinker.'

'And a far more glib conversationalist.'

'I prefer to talk only when I have something to say.'

'Hmmm. That is neither Irish nor Romany. Perhaps there's another part of you we haven't yet identified.'

'My God. I hope not.' But he was smiling, and Win felt a warm ripple of delight spread through all her limbs.

'That's the first real smile I've seen from you since I came back,' she said. 'You should smile more, Kev.'

'Should I?' he asked softly.

'Oh yes. It's beneficial for your health. Dr. Harrow says his cheerful patients tend to recover far more quickly than the sour ones.'

The mention of Dr. Harrow caused Merripen's elusive smile to vanish. 'Ramsay says you've become close with him.'

'Dr. Harrow is a friend,' she allowed.

'Only a friend?'

'Yes, so far. Would you object if he wished to court me?'

'Of course not,' Merripen muttered. 'What right would I have to object?'

'None at all. Unless you had staked some prior claim, which you certainly have not.'

She sensed Merripen's inner struggle to let the matter drop. A struggle he lost, for he said abruptly, 'Far be it from me to deny you a diet of pabulum, if that's what your appetite demands.'

'You're likening Dr. Harrow to pabulum?' Win fought to hold back a satisfied grin. The small display of jealousy was a balm to her spirits. 'I assure you, he is not at all bland. He is a man of substance and character.'

'He's a watery-eyed, pale-faced *gadjo*.'

'He is very attractive. And his eyes are not at all watery.'

'Have you let him kiss you?'

'Kev, we're on a public thoroughfare — '

'Have you?'

'Once,' she admitted, and waited as he digested the information. He scowled ferociously at the pavement before them. When it became apparent he wasn't going to say anything, Win volunteered, 'It was a gesture of affection.'

Still no response.

Stubborn ox, she thought in annoyance. 'It wasn't like your kisses. And we've never . . . ' She felt a blush rising. 'We've never done anything similar to what you and I . . . the other night . . . '

'We're not going to discuss that.'

'Why can we discuss Dr. Harrow's kisses but not yours?'

'Because my kisses aren't going to lead to courtship.'

That hurt. It also puzzled and frustrated her. Before all was said and done, Win intended to make Merripen admit just why he wouldn't pursue her. But not here, and not now.

'Well, I do have a chance of courtship with Dr.

149

Harrow,' she said, attempting a pragmatic tone. 'And at my age, I must consider any marriage prospect quite seriously.'

'Your age?' he scoffed. 'You're only twenty-five.'

'Twenty-six. And even at twenty-five, I would be considered long in the tooth. I lost several years — my best ones perhaps — because of my illness.'

'You're more beautiful now than you ever were. Any man would be mad or blind not to want you.' The compliment was not given smoothly, but with a masculine sincerity that heightened her blush.

'Thank you, Kev.'

He slid her a guarded look. 'You want to marry?'

Win's willful, treacherous heart gave a few painfully excited thuds, because at first she thought he'd asked, 'You want to marry *me*?' But no, he was merely asking her opinion of marriage as . . . well, as her scholarly father would have said, as a 'conceptual structure with a potential for realization.'

'Yes, of course,' she said. 'I want children to love. I want a husband to grow old with. I want a family of my own.'

'And Harrow says all of that is possible now?'

Win hesitated a bit too long. 'Yes, completely possible.'

But Merripen knew her too well. 'What are you not telling me?'

'I am well enough to do anything I choose now,' she said firmly.

'What does he — '

'I don't wish to discuss it. You have your forbidden topics; I have mine.'

'You know I'll find out,' he said quietly.

Win ignored that, casting her gaze to the park before them. Her eyes widened as she saw something that had not been there when she had left for France . . . a huge, magnificent structure of glass and iron. 'Is that the Crystal Palace? Oh, it must be. It's so beautiful — much more so than the engravings I've seen.'

The building, which covered an area of more than nine acres, housed an international show of art and science called the Great Exhibition. Win had read about it in the French newspapers, which had aptly termed the exhibition one of the great wonders of the world.

'How long since it was completed?' she asked, her step quickening as they headed toward the glittering building.

'Not quite a month.'

'Have you been inside? Have you seen the exhibits?'

'I've visited once,' Merripen said, smiling at her eagerness. 'And I saw a few of the exhibits, but not all. It would take three days or more to look at everything.'

'Which part did you go to?'

'The machinery court, mostly.'

'I do wish I could see even a small part of it,' she said wistfully, watching the throngs of visitors exiting and entering the remarkable building. 'Won't you take me?'

'You wouldn't have time to see anything. It's

already afternoon. I'll bring you tomorrow.'

'Now. *Please*.' She tugged impatiently on his arm. 'Oh, Kev, don't say no.'

As Merripen looked down at her, he was so handsome that she felt a pleasant little ache at the pit of her stomach. 'How could I say no to you?' he asked softly.

As he took her to the towering arched entrance of the Crystal Palace, and paid a shilling each for their admission, Win gazed at her surroundings in awe. The driving force behind the exhibition of industrial design had been Prince Albert, a man of vision and wisdom. According to the tiny printed map that was given out with the tickets, the building itself was constructed of over a thousand iron columns, and three hundred thousand panes of glass. Parts of it were tall enough to encompass full-grown elm trees. All totaled, there were one hundred thousand exhibits from around the world.

The exhibition was important in a social sense as well as a scientific one. It provided an opportunity for all classes and regions, the high and low, to mingle freely beneath one roof in a way that seldom happened. People of all manner of dress and appearance crowded inside the building.

A fashionably dressed gathering waited at the transept, or central cross-section, of the Crystal Palace. None of them seemed to take an interest in their surroundings. 'What are those people waiting for?' she asked.

'Nothing,' Merripen replied. 'They're only here to be seen. There was a similar group when

I was here before. They don't go to any of the exhibits. They merely stand there preening.'

Win laughed. 'Well, should we stand nearby and pretend to admire them, or shall we go look at something *really* interesting?'

Merripen handed her the little map.

After scrutinizing the list of courts and displays, Win said decisively, 'Fabrics and textiles.'

He escorted her through a crowded glass hallway into a room of astonishing size and breadth. The air chattered with the sounds of looms and textile machinery, with carpet bales arranged around the room and down the center. Scents of wool and dye made the atmosphere acrid and lightly pungent. Goods from Kidderminster, America, Spain, France, the Orient, filled the room with a rainbow of hues and textures . . . flatweave, knotted pile and cut pile, looped, hooked, embroidered, braided . . . Win removed her gloves and ran her hands over the gorgeous offerings.

'Merripen, look at this!' she exclaimed. 'It's a Wilton carpet. Similar to Brussels, but the pile is sheared. It feels like velvet, doesn't it?'

The manufacturer's representative, who was standing nearby, said, 'Wilton is becoming much more affordable, now that we are able to produce it on steam-powered looms.'

'Where is the factory located?' Merripen asked, running a bare hand over the soft carpet pile. 'Kidderminster, I assume?'

'There, and another in Glasgow.'

As the men conversed about the production of

153

carpet on the new looms, Win wandered farther along the rows of samples and displays. There were more machines, bewildering in their size and complexity, some made to weave fabrics, some to print patterns, some to spin tufts of wool into yarn and worsted. One of them was used in a demonstration of how stuffing mattresses and pillows would someday be mechanized.

Watching in fascination, Win was aware of Merripen coming to stand beside her. 'One wonders if everything in the world will eventually be done by machine,' she told him.

He smiled slightly. 'If we had time, I would take you to the agricultural exhibits. A man can grow twice as much food with a fraction of the time and labor it would take to do by hand. We've already acquired a threshing machine for the Ramsay estate tenants . . . I'll show it to you when we go there.'

'You approve of these technological advances?' Win asked with a touch of surprise.

'Yes, why wouldn't I?'

'The Rom doesn't believe in such things.'

He shrugged. 'Regardless of what the Rom believes, I can't ignore progress that will improve life for everyone else. Mechanization will make it easier for common people to afford clothing, food, soap . . . even a carpet for the floor.'

'But what about the men who will lose their livelihood when a machine takes their place?'

'New industries and more jobs are being created. Why put a man to work doing mindless tasks instead of educating him to do something more?'

Win smiled. 'You speak like a reformist,' she whispered impishly.

'Economic change is always accompanied by social change. No one can stop that.'

What an adept mind he had, Win thought. Her father would have been pleased by how his Gypsy foundling had turned out.

'A large workforce will be required to support all this industry,' she commented. 'Do you suppose a sufficient number of country people would be willing to move to London and the other places that — '

She was interrupted by an explosive *puff* and a few cries of surprise from the visitors around them. A thick, startling flurry of down filled the air in a choking gust. It seemed the pillow-stuffing machine had malfunctioned, sending eddies of feathers and down over everyone in sight.

Reacting swiftly, Merripen stripped off his coat and pulled it over Win, and clamped a handkerchief over her mouth and nose. 'Breathe through this,' he muttered, and hauled her through the room. The crowd was scattering, some people coughing, some swearing, some laughing, as great volumes of fluffy white down settled over the scene. There were cries of delight from children who had come from the next room, dancing and hopping to try to catch the elusive floating clumps.

Merripen didn't stop until they had reached another nave that housed a fabric court. Enormous wood and glass cases had been built for displays of fabric that flowed like rivers. The

155

walls were hung with velvets, brocades, silks, cotton, muslin, wool, every imaginable substance created for clothing, upholstery, or drapery. Towering bolts of fabric were arranged in vertical rolls affixed to more display walls that formed deep corridors within the court.

Emerging from beneath Merripen's coat, Win took one look at him and began to gasp with laughter. White down had covered his black hair and clung to his clothes like new-fallen snow.

Merripen's expression of concern changed to a scowl. 'I was going to ask if you had breathed any of the feather dust,' he said. 'But judging from all the noise you're making, your lungs seem quite clear.'

Win couldn't reply; she was laughing too hard.

As Merripen raked his hand through the midnight locks of his hair, the down became even more enmeshed.

'Don't,' Win managed, struggling to restrain her laughter. 'You'll never . . . You must let me help you; you're making it worse . . . and you s-said *I* was a pigeon to be plucked . . . ' Still chortling, she snatched his hand and tugged him into one of the fabric corridors, where they were partially concealed from view. They went beyond the half-light and into the shadows. 'Here, before anyone sees us. Oh, you're too tall for me — ' She urged him to the floor with her, where he lowered to his haunches. Win knelt amid the mass of her skirts. Untying her bonnet, she tossed it to the side.

Merripen watched Win's face as she went to work, brushing at his shoulders and hair. 'You

156

can't be enjoying this,' he said.

'Silly man. You're covered in feathers — of *course* I'm enjoying it.' And she was. He looked so . . . well, adorable, kneeling and frowning and holding still while she de-feathered him. And it was lovely to play with the thick, shiny layers of his hair, which he never would have allowed in other circumstances. Her giggles kept frothing up, impossible to suppress.

But as a minute passed, and then another, the laughter left her throat, and she felt relaxed and almost dreamlike as she continued to pull the fluff from his hair. The sound of the crowds was muffled by the velvet draped all around them, hanging like curtains of night and clouds and mist.

Merripen's eyes held a strange dark glow, the contours of his face stern and beautiful. He seemed like some dangerous pagan creature emerging from the witching hour.

'Almost done,' Win whispered, although she was already finished. Her fingers sifted gently through his hair. So vibrant, heavy, the shorn locks like velvet pile at the back of his neck.

Win's breath caught as Merripen moved. At first she thought he was rising to his feet, but he tugged her closer and took her head in his hands. His mouth was so close, his exhalations like steam against her lips.

She was stunned by the moment of suspended violence, the savage tightness of his grip. She waited, listening to his hard, angry breathing, unable to understand what had provoked him.

'I have nothing to offer you,' he finally said in a guttural voice. 'Nothing.'

Win's lips had turned dry. She moistened them, and tried to speak through a thrill of anxious trembling. 'You have yourself,' she whispered.

'You don't know me. You think you do, but you don't. The things I've done, the things I'm capable of — you and your family, all you know of life comes from books. If you understood anything — '

'*Make* me understand. Tell me what is so terrible that you must keep pushing me away.'

He shook his head.

'Then stop torturing the both of us,' she said unsteadily. 'Leave me, or let me go.'

'I can't,' he snapped. 'I can't, damn you.' And before she could make a sound, he kissed her.

Her heart thundered, and she opened to him with a low, despairing moan. Her nostrils were filled with the fragrance of smoke, and man, and the earthy autumn spice of him. His mouth shaped to hers with primitive hunger, his tongue stabbing deep, searching hungrily. They knelt together more tightly as Win rose to press her torso against his, closer, harder. And every place they touched, she ached. She wanted to feel his skin, his muscles bunched and hard beneath her hands.

The desire flared high and wild, leaving no room for sanity. If only he would press her back among all this velvet, here and now, and have his way with her. She thought of taking him inside her body, and she flushed beneath her clothes, until the crawling heat made her squirm. His mouth searched her throat, and her head tipped back to give him free access. He found the throb

158

of her pulse, his tongue stroking the vulnerable spot until she gasped.

Reaching up to his face, she shaped her fingers over his jaw, the heavy grain of shaven beard scraping deliciously against her delicate palms. She guided his mouth back to hers. Pleasure filled her as she was blindfolded by the darkness and the sensation of him all around her.

'Kev,' she whispered in between kisses, 'I've loved you for so — '

He crushed her mouth with his desperately, as if he could smother not only the words but the emotion itself. He stole as deep a taste of her as possible, ardently determined to leave nothing unclaimed. She clung to him, her body racked with sustained shivers, her nerves singing with incandescent heat. He was all she had ever wanted, all she would ever need.

But a sharp breath was torn from her throat as he pushed her back, breaking the warm, necessary contact between their bodies.

For a long moment neither of them moved, both striving to recover equilibrium. And as the glow of desire faded, Win heard Merripen say roughly, 'I can't be alone with you. This can't happen again.'

This, Win decided with a surge of anger, was an impossible situation. Merripen refused to acknowledge his feelings for her and wouldn't explain why. Surely she deserved more trust from him than that.

'Very well,' she said stiffly, struggling to her feet. As Merripen stood and reached for her, she pushed impatiently at his hand. 'No, I don't want help.' She began to shake out her skirts. 'You are absolutely right, Merripen. We should not be alone together, since the result is always a foregone conclusion: you make an advance, I respond, and then you push me away. I am no child's toy to be pulled back and forth on a string, Kev.'

He found her bonnet and handed it to her. 'I know you're not — '

'You say I don't know you,' she said furiously. 'Apparently it hasn't occurred to you that you don't know me, either. You're quite certain of who I am, aren't you? But I've changed during the past two years. You might at least make an effort to find out what kind of woman I've become.' She went to the end of the fabric corridor, peeked out to make certain the coast was clear, and she stepped out into the main part of the court.

Merripen followed. 'Where are you going?'

Glancing at him, Win was satisfied to see that he looked as rumpled and exasperated as she felt. 'I'm leaving. I'm too cross to enjoy any of the displays now.'

'Go the other direction.'

Win was silent as Merripen led her from the Crystal Palace. She had never felt so unsettled or peevish. Her parents had always called irritability an excess of spleen, but Win lacked the experience to comprehend that her ill humor stemmed from a source quite different from the spleen. All she knew was that Merripen seemed similarly vexed as he walked beside her.

It annoyed her that he didn't say a word. It

also annoyed her that he kept pace so easily with her brisk, ground-digging strides, and that when she had begun to breathe hard from exertion, he barely seemed affected by the exercise.

Only when they approached the Rutledge did Win break the silence. It pleased her that she sounded so calm. 'I will abide by your wishes, Kev. From now on, our relationship will be platonic and friendly. Nothing more.' She paused at the first step and looked up at him solemnly. 'I've been give a rare opportunity . . . a second chance at life. And I intend to make the most of it. I'm not going to waste my love on a man who doesn't want or need it. I won't bother you again.'

★ ★ ★

When Cam entered the bedroom of their suite, he found Amelia standing before a towering pile of parcels and boxes overflowing with ribbons and silk and feminine adornments. She turned with a sheepish smile as he closed the door, her heart tripping a little at the sight of him. His collarless shirt was open at the throat, his body almost feline in its lithe muscularity, his face riveting in its sensuous male beauty. Not long ago, she would never have envisioned being married at all, much less to such an exotic creature.

His gaze chased lightly over her, the pink velvet dressing gown open to reveal her chemise and naked thighs. 'I see the shopping expedition was a success.'

'I don't know what came over me,' Amelia

replied a touch apologetically. 'You know I'm never extravagant. I only meant to purchase some handkerchiefs and some stockings. But . . . ' She gestured lamely to the piles of fripperies. 'I seem to have been in an acquisitive mood today.'

A smile flashed in his dark face. 'As I've told you before, love, spend as much as you like. You couldn't beggar me if you tried.'

'I bought some things for you, too,' she said, rummaging through the pile. 'Some cravats, and books, and French shaving soap . . . although I've been meaning to discuss that with you . . . '

'Discuss what?' Cam approached her from behind, kissing the side of her throat.

Amelia drew in a breath at the hot imprint of his mouth and nearly forgot what she had been saying. 'Your shaving,' she said vaguely. 'Beards are becoming quite fashionable of late. I think you should try a goatee. You would look very dashing, and . . . ' Her voice faded as he worked his way down her neck.

'It might tickle,' Cam murmured, and laughed as she shivered.

Gently turning her to face him, he stared into her eyes. There was something different about him, she thought. A curious vulnerability she had never seen before.

'Cam,' she said carefully, 'how did your errand with Merripen go?'

The amber eyes were soft and alive with excitement. 'Quite well. I have a secret, *monisha*. Shall I tell you?' He drew her against him, wrapping his arms around her, and he whispered into her ear.

12

Kev was in a devil of a temper that evening for a variety of reasons. The uppermost being that Win was carrying out her threat. She was being *friendly* to him. Polite, courteous, damnably nice. And he was in no position to object, since this was precisely what he had wanted. But he hadn't expected that there was one thing even worse than having Win glance at him with longing. And that was indifference.

To Kev, she was affable, even affectionate, in the same way she was with Leo or Cam. She treated Kev as if he were a brother. He could hardly bear it.

The Hathaways gathered in the eating area of their suite, laughing and joking about the close quarters as they sat at the table. It was the first time in years that they had all been able to dine together: Kev, Leo, Amelia, Win, Poppy, and Beatrix, with the additions of Cam, Miss Marks, and Dr. Harrow.

Although Miss Marks had tried to demur, they had insisted that she dine with the family. 'After all,' Poppy had said, laughing, 'how else will we know how to behave? Someone must save us from ourselves.'

Miss Marks had relented, although it was clear that she would have preferred to be elsewhere. She took up as small a space as possible, a narrow, colorless figure wedged between Beatrix and Dr. Harrow. The governess rarely looked up from her plate except when Leo was speaking. Although her eyes were partially concealed by the spectacles, Kev suspected they held nothing but dislike for the Hathaways' brother.

It seemed that Miss Marks and Leo had found in each other the personification of everything they disliked most. Leo couldn't stand humorless people, or judgmental ones, and he had immediately taken to referring to the governess as 'Satan in petticoats.' And Miss Marks, for her part, despised rakes. The more charming they were, the deeper her loathing.

Most of the dinner conversation centered on the subject of Harrow's clinic, which the Hathaways regarded as a miraculous enterprise. The women fawned on Harrow to a nauseating degree, delighting in his commonplace remarks, admiring him openly.

Kev had an instinctive aversion to Harrow, although he wasn't certain if that was because of the doctor himself, or because Win's affections were at stake.

It was tempting to disdain Harrow for all his smooth-faced perfection. Except that a roguish good humor lurked in his smile, and he displayed a lively interest in the conversation around him, and he seemed never to take himself too seriously. Harrow was obviously a man who shouldered heavy responsibility — that of life and death itself — and yet he carried it lightly. He was the kind of person who always seemed to fit in no matter what the circumstances.

While the family ate and conversed, Kev

remained quiet except when called upon to answer some question about the Ramsay estate. He watched Win circumspectly, unable to discern exactly what her feelings for Harrow were. She reacted to the doctor with her usual composure, her face giving away nothing. But when their gazes met, there was an unmistakable connection, a sense of shared history. And worst of all, Kev recognized something in the doctor's expression . . . a haunting echo of his own fascination for Win.

Midway through the gruesomely pleasant dinner, Kev became aware that Amelia, who was seated at the end of the table, was unusually quiet. He looked at her closely, realizing her color was off and her cheeks were sweaty. Since he was seated at her immediate left, Kev leaned close and whispered, 'What is it?'

Amelia gave him a distracted glance. 'Ill,' she whispered back, swallowing weakly. 'I feel so . . . Oh, Merripen, do help me away from the table.'

Without another word, Kev pushed his chair back and helped her up.

Cam, who was at the other end of the long table, looked at them sharply. 'Amelia?'

'She's ill,' Kev said.

Cam reached them in a flash, his face taut with anxiety. As he gathered Amelia in his arms and carried her, protesting, from the room, one would think she'd suffered a severe injury rather than a probable case of indigestion.

'Perhaps I might be of service,' Dr. Harrow said with quiet concern, laying his napkin on the table as he made to follow them.

'Thank you,' Win said, smiling at him gratefully. 'I'm so glad you're here.'

Kev barely restrained himself from gnashing his teeth in jealousy as Harrow left the room.

The rest of the meal was largely neglected, the family going to the main receiving room to wait for a report on Amelia. It took an unnervingly long time for anyone to appear.

'What could be the matter?' Beatrix asked plaintively. 'Amelia's never ill.'

'She'll be fine,' Win soothed. 'Dr. Harrow will take excellent care of her.'

'Perhaps I should go to their room,' Poppy said, 'and ask how she is.'

But before anyone could offer an opinion, Cam appeared in the doorway of the receiving room. He looked bemused, his hazel eyes vivid as he glanced at the assorted family members around him. He appeared to search for words. Then a dazzling smile appeared despite his obvious effort to moderate it. 'No doubt the *gadje* have a more civilized way to put this,' he said, 'but Amelia is with child.'

A chorus of happy exclamations greeted the revelation.

'What did Amelia say?' Leo asked.

Cam's smile turned wry. 'Something to the effect that this wouldn't be convenient.'

Leo laughed quietly. 'Children rarely are. But she'll adore having someone new to manage.'

Kev watched Win from across the room. He was fascinated by the momentary wistfulness that hazed her expression. If he had ever doubted how much she wanted children of her own, it was clear to him then. As he stared at her, a flush of warmth rose in him, strengthening and thickening until he realized what it was. He was aroused, his body yearning to give her what she wanted. He longed to hold her, love her, fill her with his seed. The reaction was so barbaric and inappropriate that it mortified him.

Seeming to feel his gaze, Win glanced in his direction. She gave him an arrested stare, as if she could see down to all the raw heat inside him. And then she looked away from him in swift rejection.

★　★　★

Excusing himself from the receiving room, Cam went back to Amelia, who was sitting on the edge of the bed. Dr. Harrow had left the bedchamber to allow them privacy.

Cam closed the door and leaned back against it, letting his caressing gaze fall on the small, tense form of his wife. He knew little of these matters. In both Romany and *gadjo* cultures, pregnancy and childbirth were a strictly female domain. But he did know that his wife was uneasy in situations she had no control over. He also knew that women in her condition needed reassurance and tenderness. And he had an inexhaustible supply of both for her.

'Nervous?' Cam asked softly, approaching her.

'Oh no, not in the slightest; it's an ordinary

167

circumstance, and only to be expected after — '
Amelia broke off with a little gasp as he sat
beside her and pulled her into his arms. 'Yes, I'm
a bit nervous. I wish . . . I wish I could talk to my
mother. I'm not exactly certain how to do this.'

Of course. Amelia liked to manage everything,
to be authoritative and competent no matter
what she did. But the entire process of
childbearing would be one of increasing
dependence and helplessness, until the final
stage, when nature took over entirely.

Cam pressed his lips into her gleaming dark
hair, which smelled like sweetbriar. He began to
rub her back in the way he knew she liked best.
'We'll find some experienced women for you to
talk to. Lady Westcliff, perhaps. You like her, and
God knows she would be forthright. And
regarding what you're going to do . . . you'll let
me take care of you, and spoil you, and give you
anything you want.' He felt her relax a little.
'Amelia, love,' he murmured, 'I've wanted this
for so long.'

'Have you?' She smiled and snuggled tightly
against him. 'So have I. Although I had hoped it
would happen at a more convenient time, when
Ramsay House was finished, and Poppy was
betrothed, and the family was settled — '

'Trust me, with your family there will never be
a convenient time.' Cam eased her back to lie on
the bed with him. 'What a pretty little mother
you'll be,' he whispered, cuddling her. 'With your
blue eyes, and your pink cheeks, and your belly
all round with my child . . . '

'When I grow large, I hope you won't strut

and swagger, and point to me as an example of your virility.'

'I do that already, *monisha*.'

Amelia looked up into his smiling eyes. 'I can't imagine how this happened.'

'Didn't I explain that on our wedding night?'

She chuckled and put her arms around his neck. 'I was referring to the fact that I've been taking preventative measures. All those cups of nasty-tasting tea. And I *still* ended up conceiving.'

'Rom,' he said by way of explanation, and kissed her passionately.

★　★　★

When Amelia felt well enough to join the other women for tea in the receiving room, the men went downstairs to the Rutledge's gentlemen's room. Although the room was ostensibly for the use of hotel guests, it had become a favorite haunt of the peerage, who wished to share the company of the Rutledge's many notable foreign visitors.

The ceilings were comfortably dark and low, paneled in glowing rosewood, the floors covered in thick Wilton carpeting. The gentlemen's room was cornered with large, deep apses that provided private spaces for reading, drinking, and conversing. The main space was furnished with velvet-upholstered chairs and tables laden with cigar boxes and newspapers. Servants moved unobtrusively through the room, bringing snifters of warmed brandy and glasses of port.

Settling in one of the unoccupied octagonal apses, Kev requested brandy for the table. 'Yes, Mr. Merripen,' the servant said, hastening to comply.

'What well-trained staff,' Dr. Harrow remarked. 'I find it commendable that they give impartial service to all the guests.'

Kev slanted him a questioning glance. 'Why wouldn't they?'

'I imagine that a gentleman of your origins does not receive service at every establishment you frequent.'

'I find that most establishments pay more attention to the quality of a man's clothes than the shade of his complexion,' Kev replied evenly. 'Usually it doesn't matter that I'm a Rom, so long as I can afford their wares.'

'Of course.' Harrow looked uncomfortable. 'My apologies. I'm not usually so tactless, Merripen.'

Kev gave him a short nod to indicate that no offense had been taken.

Harrow turned to Cam, seeking to change the subject. 'I hope you'll allow me to recommend a colleague to attend Mrs. Rohan during the remainder of your stay in London. I'm acquainted with many excellent physicians here.'

'I would appreciate that,' Cam said, accepting a brandy from a servant. 'Although I suspect we won't remain in London much longer.'

'Miss Winnifred seems to have a great fondness for children,' Harrow mused. 'In light of her condition, it's fortunate that she will have nieces and nephews to dote on.'

The other three men looked at him sharply.

170

Cam had paused in the act of lifting the brandy to his lips. 'Condition?' he asked.

'Her inability to have children of her own,' Harrow clarified.

'What the devil do you mean, Harrow?' Leo asked. 'Haven't we all been trumpeting about my sister's miraculous recovery, due to your stellar efforts?'

'She has indeed recovered, my lord.' Harrow frowned thoughtfully as he stared into his brandy snifter. 'But she will always be somewhat fragile. In my opinion, she should never try to conceive. In all likelihood the process would result in her death.'

A heavy silence followed this pronouncement. Even Leo, who usually affected an air of insouciance, couldn't manage to conceal his reaction. 'Have you made my sister aware of this?' he asked. 'Because she has given me the impression that she fully expects to marry and have her own family someday.'

'I have discussed it with her, of course,' Harrow replied. 'I have told her that if she marries, her husband would have to agree that it would be a childless union.' He paused. 'However, Miss Hathaway is not yet ready to accept the idea. In time, I hope to persuade her to adjust her expectations.' He smiled slightly. 'Motherhood, after all, is not necessary for every woman's happiness, much as society glorifies the notion.'

Cam stared at him intently. 'My sister-in-law will find it a disappointment, to say the least.'

'Yes. But Miss Hathaway will live longer and enjoy a higher quality of life as a childless woman. And she will learn to accept her altered circumstances. That is her strength.' He swallowed some brandy before continuing quietly, 'Miss Hathaway was probably never destined for childbearing, even before the scarlet fever. Such a narrow frame. Elegant, but hardly ideal for breeding purposes.'

Kev tossed back his brandy, letting the amber fire wash down his throat. He pushed back from the table and stood, unable to bear another moment of the bastard's proximity. The mention of Win's 'narrow frame' had been the last straw. Excusing himself with a rough mutter, he walked out of the hotel and into the night. His senses drew in the cool air, the foul, sharp city smells, the stirrings and rattlings and cries of the London night coming to life. Christ, he wanted to be away from this place.

He wanted to take Win to the country with him, to some place that was fresh and wholesome. Away from the gleaming Dr. Harrow, whose clean, fastidious perfection filled Kev with dread. Every instinct warned that Win wasn't safe from Harrow.

But she wasn't safe from him, either.

His own mother had died giving birth. The thought of killing Win with his own body, his spawn swelling inside her until —

His entire being shied at the thought. His deepest terror was harming her. Losing her.

Kev wanted to talk to her, to listen to her, help her somehow to come to terms with the limitations she'd been given. But he'd put a barrier between them, and he didn't dare cross it. Because if Harrow's flaw was a lack of empathy, Kev's was just the opposite. Too much feeling, too much need.

Enough to kill her.

★ ★ ★

Later that evening Cam came to Kev's room. Kev had just returned from his walk, a glaze of evening mist still clinging to his coat and hair.

Answering the knock at the door, Kev stood at the threshold and scowled. 'What is it?'

'I had a private talk with Harrow,' Cam said, his face expressionless.

'And?'

'He wants to marry Win. But he intends the marriage to be in name only. She doesn't know it yet.'

'Bloody hell,' Kev muttered. 'She'll be the latest addition to his collection of fine objects. She'll stay chaste while he has his affairs — '

'I don't know her well,' Cam murmured, 'but I don't think she would ever agree to such an arrangement. Especially if you offered her an alternative, *phral*.'

'There is only one alternative, and that is to stay safe with her family.'

'There's one more. You could offer for her.'

'That's not possible.'

'Why not?'

Kev felt his face burn. 'I couldn't stay celibate with her. I could never hold to it.'

'There are ways to prevent conception.'

That elicited a contemptuous snort from Kev.

173

'That worked well for you, didn't it?' He rubbed his face wearily. 'You know the other reasons I can't offer for her.'

'I know the way you once lived,' Cam said, choosing his words with obvious care. 'I understand your fear of harming her. But in spite of all that, I find it hard to believe that you would really let her go to another man.'

'I would if that was best for her.'

'Can you actually say that the best Winnifred Hathaway deserves is someone like Harrow?'

'Better him,' Kev managed to say, 'than someone like me.'

★ ★ ★

Although the social season was not yet over, it was agreed that the family would go to Hampshire. There was Amelia's condition to consider — she would be better off in the healthful surroundings — and Win and Leo wanted to see the Ramsay estate. The only question was the fairness of depriving Poppy and Beatrix of the remainder of the season. But they both claimed to be quite happy to quit London.

This attitude was not unexpected coming from Beatrix, who still seemed far more interested in books and animals and romping through the countryside like a wild creature. But Leo was surprised that Poppy, who was candid about wanting to find a husband, would be so willing to depart.

'I've seen all this season's prospects,' Poppy told Leo grimly as they rode through Hyde Park in an open carriage. 'Not one of them is worth staying in town for.'

Beatrix sat in the opposite seat, with Dodger the ferret curled in her lap. Miss Marks had wedged herself in the corner, her bespectacled gaze fixed on the scenery.

Leo had rarely encountered such an off-putting female. Abrasive, pale, her form an accumulation of pointy elbows and angular bones, her character stiff and knotty and dry.

Clearly Catherine Marks hated men. Which Leo wouldn't have blamed her for, since he was well aware of the faults of his gender. Except that she didn't seem to like women very much, either. The only people she seemed to unbend with were Poppy and Beatrix, who had reported that Miss Marks was exceptionally intelligent and could be very witty at times, and she had a lovely smile.

Leo had a difficult time imagining the tight little seam of Miss Marks's mouth curving in a smile. He rather doubted she even had teeth, since he had never seen them.

'She'll ruin the view,' he had complained that morning, when Poppy and Beatrix had told him they were bringing him on their drive. 'I won't enjoy the scenery with the Grim Reaper casting her shadow over it.'

'Don't call her such horrid names, Leo,' Beatrix had protested. 'I like her very much. And she's very nice when you're not around.'

'I believe she was treated very wrongly by a man in her past,' Poppy said sotto voce. 'In fact, I've heard a rumor or two that Miss Marks became a governess because she was involved in a scandal.'

Leo was interested despite himself. 'What kind of scandal?'

Poppy lowered her voice to a whisper. 'They say she *squandered her favors*.'

'She doesn't look like a woman who would squander her favors,' Beatrix said in a normal voice.

'Hush, Bea!' Poppy exclaimed. 'I don't want Miss Marks to overhear. She might think we were gossiping about her.'

'But we *are* gossiping about her. Besides, I don't believe she would do . . . you know, *that* . . . with anyone. She doesn't seem at all that sort of woman.'

'I believe it,' Leo had said. 'Usually the ladies most inclined to squander their favors are the ones who don't have any.'

'I don't understand,' Bea said.

'He means unattractive ladies are more easily seduced,' Poppy had said wryly, 'which I don't agree with. And besides, Miss Marks isn't unattractive at all. She's only a bit . . . stern.'

'And scrawny as a Scottish chicken,' Leo had muttered.

As the carriage passed Marble Arch and proceeded to Park Lane, Miss Marks glued her gaze to the spring floral displays.

Glancing at her idly, Leo noted that she had a decent profile — a sweet little tip of a nose supporting the spectacles, a gently rounded chin. Too bad the clenched mouth and frowning forehead ruined the rest of it.

He turned his attention back to Poppy, pondering her lack of desire to stay in London. Surely any other girl her age would have been begging to finish the season and enjoy all the balls and parties.

'Tell me about this season's prospects,' he said to Poppy. 'Can it be that not one of them holds any interest for you?'

She shook her head. 'Not one. I've met a few whom I do like, such as Lord Bromley, or — '

'Bromley?' Leo repeated, his brows lifting. 'But he's twice your age. Are there any younger ones you might consider? Someone born in this century, perhaps?'

'Well, there's Mr. Radstock.'

'Portly and plodding,' Leo said, having met the porker on a few previous occasions. The upper circles of London were a relatively small community. 'Who else?'

'There is Lord Wallscourt, very gentle and friendly, but . . . he's a rabbit.'

'Curious and cuddly?' Beatrix asked, having a high opinion of rabbits.

Poppy smiled. 'No, I meant he was rather colorless and . . . oh, just *rabbity*. Which is a fine thing in a pet, but not a husband.' She made a project of neatening the bonnet ribbons tied beneath her chin. 'You'll probably advise me to lower my expectations, Leo, but I've already dropped them to the extent that even a worm couldn't squeeze itself beneath my expectations. I must tell you, the London season is a grave disappointment.'

'I'm sorry, Poppy,' Leo said gently. 'I wish I

knew a fellow to recommend to you, but the only ones I know are ne'er-do-wells and drunkards. Excellent friends. But I'd rather shoot one of them than have him as a brother-in-law.'

'That leads to something I've wanted to ask you.'

'Oh?' He looked into her sweet, serious face, this perfectly lovely sister who aspired so desperately to have a calm and ordinary life.

'Now that I've been out in society,' Poppy said, 'I've heard rumors . . .'

Leo's smile turned rueful as he understood what she wanted to know. 'About me.'

'Yes. Are you really as wicked as some people say?'

Despite the private nature of the query, Leo was aware of both Miss Marks and Beatrix turning their full attention to him.

'I'm afraid so, darling,' he said, while a sordid parade of his past sins swept through his mind.

'Why?' Poppy asked with a frankness he ordinarily would have found endearing. But not with Miss Marks's sanctimonious gaze fastened on him.

'It's much easier to be wicked,' he said. 'Especially if one has no reason to be good.'

'What about earning a place in heaven?' Catherine Marks asked. He would have thought she had a pretty voice, if it hadn't come from such an unappealing source. 'Isn't that reason enough to conduct yourself with some modicum of decency?'

'That depends,' he said sardonically. 'What is heaven to you, Miss Marks?'

178

She considered the question with more care than he would have expected. 'Peace. Serenity. A place where there is no sin, nor gossip, nor conflict.'

'Well, Miss Marks, I'm afraid your idea of heaven is my idea of hell. Therefore my wicked ways shall happily continue.' Turning back to Poppy, he spoke far more kindly. 'Don't lose hope, Sis. There's someone out there, waiting for you. Someday you'll find him, and he'll be everything you were hoping for.'

'Do you really think so?' Poppy asked.

'No. But I've always thought that was a nice thing to say to someone in your circumstances.'

Poppy snickered and poked Leo in the side, while Miss Marks gave him a stare of pure disgust.

13

On their last evening in London, the family attended a private ball given at the home of Mr. and Mrs. Simon Hunt in Mayfair. Mr. Hunt, a railway entrepreneur and part owner of a British locomotive works, was a self-made man, the son of a London butcher. He was part of a new and growing class of investors, businessmen, and managers who were unsettling the long-held traditions and authority of the peerage itself.

A fascinating and rather volatile mix of guests attended the Hunts' annual spring ball . . . politicians, foreigners, aristocrats, and businesspeople. It was said the invitations were highly sought after, since even the peers who outwardly disdained the pursuit of wealth were eager to have some connection to the extraordinarily powerful Mr. Hunt.

The Hunt mansion could well have been described as the symbol of the success of private enterprise. Large, luxurious, and technologically advanced, the house was lit with gas in every room and filled with plasterwork made from modern flexible molds that were currently being displayed at the Crystal Palace.

Floor-length windows gave access to broad walks and gardens outside, not to mention a remarkable glass-roofed conservatory heated with a complex system of underfloor pipework.

Just before the Hathaways arrived at the Hunt

180

mansion, Miss Marks whispered a few last-minute reminders to her charges, telling them not to fill their dance cards too quickly in case a prepossessing gentleman might arrive later at the ball, and never to be seen without their gloves, and never to refuse a gentleman who asked them to dance unless they were already engaged to dance with another. But by all means, they must never allow one gentleman more than three dances — such excessive familiarity would cause gossip.

Win was touched by the careful way in which Miss Marks relayed the instructions, and the earnest attention Poppy and Beatrix gave her. Clearly the three of them had labored long and hard on the intricate labyrinth of etiquette.

Win was at a disadvantage compared to her two younger sisters. Since she had spent so long away from London, her own knowledge of social mores was lacking. 'I hope I won't embarrass any of you,' she said lightly. 'Though I should warn you that the chances of my making a social misstep are quite high. I hope you'll undertake to teach me as well, Miss Marks.'

The governess smiled a little, revealing even white teeth and soft lips. Win couldn't help thinking that if Miss Marks were a bit more filled out, she would be quite pretty. 'You have such a natural sense of propriety,' she told Win, 'I can't imagine you being anything less than a perfect lady.'

'Oh, Win never does anything wrong,' Beatrix told Miss Marks.

'Win is a saint,' Poppy agreed. 'It's very trying.

But we do our best to tolerate her.'

Win smiled at them. 'For your information,' she told them lightly, 'I intend to break at least three rules of etiquette before the ball is over.'

'Which three?' Poppy and Beatrix asked in unison. Miss Marks merely looked perplexed, as if she was trying to understand why anyone would deliberately do such a thing.

'I haven't decided yet.' Win folded her gloved hands in her lap. 'I'll have to wait for the opportunities to present themselves.'

As the guests entered the mansion, domestics came to take the cloaks and shawls, and the gentlemen's hats and coats. Seeing Cam and Merripen standing near each other, shrugging off their coats with the same deft gestures, Win felt a whimsical smile touch her lips. She wondered how it was that everyone couldn't see that they were brothers. Their kinship was so clear to her, even though they weren't identical. The same wavy dark hair, although Cam's was longer and Merripen kept his neatly cropped. The same long, athletic build, although Cam was slimmer and more supple, whereas Merripen had the sturdier, more muscular build of a boxer.

Their greatest difference, however, was not that of their external appearances, but the way each approached the world. Cam with a sense of amused tolerance and charm and shrewd confidence. And Merripen with his battered dignity and smoldering intensity, and most of all, the strength of feeling that he fought so desperately to hide.

Oh, how she wanted him. But he would not be

182

easily won, if ever. Win thought it was rather like trying to coax a wild creature to come to her hand: the endless advances and retreats, the hunger and need for connection warring with fear.

She wanted him even more as she saw him here among this glittering crowd, his aloof and powerful form dressed in the austere evening scheme of black and white. Merripen did not consider himself inferior to the people around him, but he was well aware that he was not one of them. He understood their values, even though he didn't always agree with them. And he had learned how to acquit himself well in the *gadjo* world — he was the kind of man who would adapt to any circumstances. After all, Win thought with private amusement, not just any man could break a horse, build a stone fence by hand, recite the Greek alphabet, *and* discuss the relative philosophical merits of empiricism and rationalism. Not to mention rebuild an estate and run it as if he were to the manor born.

There was a sense of impenetrable mystery about Kev Merripen. She was obsessed with the tantalizing thought of what it would be like to slip past all his secrets, to reach the extraordinary heart he guarded so closely.

Melancholy swept over her as she glanced at the beautiful interior of the mansion, the guests laughing and chatting while music floated lightly over the scene. So much to enjoy and appreciate, and yet all Win wanted was to be alone with the most unavailable man in the room.

However, she wasn't going to play the wallflower. She was going to dance and laugh and do all the things she had imagined for years while lying in her sickbed. And if it displeased Merripen or made him jealous, so much the better.

Divested of her cloak, Win went forward with her sisters. They were all dressed in pale satins, Poppy in pink, Beatrix in blue, Amelia in lavender, and herself in white. Her gown was uncomfortable, which Poppy had laughingly said was a good thing, as a comfortable gown would almost certainly not be stylish. It felt too light on the top, the bodice low and square, the sleeves short and tight. And it felt too heavy from the waist down, with wide triple skirts caught up in flounces. But the main source of discomfort was her corset, which she had gone without for so long that she found herself resenting even the slightest constriction. Though it was only lightly laced, the corset stiffened her torso and pushed her breasts artificially high. It hardly seemed decent. And yet it was considered *indecent* to go without one.

All things considered, however, it seemed worth the discomfort when she saw Merripen's reaction. His face went blank at the sight of her in the low-cut ball gown, his gaze traveling from the tip of one satin slipper peeking from beneath the hem up to her face. He stared an extra few moments at her breasts, lifted high as if they had been cupped by his hands. When his eyes finally looked into hers, they flickered with obsidian fire. A responsive shiver chased beneath the framework of Win's corset. With difficulty, she looked away from him.

The Hathaways went farther into the entrance hall, where a chandelier shed sparkling light over the parquetry floor.

'What an extraordinary creature,' Win heard Dr. Harrow murmur nearby. She followed his gaze to the lady of the house, Mrs. Annabelle Hunt, who was greeting guests.

Although Win had never met Mrs. Hunt, she recognized her from descriptions she had heard. Mrs. Hunt was said to be one of the greatest beauties of England, with her beautifully turned figure and heavily lashed blue eyes, and hair that gleamed with rich shades of honey and gold. But it was her luminous, lively expressiveness that made her truly engaging.

'That's her husband, standing next to her,' Poppy murmured. 'He's intimidating, but very nice.'

'I beg to differ,' Leo said.

'You don't think he's intimidating?' Win asked.

'I don't think he's nice. Whenever I happen to be in the same room as his wife, he looks at me as if he'd like to dismember me.'

'Well,' Poppy said prosaically, 'one can't fault his judgment.' She leaned toward Win and said, 'Mr. Hunt is besotted with his wife. Their marriage is a love match, you see.'

'How unfashionable,' Dr. Harrow commented with a grin.

'He even dances with her,' Beatrix told Win, 'which husbands and wives are *never* supposed to do. But considering Mr. Hunt's fortune, people find reasons to excuse him for such behavior.'

185

'See how small her waist is,' Poppy murmured to Win. 'And that's after three children — two of them very large boys.'

'I will have to lecture Mrs. Hunt on the evils of tight-lacing,' Dr. Harrow said sotto voce, and Win laughed.

'I'm afraid the choice between health and fashion is not an easy one for women,' she told him. 'I'm still surprised that you allowed me to wear stays tonight.'

'You hardly need them,' he said, his gray eyes twinkling. 'Your natural waist is hardly wider than Mrs. Hunt's corseted one.'

Win smiled into Julian's handsome face, thinking that whenever she was in his presence, she felt safe and reassured. It had been like that ever since she had first met him. He had been a godlike figure to her, and to everyone at the clinic. But she still had no real sense of him as a flesh-and-blood man. No idea if there was potential for them to be more together than they were individually.

'The mysterious missing Hathaway sister!' Mrs. Hunt exclaimed, and took both Win's hands in her gloved ones.

'Not so mysterious,' Win said, smiling.

'Miss Hathaway, what a delight to meet you at last, and even more to see you in good health.'

'Mrs. Hunt always asks about you,' Poppy told Win, 'so we've kept her informed about your progress.'

'Thank you, Mrs. Hunt,' Win said shyly. 'I am quite well now, and honored to be a guest at your lovely home.'

Mrs. Hunt gave Win a dazzling smile, retaining her hands as she spoke to Cam. 'Such graceful manners. I think, Mr. Rohan, that Miss Hathaway will easily attain the popularity of her sisters.'

'Next year, I'm afraid,' Cam said easily. 'This ball marks the end of the season for us. We're all traveling to Hampshire within the week.'

Mrs. Hunt made a little face. 'So soon? But I suppose that is only to be expected. Lord Ramsay will want to see his estate.'

'Yes, Mrs. Hunt,' Leo said. 'I adore bucolic settings. One can never view too many sheep.'

At the sound of Mrs. Hunt's laughter, her husband joined the conversation. 'Welcome, my lord,' Simon Hunt said to Leo. 'The news of your return is being celebrated throughout London. Apparently the gaming and wine establishments suffered greatly in your absence.'

'Then I shall do my best to reinvigorate the economy,' Leo said.

Hunt grinned briefly. 'You owe quite a lot to this fellow,' he said to Leo, turning to shake Merripen's hand. Merripen, as usual, had been standing unobtrusively at the side of the group. 'According to Westcliff and the other neighboring estate, Merripen has made a rousing success of the Ramsay estate in a very short time.'

'Since the name 'Ramsay' is so seldom coupled with the word 'success,'' Leo replied, 'Merripen's accomplishment is all the more impressive.'

'Perhaps later in the evening,' Hunt said to Merripen, 'we might find a moment to discuss your impressions of the threshing machine you purchased for the estate. With the locomotive works so firmly established, I'm considering expanding the business into agricultural machinery. I've heard of a new design for the thresher, as well as a steam-powered hay press.'

'The entire agricultural process is becoming mechanized,' Merripen replied. 'Spindle harvesters, cutters, and binders . . . many of the prototypes are on display at the exhibition.'

Hunt's dark eyes glinted with interest. 'I'd like to hear more.'

'My husband is endlessly fascinated by machines,' Mrs. Hunt said, laughing. 'I believe they've eclipsed all his other interests.'

'Not all,' Hunt said softly. Something about the way he glanced at his wife caused her cheeks to flush.

Amused, Leo smoothed over the moment by saying, 'Mr. Hunt, I would like to introduce Dr. Harrow, the physician who helped my sister to recover her health.'

'A pleasure, sir,' Dr. Harrow said, and shook Hunt's hand.

'Likewise,' Hunt replied cordially, returning the shake. But he gave the doctor an odd, speculative look. 'You are the Harrow who runs the clinic in France?'

'I am.'

'And you reside there still?'

'Yes, although I try to visit friends and family in Great Britain as often as my schedule allows.'

'I believe I am acquainted with the family of your late wife,' Hunt murmured, staring hard at him.

188

After a quick double blink, Harrow responded with a regretful smile, 'The Lanhams. Estimable people. I haven't seen them for years. The memories, you understand.'

'I understand,' Hunt said quietly.

Win was puzzled by the long, awkward pause that followed, and the sense of discord that emanated from the two men. She glanced at her family, and Mrs. Hunt, who clearly didn't comprehend, either.

'Well, Mr. Hunt,' Mrs. Hunt said brightly, 'are we going to shock everyone by dancing together? They're going to play a waltz quite soon — and you know you are my favorite partner.'

Hunt's attention was immediately distracted by the flirtatious note in his wife's voice. He grinned at her. 'Anything for you, love.'

Harrow caught Win's gaze with his own. 'I haven't waltzed in far too long,' he said. 'Might you save a place for me on your dance card?'

'Your name is already there,' she replied, and placed a light hand on his proffered arm. They followed the Hunts to the drawing room.

Poppy and Beatrix were already being approached by prospective partners, while Cam closed his gloved fingers over Amelia's. 'I'll be damned if Hunt's the only one who's allowed to be shocking. Come dance with me.'

'I'm afraid we won't shock anyone at all,' she said, accompanying him without hesitation. 'People already assume we don't know any better.'

Leo watched the procession into the drawing room with narrowed eyes. 'I wonder,' he said to

Merripen, 'what Hunt knows about Harrow? Do you know him well enough to ask?'

'Yes,' Merripen said. 'But even if I didn't, I wouldn't leave this place until I made him tell me.'

That made Leo chuckle. 'You may be the only one in this entire mansion who would dare try to 'make' Simon Hunt do anything. He's a bloody big bastard.'

'So am I,' came Merripen's grim reply.

*   *   *

It was a lovely ball, or would have been, if Merripen had behaved like a reasonable human being. He watched Win constantly, hardly bothering to be discreet about it. While she stood in one group or another and he conversed with a group of men that included Mr. Hunt, Merripen's gaze never strayed far from Win.

At least three times Win was approached by various men with whom she had engaged to dance, and each time Merripen appeared at her side and glowered at the would-be dance partner until he slunk away.

Merripen was frightening off suitors right and left.

Even Miss Marks was unable to deter him. The governess had told Merripen most firmly that his chaperonage was unnecessary, as she had the situation well in hand. But he had replied obstinately that if she were to act as chaperon, she had better do a better job of keeping undesirable men away from her charge.

'What do you think you're doing?' Win whispered to Merripen furiously, as he sent off yet another abashed gentleman. 'I wanted to dance with him! I had promised him I would!'

'You're not going to dance with scum like him,' Merripen muttered.

Win shook her head in bewilderment. 'He's a viscount from a respected family. What could you possibly object to?'

'He's a friend of Leo's. That's reason enough.'

Win glared up at Merripen. She struggled to retain a grasp on her composure. She had always found it so easy to conceal her emotions beneath a serene facade, but lately she was finding that more and more difficult. All her feelings were lurking too close to the surface. 'If you are trying to ruin my evening,' she told him, 'you're doing a splendid job of it. I want to dance, and you're scaring away everyone who approaches me. Leave me alone.' She turned her back to him, and sighed with relief as Julian Harrow came to them.

'Miss Hathaway,' he said, 'will you do me the honor — '

'Yes,' she said before he could even finish the sentence. Taking his arm, she let him lead her into the mass of swirling, waltzing couples. Glancing over her shoulder, she saw Merripen staring after her, and she sent him a threatening look. He returned it with a scowl.

As Win walked away, she felt the pressure of a frustrated laugh in her throat. She swallowed it back, thinking that Kev Merripen was the most infuriating man alive. He was a dog in the manger, refusing to have a relationship with her

191

and yet not allowing her to be with anyone else. And knowing his capacity for endurance, it would probably go on for years. Forever. She couldn't live like this.

'Winnifred,' Julian Harrow said, his gray eyes concerned. 'This is far too lovely a night for you to be distressed. What were you arguing about?'

'Nothing of import,' she said, trying to speak lightly but succeeding only in sounding stiff. 'Just a family squabble.'

She curtseyed and Julian bowed, and he took her in his arms. His hand was firm on her back, guiding her easily as they danced.

Julian's touch reawakened memories of the clinic, the way he had encouraged and helped her, the times he had been stern when she had needed it, and the times they had celebrated when she had reached another milestone in her progress. He was a good, kind, high-minded man. A handsome man. Win was hardly oblivious to the admiring feminine gazes he attracted. Most of the unmarried girls in this room would have given anything to have such a splendid suitor.

I could marry him, she thought. He had made it clear that all it would take was a bit of encouragement on her part. She could become a doctor's wife and live in the south of France, and perhaps help somehow in his work at the clinic. To help other people who were suffering the way she had . . . to do something positive and worthwhile with her life . . . wouldn't that be better than this?

Anything was preferable to the pain of loving a

man she couldn't have. And, God help her, living in close proximity. She would become bitter and frustrated. She might even come to hate Merripen.

She felt herself relaxing in Julian's arms. The bleak, angry feeling faded, soothed by the music and the waltz rhythm. Julian swept her around the drawing room, guiding her carefully among the dancing couples.

'This is what I dreamed of,' Win told him. 'Being able to do this . . . just like everyone else.'

His hand tightened on her waist. 'And so you are. But you're not like everyone else. You're the most beautiful woman here.'

'No,' she said, laughing.

'Yes. Like an angel in an Old Masters work. Or perhaps the *Sleeping Venus*. Are you familiar with that painting?'

'I'm afraid not.'

'I'll take you to see it someday. Though you might find it a bit shocking.'

'I suppose Venus is unclothed in that work?' Win tried to sound worldly, but she felt herself blushing. 'I've never understood why such depictions of beauty are always in the nude, when a bit of tactful drapery would yield the same effect.'

'Because there is nothing more beautiful than the unveiled female form.' Julian laughed quietly as he saw her heightened color. 'Have I embarrassed you with my frankness? I'm sorry.'

'I don't think you are. I think you meant to disconcert me.' It was a new sensation, flirting with Julian.

'You're right. I want to set you a bit off-balance.'

'Why?'

'Because I would like for you to see me as someone other than predictable, tedious old Dr. Harrow.'

'You're none of those things,' she said, laughing.

'Good,' he murmured, smiling at her. The waltz ended, and gentlemen began to lead their partners out of the dancing area, while others took their places.

'It's warm in here, and far too crowded,' Julian said. 'Would you like to be scandalous and slip away with me for a moment?'

'I would love to.'

He took her to a corner partially screened by some massive potted plants. At an opportune moment, he led her out of the drawing room and into a huge glass conservatory. The space was filled with paths and indoor trees and flowers, and secluded little benches. Beyond the conservatory, a wide terrace overlooked the fenced gardens and the other mansions of Mayfair. The city was outlined in the distance, bristling with chimneys that frosted the midnight sky with streams of smoke.

They sat on a bench, Win's skirts billowing around them. Julian turned partially to face her. The glaze of moonlight gave his polished-ivory skin a slight luminescence. 'Winnifred,' he murmured, and the timbre of his voice was low and intimate. Staring into his gray eyes, Win realized that he was going to kiss her.

194

But he surprised her by removing one of her gloves with exquisite care, the moonlight shimmering over his black hair. Lifting her slender hand to his lips, he kissed the backs of her fingers, and then the fragile inside of her wrist. He held her hand like a half-open flower against his face. His tenderness disarmed her.

'You know why I've come to England,' he said softly. 'I want to know you much better, my dear, in a way that wasn't possible at the clinic. I want — '

But a sound from nearby caused Julian to break off, his head lifting.

Together, he and Win stared at the intruder.

It was Merripen, of course, huge and dark and aggressive as he strode toward them.

Win's jaw sagged in disbelief. He had followed her out here? She felt like a hunted creature. For heaven's sake, was there no place she could evade his outrageous stalking?

'Go . . . away,' she said, enunciating each word with scornful precision. 'You are not my chaperon.'

'You should be with your chaperon,' Merripen snapped. 'Not here with *him*.'

Win had never found it so difficult to master her emotions. She shoved them back, closing them behind an expressionless face. But she could feel the temper seething impatiently inside her. Her voice shook only a little as she turned to Julian. 'Would you be so kind as to leave us, Dr. Harrow? There is something I must settle with Merripen.'

Julian glanced from Merripen's set face to

hers. 'I'm not sure I should,' he said slowly.

'He's been plaguing me all evening,' Win said. 'I'm the only one who can put a stop to it. Please allow me a moment with him.'

'Very well.' Julian stood from the bench. 'Where shall I wait for you?'

'Back in the drawing room,' Win replied, grateful that there was no argument from Julian. Clearly he respected her, and her abilities, enough to allow her to manage the situation. 'Thank you, Dr. Harrow.'

She was barely aware of Julian's departure, she was so focused on Merripen. She stood and went to him with a furious scowl. 'You are driving me mad!' she exclaimed. 'I want you to stop this, Kev! Do you have any idea how ridiculous you're being? How badly you've behaved tonight?'

'*I've* behaved badly?' he thundered. 'You were about to let yourself be compromised.'

'Perhaps I want to be compromised.'

'That's too bad,' he said, reaching out to grip her upper arm, preparing to haul her from the conservatory. 'Because I'm going to make certain you stay safe.'

'Don't touch me!' Win wrenched free of him, incensed. 'I've been safe for years. Tucked safely in bed, watching everyone around me enjoying their lives. I've had enough *safety* to last a lifetime, Kev. And if that's what you want, for me to continue to be alone and unloved, then you can go to the devil.'

'You were never alone,' he said harshly. 'You've never been unloved.'

'I want to be loved as a *woman*. Not as a

child, or a sister, or an invalid — '

'That's not how I — '

'Perhaps you're not even capable of such love.' In her blazing frustration, Win experienced something she had never felt before. The desire to hurt someone. 'You don't have it in you.'

Merripen moved through a shaft of moonlight that had slipped through the conservatory glass, and Win felt a little shock as she saw his murderous expression. In just a few words she had managed to cut him deeply, enough to open a vein of dark and furious feeling. She fell back a step, alarmed as he seized her in a brutal grip.

He jerked her upward. 'All the fires of hell could burn for a thousand years and it wouldn't equal what I feel for you in one minute of the day. I love you so much there is no pleasure in it. Nothing but torment. Because if I could dilute what I feel for you to the millionth part, it would still be enough to kill you. And even if it drives me mad, I would rather see you live in the arms of that cold, soulless bastard than die in mine.'

Before she could begin to comprehend what he'd said, and all the implications, he took her mouth with savage hunger. For a full minute, perhaps two, she couldn't even move, could only stand there helplessly, falling apart, every rational thought dissolving. She felt faint, but not from illness. Her hand fluttered to the back of his neck, the muscles rigid above the crisp edge of his collar, the locks of his hair like raw silk.

Her fingers unconsciously caressed his nape, trying to soothe his hard-breathing fervor. His mouth slanted deeper over hers, sucking and teasing, his taste drugging and sweet. And then something quieted his frenzy, and he became gentle. His hand trembled as he touched her face, his fingers smoothing over her cheek, his palm cradling her jaw. The hungry pressure of his mouth lifted from hers, and he kissed her eyelids and nose and forehead.

In his drive to press close, he had urged her back against the conservatory wall. She gasped as her bare upper shoulders were flattened on a pane of glass, causing gooseflesh to rise. Cold glass . . . but his body was so warm, his scalding-soft mouth traveling down to her throat, her chest, the hint of cleavage.

Merripen slipped two fingers inside her bodice, stroking the cool cushion of her breast. It wasn't enough. He tugged impatiently at the edge of the bodice and the shallow cup of the corset beneath. Win closed her eyes, offering not so much as a word of protest, still except for the heaves of her breathing.

Merripen gave a soft grunt of satisfaction as her breast popped free. He lifted her higher against the glass, nearly lifting her off her feet, and he closed his mouth over the tip of her breast.

Win bit her lip to keep from crying out. Each swirling lick of his tongue sent darts of heat down to her toes. She slid her hands into his hair, one gloved, one ungloved, her body arching against the tender stimulation of his mouth.

When her nipple was taut and throbbing, he moved back up to her neck, dragging his mouth along the delicate skin. 'Win.' His voice was ragged. 'I want to — ' But he bit back the words and kissed her again, deep and feverish, while he took the hard peak of her breast in his fingers. He squeezed and rolled it softly, until the wickedly gentle harassment caused her to writhe and sob in pleasure.

Then it all ended with cruel suddenness. He froze inexplicably and jerked her away from the window, pulling the front of her body into his. As if he was trying to hide her from something. A quiet curse escaped him.

'What . . . ' Win found it difficult to speak. She was as dazed as if she were emerging from a deep sleep, her thoughts tumbling over on themselves. 'What is it?'

'I saw movement on the terrace. Someone may have seen us.'

That startled Win back into a semblance of normalcy. She turned from him, clumsily pulling her bodice back into place. 'My glove,' she whispered, seeing it lying by the bench like a tiny abandoned flag of truce.

Merripen went to retrieve it for her.

'I . . . I'm going to the ladies' dressing room,' she said shakily. 'I'll put myself to rights, and return to the drawing room as soon as I'm able.'

She wasn't altogether certain what had just happened, what it had meant. Merripen had admitted he loved her. He had finally said it. But she had always imagined it as a joyful confession, not an angry and bitter one. Everything seemed so terribly wrong.

If only she could go back to the hotel, now, and be alone in her room. She needed privacy in which to think. What was it he had said? . . . *I would rather see you live in the arms of that cold, soulless bastard than die in mine.* But that made no sense. Why had he said such a thing?

She wanted to confront him, but this was not the time or place. This was a matter that must be handled with great care. Merripen was more complicated than most people realized. Although he gave the impression of being less sensitive than most men, the truth was, he harbored such powerful feelings that even he wasn't able to manage them well.

'We must talk later, Kev,' she said.

He gave a short nod, his shoulders and neck set as if he were carrying an unbearable burden.

★   ★   ★

Win went as discreetly as possible to the ladies' dressing room upstairs, where maids were busy repairing torn flounces, helping to blot the shine from perspiring faces, and anchoring coiffures with extra hairpins. Women had gathered in small groups, giggling and gossiping about things they'd seen and overheard. Win sat before a looking glass and inspected her reflection. Her cheeks were flushed, a marked contrast to her usual composed paleness, and her lips were red and swollen. Her color deepened as she wondered if everyone could see what she had been doing.

A maid came to blot Win's face and dust it with rice powder, and she murmured her thanks. She took several calming breaths — as deep as the dratted corset would allow — and tried inconspicuously to make certain her bodice was fully covering her breasts.

By the time Win felt ready to go downstairs once more, approximately thirty minutes had passed. She smiled as Poppy entered the ladies' dressing room and came to her.

'Hello, dear,' Win said, standing from the chair. 'Here, take my chair. Do you need hairpins? Powder?'

'No, thank you.' Poppy wore a tense, anxious expression, looking nearly as flushed as Win had been earlier.

'Are you enjoying yourself?' Win asked with a touch of concern.

'Not really,' Poppy said, drawing her to the corner to keep from being overheard. 'I was looking forward to meeting someone other than the usual crowd of stuffy old peers, or worse, the stuffy young ones. But the only new men I met were climbers and businessmen. Either they want to talk about money — which is vulgar and I don't know anything about it — or they have careers they claim they can't discuss, which means they're probably involved in something illegal.'

'And Beatrix? How is she faring?'

'She's quite popular, actually. She goes around saying outrageous things, and people laugh and think she's being witty when they don't realize she's perfectly serious.'

Win smiled. 'Shall we go downstairs and find her?'

'Not yet.' Poppy reached out to take her hand,

and gripped it tightly. 'Win, dear . . . I've come to find you because . . . there's a sort of upheaval going on downstairs. And . . . it involves you.'

'An upheaval?' Win shook her head, feeling cold in the marrow of her bones. Her stomach gave a sick plunge. 'I don't understand.'

'A rumor is quickly spreading that you were seen in the conservatory in a compromising position. A *very* compromising one.'

Win felt her face turn white. 'It's only been thirty minutes,' she whispered.

'This is London society,' Poppy said grimly. 'Gossip travels at full throttle.'

A pair of young women entered the dressing room, saw Win, and immediately whispered to each other.

Win's stricken gaze met Poppy's. 'There's going to be a scandal, isn't there?' she asked faintly.

'Not if it's managed properly and quickly.' Poppy squeezed her hand. 'I'm to take you to the library, dear. Amelia and Mr. Rohan are there — we're going to meet them and put our heads together, and decide on a course of action.'

Win almost wished she could go back to being an invalid with frequent fainting spells. Because at the moment, a good long swoon sounded quite appealing. 'Oh, what have I done?' she whispered.

That elicited a faint smile from Poppy. 'That seems to be the question on everyone's mind.'

202

14

The Hunts' library was a handsome room lined with mahogany bookcases with fronts of glazed glass. Cam Rohan and Simon Hunt were standing beside a large inlaid sideboard laden with glittering spirit decanters. Holding a glass half-filled with amber liquid, Hunt gave Win an inscrutable glance as she entered the library. Amelia, Mrs. Hunt, and Dr. Harrow were also there. Win had the curious feeling that it couldn't really be happening. She had never been involved in a scandal before, and it wasn't nearly as exciting or interesting as she had imagined while lying in her sickbed.

It was frightening.

Because in spite of her earlier words to Merripen about wanting to be compromised, she hadn't meant any of it. No sane woman would wish for such a thing. Causing a scandal meant ruining not only Win's prospects, but those of her younger sisters. It would cast a shadow over the entire family. Her carelessness was going to harm all the people she loved.

'Win.' Amelia came to her at once, embracing her firmly. 'It's all right, dear. We'll manage this.'

Had Win not been so distressed, she would have smiled. Her older sister was famous for her confidence in her ability to manage anything, including natural disasters, foreign invasions, and stampeding wildlife. None of those, however, could come close to the havoc of a London society scandal.

'Where is Miss Marks?' Win asked in a muffled voice.

'In the drawing room with Beatrix. We're trying to keep appearances as normal as possible.' Amelia sent a tense, rueful smile to the Hunts. 'But our family has never been especially good at that.'

Win stiffened as she saw Leo and Merripen enter the room. Leo came straight to her, while Merripen went to lurk in the corner as usual. He wouldn't meet her gaze. The room was filled with a charged silence that caused the down on the back of her neck to rise.

She hadn't gotten herself into this all alone, Win thought with a flare of anger.

Merripen would have to help her now. He would have to protect her with any means at his disposal. Including his name.

Her heart began to pound so heavily that it almost hurt.

'It appears you've been making up for lost time, Sis,' Leo said flippantly, but there was a flicker of concern in his light eyes. 'We have to be quick about this, since people will talk even more in light of our collective absence. Tongues are wagging so fast, they've created a strong breeze in the drawing room.'

Mrs. Hunt approached Amelia and Win. 'Winnifred.'

Her voice was very gentle. 'If this rumor is not true, I will take action at once to deny it on your behalf.'

Win drew in a trembling breath. 'It is true,' she said.

Mrs. Hunt patted her arm and gave her a reassuring glance. 'Trust me, you are not the first nor will you be the last to find yourself in this predicament.'

'In fact,' came Mr. Hunt's lazy drawl, 'Mrs. Hunt has firsthand experience in just such a — '

'Mr. Hunt,' his wife said indignantly, and he grinned. Turning back to Win, Mrs. Hunt said, 'Winnifred, you and the gentleman in question must resolve this at once.' A delicate pause. 'May I ask whom you were seen with?'

Win couldn't answer. She let her gaze fall to the carpet, and she studied the pattern of medallions and flowers dazedly as she waited for Merripen to speak. The silence only lasted a matter of seconds, but it seemed like hours. *Say something*, she thought desperately. *Tell them it was you!*

But there was no movement or sound from Merripen.

And then Julian Harrow stepped forward. 'I am the gentleman in question,' he said quietly.

Win's head jerked up. She gave him an astonished glance as he took her hand. 'I apologize to all of you,' Julian continued, 'and especially to Miss Hathaway. I didn't intend to expose her to gossip or censure. But this precipitates something I had already resolved to do, which is to ask for Miss Hathaway's hand in marriage.'

Win stopped breathing. She looked directly at Merripen, and a silent cry of anguish seared through her heart. Merripen's hard face and coal-black eyes revealed nothing.

He said nothing.

Did nothing.

Merripen had compromised her and now he was letting another man assume the responsibility for it. Letting someone else rescue her. The betrayal was worse than any illness or pain she had ever experienced before. Win hated him. She would hate him until her dying day and beyond.

What choice did she have but to accept Julian? It was either that or allow herself and her sisters to be ruined.

Win felt her face drain of all color, but she summoned a paper-thin smile as she glanced at her brother.

'Well, my lord?' she asked Leo. 'Should we ask your permission first?'

'You have my blessing,' her brother said dryly. 'After all, I certainly don't want my pristine reputation to be marred by your scandals.'

Win turned to face Julian. 'Then yes, Dr. Harrow,' she said in a steady voice. 'I will marry you.'

A frown notched between Mrs. Hunt's fine dark brows as she stared at Win. She nodded in a businesslike manner. 'I will go out and explain quietly to the appropriate parties that what they saw was a betrothed couple embracing . . . a bit intemperate perhaps, but quite forgivable in light of a betrothal.'

'I'll go with you,' Mr. Hunt said, coming to his wife's side. He extended a hand to Dr. Harrow and shook it. 'My congratulations, sir.' His tone was cordial but far from enthusiastic. 'You are most fortunate to have won Miss Hathaway's hand.'

As the Hunts left, Cam approached Win. She forced herself to stare directly into his perceptive hazel eyes, though it cost her.

'Is this what you want, little sister?' he asked softly.

His sympathy nearly undid her. 'Oh yes.' She set her jaw against a wretched quiver, and managed to smile. 'I'm the luckiest woman in the world.'

And when she brought herself to look at Merripen, she saw that he was gone.

★   ★   ★

'What a ghastly evening,' Amelia muttered after everyone had left the library.

'Yes.' Cam led her into the hallway.

'Where are we going?'

'Back to the drawing room to make an appearance. Try to look pleased and confident.'

'Oh, good God.' Amelia pulled away from him and strode to a large arched wall niche, where a Palladian window revealed a view of the street below. She pressed her forehead against the glass and sighed heavily. A repeated tapping noise echoed through the hallway.

Serious as the situation was, Cam couldn't prevent a quick grin. Whenever Amelia was worried or angry, her nervous habit asserted itself. As he had once told her, she reminded him of a hummingbird tamping down her nest with one foot.

Cam went to her, and rested his warm palms on the cool slopes of her shoulders. He felt her shiver at his touch. 'Hummingbird,' he whispered, and slid his hands up to the back of her neck to knead the small frozen muscles there. As her tension ebbed, the foot tapping gradually died away. Finally Amelia relaxed enough to tell him her thoughts.

'Everyone in that library was aware that Merripen was the one who compromised her,' she said curtly. '*Not* Harrow. I can't believe it. After all Win has gone through, it comes to this? She'll marry a man she doesn't love and go to France, while Merripen won't lift a finger to stop her? What is the *matter* with him?'

'More than can be explained here and now. Calm yourself, love. It won't help Win for you to appear distressed.'

'I can't help it. This is all wrong. Oh, the look on my sister's face . . . '

'We have time to sort it out,' Cam murmured. 'A betrothal isn't the same as marriage.'

'But a betrothal is binding,' Amelia said with miserable impatience. 'You know people regard it as a contract that can't be broken easily.'

'Perhaps semi-binding,' he allowed.

'Oh, Cam.' Her shoulders drooped. 'You would never let anything come between us, would you? You would never let us be parted?'

The question was so patently ridiculous that Cam hardly knew what to say. He turned Amelia to face him, and saw with a jolt of surprise that his practical, sensible wife was close to tears. The pregnancy was making her emotional, he thought. The glitter of moisture in her eyes sent a rush of fierce tenderness through him. He curved a protective arm around her and used his free hand to grip the back of her hair, not caring that it mussed her coiffure. 'You are the reason I live,' he said in a low voice, holding her close. 'You're everything to me. Nothing could ever make me leave you. And if anyone ever tried to separate us, I would kill him.' He covered her mouth with his and kissed her with devastating sensuality, not stopping until she was weak and flushed and leaning hard against him. 'Now,' he said, only half-joking, 'where is that conservatory?'

That provoked a watery chuckle from her. 'I think there's been enough gossip fodder for one night. Are you going to talk to Merripen?'

'Of course. He won't listen, but that's never stopped me before.'

'Do you think he — ' Amelia broke off as she heard footsteps coming along the hallway, along with the crisp, abundant rustling of heavy skirts. She shrank farther into the niche with Cam, burrowing into his arms. She felt him smile against her hair. Together they were still and silent as they listened to a pair of ladies chattering.

' . . . in heaven's name did the Hunts invite them?' one of them was asking indignantly.

Amelia thought she recognized the voice — it belonged to one of the prune-faced chaperons who had been sitting at the side of the drawing room. Someone's maiden aunt, relegated to spinster status.

'Because they're monstrously wealthy?' her companion suggested.

'I suspect it is more because Lord Ramsay is a viscount.'

'You're right. An unmarried viscount.'

'But all the same . . . *Gypsies* in the family! The very thought of it! One can never expect them to behave in a civilized manner — they live by their animal instincts. And we're expected to hobnob with such people as if they're our equals.'

'The Hunts are *bourgeois* themselves, you know. No matter that Hunt owns half of London by now, he's still a butcher's son.'

'They and many of the guests here are not at all of suitable caliber for us to associate with. I have no doubt at least a half-dozen other scandals will erupt before the night is out.'

'Dreadful, I agree.' A pause, and then the second woman added wistfully, 'I do hope we'll be invited back next year . . . '

As the voices faded, Cam looked down at his wife with a frown. He didn't give a damn what anyone said — by now he was inured to anything that could be said about Gypsies. But he hated that the arrows were sometimes directed at Amelia.

To his surprise, she was smiling up at him steadily, her eyes midnight blue.

His expression turned quizzical. 'What's so amusing?'

Amelia toyed with a button on his coat. 'I was just thinking . . . tonight those two old hens will probably go to their beds, cold and alone.' An impish grin curved her lips. 'Whereas *I* will be with a wicked, handsome Rom who will keep me warm all night.'

* * *

Kev watched and waited until he found an opportunity to approach Simon Hunt, who had just managed to extricate himself from a conversation with a pair of giggling women. 'May I have a word with you?' Kev asked quietly.

Hunt didn't appear at all surprised. 'Let's go to the back terrace.'

They made their way to a side door of the drawing room, which opened directly onto the terrace. A group of gentlemen were gathered at one corner of the terrace, enjoying cigars. The rich scent of tobacco drifted on the cool breeze.

Simon Hunt smiled pleasantly and shook his head as the men beckoned for him and Kev to join them. 'We have some business to discuss,' he told them. 'Perhaps later.'

Leaning casually against the iron balustrade, Hunt regarded Kev with assessing dark eyes.

On the few occasions when they had met in Hampshire at Stony Cross Park, the estate that bordered the Ramsay lands, Kev had liked Hunt. He was a man's man who spoke in a straightforward manner. An openly ambitious man who enjoyed the pursuit of money and the pleasures it afforded him. And although most men in his position would have taken themselves far too seriously, Hunt had an irreverent and self-deprecating sense of humor.

'I assume you're going to ask what I know about Harrow,' Hunt said.

'Yes.'

'In light of recent events, this seems a bit like shutting the door after the house is robbed. And I should add that I have no proof of anything. But the accusations the Lanhams have made against Harrow are sufficiently serious to merit consideration.'

'What accusations?' Kev growled.

'Before Harrow built the clinic in France, he married the Lanhams' eldest daughter, Louise. She was said to be an unusually beautiful girl, a bit spoiled and willful, but on the whole an advantageous match for Harrow. She came with a large dowry and a well-connected family.'

Reaching into his coat, Hunt extracted a slender silver cigar case. 'Care for one?' he asked. Kev shook his head. Hunt pulled out a cigar, deftly bit off the tip, and lit it. The end of the cigar glowed as Hunt drew on it.

'According to the Lanhams,' Hunt continued, exhaling a stream of aromatic smoke, 'a year into the marriage, Louise changed. She became quite docile and distant, and seemed to have lost interest in her former pursuits. When the Lanhams approached Harrow with their concerns, he claimed the changes in her were simply evidence of maturity and marital contentment.'

'But they didn't believe that?'

'No. When they questioned Louise, however, she claimed to be happy and she asked them not to interfere.' Hunt raised the cigar to his lips again and stared thoughtfully at the lights of

London winking through the night haze. 'Sometime during the second year, Louise went into a decline.'

Kev felt a discomforting chill at the word 'decline,' commonly used for any illness a doctor couldn't diagnose or comprehend. The inexorable physical failing that no treatment could prevent.

'She became weak and dispirited and bedridden. No one could do anything for her. The Lanhams insisted on bringing their own doctor to attend her, but he couldn't find any cause for illness. Louise's condition deteriorated over a month or so, and then she died. The family blamed Harrow for her demise. Before the marriage, Louise had been a healthy, high-spirited girl, and not quite two years later, she was gone.'

'Sometimes declines happen,' Kev remarked, feeling the need to play devil's advocate. 'It wasn't necessarily Harrow's doing.'

'No. But it was Harrow's reaction that convinced the family that he was responsible in some way for Louise's death. He was too composed. Dispassionate. A few crocodile tears for appearance's sake, and that was it.'

'And after that he went to France with the dowry money?'

'Yes.' Hunt's broad shoulders lifted in a shrug. 'I despise gossip, Merripen. I rarely choose to pass it along. But the Lanhams are respectable people and not given to dramatics.' Frowning, he tapped the ash from his cigar over the edge of the balustrade. 'And despite all the good Harrow

213

has reportedly done for his patients . . . I can't help but feel there is something amiss with him. It's nothing I can put into words.'

Kev felt an ineffable relief to have his own thoughts echoed by a man like Hunt. 'I've had the same feeling about Harrow, ever since I first met him,' he said. 'But everyone else seems to revere him.'

There was a wry glint in Hunt's black eyes. 'Yes, well . . . this wouldn't be the first time I didn't agree with popular opinion. But I think anyone who cares for Miss Hathaway should be concerned for her sake.'

15

Merripen was gone by morning. He had checked out of the Rutledge and had left word that he would be traveling alone to the Ramsay estate.

Win had awoken with memories rising to the forefront of her bewildered mind. She felt heavy and weary and sullen. Merripen had been a part of her for too long. She had carried him in her heart, had absorbed him into the marrow of her bones. To let go of him now would feel like amputating part of herself. And yet it had to be done. Merripen himself had made it impossible for her to choose otherwise.

She washed and dressed with the help of a maid, and arranged her hair in a plaited chignon. There would be no meaningful talks with anyone in her family, she decided numbly. There would be no weeping or regrets. She was going to marry Dr. Julian Harrow and live far away from Hampshire. And she would try to find a measure of peace in that great, necessary distance.

'I want to be married as quickly as possible,' she told Julian later that morning, as they had tea in the family suite. 'I miss France. I want to return there without delay. As your wife.'

Julian smiled and touched the curve of her cheek with smooth, tapered fingertips. 'Very well, my dear.' He took her hand in his, brushing across her knuckles with his thumb. 'I have some business in London to take care of, and I'll join you in Hampshire in a few days. We'll make our plans there. We can marry at the estate chapel, if you like.'

The chapel that Merripen had rebuilt. 'Perfect,' Win said evenly.

'I'll buy a ring for you today,' Julian said. 'What kind of stone would you like? A sapphire to match your eyes?'

'Anything you choose will be lovely.' Win let her hand remain in his as they both fell silent. 'Julian,' she murmured, 'you haven't yet asked what . . . what transpired between Merripen and me last night.'

'There is no need,' Julian replied. 'I'm far too pleased by the result.'

'I . . . I want you to understand that I will be a good wife to you,' Win said earnestly. 'I . . . My former attachment to Merripen . . .'

'That will fade in time,' Julian said gently.

'Yes.'

'And I warn you, Winnifred . . . I will launch quite a battle for your affections. I will prove such a devoted and generous husband, there will be no room in your heart for anyone else.'

She thought about bringing up the subject of children, asking if perhaps he would relent someday if her health improved even more. But from what she did know about Julian, he would not reverse his decisions easily. And she wasn't certain it mattered. She was trapped.

Whatever life held in store for her now, she would have to make the best of it.

★   ★   ★

216

After two days of packing, the family was on its way to Hampshire. Cam, Amelia, Poppy, and Beatrix were in the first carriage, while Leo, Win, and Miss Marks were in the second. They had departed before day had broken, to gain as much headway as possible on the twelve-hour journey.

God knew what was being discussed in the second carriage. Cam only hoped Win's presence would help to blunt the animosity between Leo and Miss Marks.

The conversation in the first carriage, as Cam had expected, was nothing but animated. It both touched and amused him that Poppy and Beatrix had launched a campaign to put Merripen forth as a candidate to be Win's husband. Naively the girls had assumed that the only thing standing in the way was Merripen's lack of fortune.

' — so if you could give him some of your money — ,' Beatrix was saying eagerly.

' — or give him part of Leo's fortune,' Poppy interceded. 'Leo would only waste it — '

' — make Merripen understand that it would be Win's dowry,' Beatrix said, 'so it wouldn't hurt his pride — '

' — and they wouldn't need very much,' Poppy said. 'Neither of them gives a fig for mansions or fine carriages or — '

'Wait, both of you,' Cam said, lifting his hands in a defensive gesture. 'The problem is more complex than a matter of money, and — no, stop chirping for a moment and hear me out.' He smiled into the two pairs of blue eyes regarding him so anxiously. He found their concern for Merripen and Win more than a little endearing.

'Merripen has ample means to offer for Win. What he earns as the Ramsay estate manager is a handsome living in itself, and he also has unlimited access to the Ramsay accounts.'

'Then why is Win going to marry Dr. Harrow and not Merripen?' Beatrix demanded.

'For reasons Merripen wants to keep private, he believes he would not be an appropriate husband for her.'

'But he loves her!'

'Love doesn't solve every problem, Bea,' Amelia said gently.

'That sounds like something Mother would have said,' Poppy remarked with a slight smile, while Beatrix looked disgruntled.

'What would your father have said?' Cam asked.

'He would have led us all into some lengthy philosophical exploration of the nature of love, and it would have accomplished nothing whatsoever,' Amelia said. 'But it would have been fascinating.'

'I don't care how complicated everyone says it is,' Beatrix said. 'Win should marry Merripen. Don't you agree, Amelia?'

'It's not our choice,' Amelia replied. 'And it's not Win's, either, unless the big dunderhead offers her an alternative. There's nothing Win can do if he won't propose to her.'

'Wouldn't it be nice if ladies could propose to gentlemen?' Beatrix mused.

'Heavens, no,' Amelia said promptly. 'That would make it far too easy for the gentlemen.'

'In the animal kingdom,' Beatrix commented,

218

'males and females enjoy equal status. A female may do anything she wishes.'

'The animal kingdom allows many behaviors that we humans cannot emulate, dear. Scratching in public, for example. Regurgitating food. Flaunting themselves to attract a mate. Not to mention . . . Well, I needn't go on.'

'I wish you would,' Cam said with a grin. He settled Amelia more comfortably against his side and spoke to Beatrix and Poppy. 'Listen, you two. Neither of you is to bedevil Merripen about the situation. I know you want to help, but all you'll succeed in doing is provoking him.'

They both grumbled and nodded reluctantly, and snuggled in their respective corners. It was still dark outside, and the rocking motion of the carriage was soothing. In a matter of minutes, both sisters were drowsing.

Glancing at Amelia, Cam saw that she was still awake. He stroked the fine-grained skin of her face and throat, looking down into her pure blue eyes.

'Why didn't he step forward, Cam?' she whispered. 'Why did he give Win to Dr. Harrow?'

Cam took his time about answering. 'He's afraid.'

'Of what?'

'What he might do to her.'

Amelia frowned in bewilderment. 'That makes no sense. Merripen would never hurt her.'

'Not intentionally.'

'You're referring to the danger of getting her with child? But Win doesn't agree with Dr.

Harrow's opinion, and she says that even he can't say of a certainty what might happen.'

'It's not just that.' Cam sighed and settled her more closely against him. 'Did Merripen ever tell you that he was *asharibe*?'

'No, what does that mean?'

'It's a word used to describe a Romany warrior. Boys as young as five or six are trained in bare-knuckle fighting. There are no rules or time limits. The goal is to inflict the worst damage as quickly as possible until someone drops. The boys' handlers take money from paying crowds. I've seen *asharibe* who were badly hurt, blinded, even killed during the matches. They fight with fractured wrists and broken ribs if necessary.' Absently Cam smoothed Amelia's hair as he added, 'There were none in our tribe. Our leader decided it was too cruel. We learned to fight, of course, but it was never a way of life for us.'

'Merripen . . . ,' Amelia whispered.

'From what I can tell, it was even worse than that for him. The man who raised him . . . ' Cam, always so articulate, found it difficult to go on.

'His uncle?' Amelia prompted.

'Our uncle.' Cam had already told her that he and Merripen were brothers. But he hadn't yet confided the rest of what Shuri had said. 'Apparently he raised Merripen as if he were a game dog.'

Amelia turned pale. 'What do you mean?'

'Merripen was brought up to be as vicious as a pit animal. He was starved and maltreated until he was conditioned to fight anyone, under any circumstances. And he was taught to take any abuse that was meted out to him and turn his aggression against his opponent.'

'Poor boy,' Amelia murmured. 'That explains much about the way he was when he first came to us. He was only half-tame. But . . . that was all a long time ago. His life has been very different since then. And having once suffered so terribly, doesn't he want to be loved now? Doesn't he want to be happy?'

'It doesn't work that way, sweetheart.' Cam smiled into her puzzled face. It was no surprise that Amelia, who had been brought up in a large and affectionate family, should find it difficult to understand a man who feared his own needs as if they were his worst enemy. 'What if you were taught all during your childhood that the only reason for your existence was to inflict pain on others? That violence was all you were good for? How do you unlearn such a thing? You can't. So you cover it as best you can, always aware of what lies beneath the veneer.'

'But . . . obviously Merripen has changed. He's a man with many fine qualities.'

'Merripen wouldn't agree.'

'Well, Win has made it clear that she would have him regardless.'

'It doesn't matter that she would have him. He's determined to protect her from himself.'

Amelia hated being confronted with problems that had no definite solution. 'Then what can we do?'

Cam lowered his head to kiss the tip of her nose. 'I know how you hate to hear this, love

. . . but not much. It's in their hands.'

She shook her head and grumbled something against his shoulder.

'What did you say?' he asked, amused.

Her gaze lifted to his, and a self-deprecating smile curved her lips. 'Something to the effect that I *hate* having to leave Merripen and Win's future in their hands.'

★ ★ ★

The last time Win and Leo had seen Ramsay House it had been dilapidated and half-burned, the grounds barren except for weeds and rubble. And unlike the rest of the family, they had not seen the stages of its progress as it was being rebuilt.

The affluent southern county of Hampshire encompassed coastal land, heathland, and ancient forests filled with abundant wildlife. Hampshire had a milder, sunnier climate that most other parts of England, owing to the stabilizing effect of its location. Although Win had not lived in Hampshire for very long before she had gone to Dr. Harrow's clinic, she had the feeling of coming home. It was a welcoming, friendly place, with the lively market town of Stony Cross just within walking distance of the Ramsay estate.

It seemed the Hampshire weather had decided to present the estate to its best effect, with profuse sunshine and a few picturesque clouds in the distance.

The carriage passed the gatekeeper's lodge,

constructed of grayish blue bricks with cream stone detailing. 'They refer to that as the Blue House,' Miss Marks said, 'for obvious reasons.'

'How lovely!' Win exclaimed. 'I've never seen bricks that color in Hampshire before.'

''Staffordshire blue' brick,' Leo said, craning his neck to see the other side of the house. 'Now that they're able to bring brick from other places on the railway, there's no need for the builder to make them on site.'

They went along the lengthy drive toward the house, which was surrounded by velvety green lawn and white-graveled walking paths, and young hedges and rosebushes. 'My God,' Leo murmured as they approached the house itself. It was a multi-gabled cream stone structure with cheerful dormers. The blue slate roof featured hips and bays outlined with contrasting terra-cotta ridge tiles. Although the place was similar to the old house, it had been much improved. And what remained of the original structure had been so lovingly restored that one could hardly tell the old sections from the new.

Leo didn't take his gaze off the place. 'Merripen said they'd kept some of the odd-shaped rooms and nooks. I see many more windows. And they've added a service wing.'

People were working everywhere, carters, stockmen, sawyers, and masons, gardeners clipping hedges, stable boys and footmen coming out to the arriving carriages. The estate had not only come to life; it was thriving.

Watching her brother's intent profile, Win felt a surge of gratitude toward Merripen, who had made all this happen. It was good for Leo to come home to this. It was an auspicious beginning to a new life.

'The household staff is in need of expansion,' Miss Marks said, 'but the ones Mr. Merripen has hired are quite efficient. Mr. Merripen is an exacting manager, but also kind. They would do anything to please him.'

Win descended from the carriage with a footman's help, and allowed him to escort her to the front doors. A marvelous set of double doors, with lower panels of solid timber and leaded glass panes set within the upper panels. As soon as Win reached the top step, the doors opened to reveal a middle-aged woman with ginger hair and a fair freckled complexion. Her figure was shapely and sturdy in a high-necked black dress. 'Welcome, Miss Hathaway,' she said warmly. 'I am Mrs. Barnstable, the housekeeper. How glad we all are to have you back in Hampshire.'

'Thank you,' Win murmured, following her into the entrance hall.

Win's eyes widened at the interior of the place, so light and sparkling, the two-story-high hall lined with paneling painted a creamy white. A gray stone staircase was set in the back of the hall, its iron balustrades gleaming black and spotless. Everywhere, it smelled of soap and fresh wax.

'Remarkable,' Win breathed. 'It's not the same place at all.'

Leo came up beside her. For once he had no glib remark to make, nor did he bother to hide his admiration. 'It's a bloody miracle,' he said.

'I'm astonished.' He turned to the housekeeper. 'Where is Merripen, Mrs. Barnstable?'

'Out at the estate timber yard, my lord. He is helping to unload a wagon. The logs are quite heavy, and the workers sometimes need Mr. Merripen's help with a difficult load.'

'We have a timber yard?' Leo asked.

Miss Marks replied, 'Mr. Merripen is planning to construct houses for the new tenant farmers.'

'This is the first I've heard of it. Why are we providing houses for them?' Leo's tone was not at all censuring, merely interested. But Miss Marks's lips thinned, as if she had interpreted his question as a complaint.

'The most recent tenants to join the estate were lured by the promise of new houses. They are already successful farmers, educated and forward-looking, and Mr. Merripen believes their presence will add to the estate's prosperity. Other local estates, such as Stony Cross Park, are also building homes for their tenants and laborers — '

'It's all right,' Leo interrupted. 'No need to be defensive, Marks. God knows I wouldn't think of interfering with Merripen's plans after seeing all he's done so far.' He glanced at the housekeeper. 'If you'll point the way, Mrs. Barnstable, I'll go out and find Merripen. Perhaps I might help to unload the timber wagon.'

'A footman will show you the way,' the housekeeper said at once. 'But the work is occasionally hazardous, my lord, and not fitting for a man of your station.'

Miss Marks added in a light but caustic tone,

225

'Besides, it is doubtful you could be of any help.'

The housekeeper's mouth fell open.

Win had to bite back a grin. Miss Marks had spoken as if Leo were a small weed of a man instead of a strapping six-footer.

Leo gave the governess a sardonic smile. 'I'm more physically capable than you suspect, Marks. You have no idea what lurks beneath this coat.'

'I am profoundly grateful for that.'

'Miss Hathaway,' the housekeeper broke in hurriedly, trying to smooth over the conflict, 'may I show you to your room?'

'Yes, thank you.' Hearing her sisters' voices, Win turned to see them entering the hall along with Mr. Rohan.

'Well?' Amelia asked with a grin, spreading her hands to indicate their surroundings.

'Lovely beyond words,' Win replied.

'Let's freshen ourselves and brush off the travel dust, and then I'll take you around.'

'I'll only be a few minutes.'

Win went to the staircase with the housekeeper. 'How long have you been employed here, Mrs. Barnstable?' she asked as they ascended to the second floor.

'A year, more or less. Ever since the house became habitable. I had previously been employed in London, but the old master passed on to his reward, and the new master dismissed most of the staff and replaced them with his own. I was in desperate need of a position.'

'I'm sorry to hear that. But very pleased for the Hathaways' sake.'

'It has been a challenging undertaking,' the housekeeper said, 'putting together a staff and training them all. I will confess I had a few trepidations, given the unusual circumstances of this position. But Mr. Merripen was very persuasive.'

'Yes,' Win said absently, 'it is difficult to say no to him.'

'He has a strong and steady presence, that Mr. Merripen. I've often marveled to see him in the center of a dozen simultaneous undertakings — the carpenters, the painters, the blacksmith, the head groomsman, all clamoring for his attention. And he always keeps a cool head. We can scarcely do without him. He is the fixed point of the estate.'

Win nodded morosely, glancing into the rooms they passed. More cream paneling, and light cherry furniture, and upholsteries of soft-colored velvets rather than the gloomy dark shades that were currently fashionable. She thought it a pity that she would never be able to enjoy this house except for occasional visits.

Mrs. Barnstable took her to a beautiful room with windows overlooking the gardens. 'This is yours,' the housekeeper said. 'No one has occupied it before.' The bed was made of light blue upholstered panels, the bedclothes of white linen. There was a graceful lady's writing desk in the corner, and a satin maple wardrobe with a looking glass set in the door.

'Mr. Merripen personally selected the wallpaper,' Mrs. Barnstable said. 'He nearly drove the interior architect mad with his insistence on seeing hundreds of samples until he found this pattern.'

The wallpaper was white, with a delicate pattern of flowering branches. And at sparse intervals, there was the motif of a little robin perched on one of the twigs.

Slowly Win went to one of the walls and touched one of the birds with her fingertips. Her vision blurred.

During her long recuperation from the scarlet fever, when she had grown tired of holding a book in her hands and no one had been available to read to her, she had stared out the window at a robin's nest in a nearby maple tree. She had watched the fledglings hatch from their blue eggs, their bodies pink and veined and fuzzy. She had watched their feathers grow in, and she had watched the mother robin working to fill their ravenous beaks. And Win had watched as, one by one, they had flown from the nest while she remained in bed.

Merripen, despite his fear of heights, had often climbed a ladder to wash the second-floor window for her. He had wanted her view of the outside world to be clear.

He had said the sky should always be blue for her.

'You're fond of birds, Miss Hathaway?' the housekeeper asked.

Win nodded without looking around, afraid that her face was red with unexpressed emotion. 'Robins especially,' she half-whispered.

'A footman will bring your trunks up soon, and one of the maids will unpack them. In the meantime, if you would like to wash, there is fresh water at the washstand.'

'Thank you.' Win went to the porcelain pitcher and basin and sluiced clumsy handfuls of cooling water on her face and throat, heedless of the drips that fell onto her bodice. Blotting her face with a cloth, she felt only momentary relief from the aching heat that had suffused her.

Hearing the creak of a floorboard, Win turned sharply.

Merripen was at the threshold, watching her.

The damnable flush wouldn't stop.

She wanted to be on the other side of the world from him. She wanted never to see him again. And at the same time her senses pulled him in greedily . . . the sight of him in an open-throated shirt, white linen clinging to the nutmeg tan of his skin . . . the short dark layers of his hair, the scent of his exertions reaching her prickling nostrils. The sheer size and presence of him paralyzed her with need. She wanted the taste of his skin against her lips. She wanted to feel the throb of his pulse against her own. If only he would come to her just as he was, this moment, and crush her onto the bed with his hard, heavy body, and take her. Ruin her.

'How was the journey from London?' he asked, his face expressionless.

'I'm not going to make pointless conversation with you.' Win went to the window and focused blindly on the dark woodland in the distance.

'Is the room to your liking?'

She nodded without looking at him.

'If there is anything you need — '

229

'I have everything I need,' she interrupted. 'Thank you.'

'I want to talk to you about the other — '

'That's quite all right,' she said, managing to sound composed. 'You don't need to come up with excuses about why you didn't offer for me.'

'I want you to understand — '

'I do understand. And I've already forgiven you. Perhaps it will ease your conscience to hear that I'll be much better off this way.'

'I don't want your forgiveness,' he said curtly.

'Fine, you're not forgiven. Whatever pleases you.' She couldn't bear to be alone with him for another moment. Her heart was breaking; she could feel it fracturing. Putting her head down, she began to walk past his motionless form.

Win didn't intend to stop. But before she crossed the threshold, she halted within arm's length of him. There was one thing she wanted to tell him. The words would not be contained.

'Incidentally,' she heard herself say tonelessly, 'I went to visit a London doctor yesterday. A highly respected one. I told him my medical history, and I asked if he would evaluate my general state of health.' Aware of the intensity of Merripen's gaze, Win continued evenly. 'In his professional opinion, there is no reason I shouldn't have children if I want them. He said there is no guarantee for any woman that childbirth will be free of risk. But I will lead a full life. I will have marital relations with my husband, and God willing, I will become a mother someday.' She paused, and added in a bitter voice that didn't sound at all like her

230

own, 'Julian will be so pleased when I tell him, don't you think?'

If the jab had pierced through Merripen's guard, there was no sign of it. 'There is something you need to know about him,' Merripen said quietly. 'His first wife's family — the Lanhams — suspect he had something to do with her death.'

Win's head whipped around, and she stared at Merripen with narrowed eyes. 'I can't believe you would sink so low. Julian told me all about it. He loved her. He did everything he could to bring her through the illness. When she died, he was devastated, and then he was victimized further by her family. In their grief, they needed someone to blame. Julian was a convenient scapegoat.'

'The Lanhams claim he behaved suspiciously after her death. He didn't fit anyone's idea of a bereaved husband.'

'Not all people show their grief in the same way,' she snapped. 'Julian is a doctor — he has trained himself to be impassive in the course of his work, because that is best for his patients. Naturally he wouldn't let himself fall apart, no matter how deep his sorrow. How dare you judge him?'

'Don't you realize you may be in danger?'

'From *Julian*? The man who made me well?' She shook her head with a disbelieving laugh. 'For the sake of our past friendship, I'm going to forget you said anything about this, Kev. But remember in the future that I will not tolerate any insult to Julian. Remember that he stood by me when you did not.'

She brushed by him without waiting for his reaction, and saw her older sister coming along the hallway. 'Amelia,' she said brightly. 'Shall we begin the tour now? I want to see everything.'

16

Although Merripen had made it clear to the Ramsay household that Leo, not he, was master, the servants and laborers still considered him the authority. Merripen was the one they first approached with all concerns. And Leo was content to let it remain so while he familiarized himself with the reinvigorated estate and its inhabitants.

'I'm not a complete idiot, despite appearances to the contrary,' he told Merripen dryly as they rode out to the east corner of the estate one morning. 'The arrangements you've made are obviously working. I don't intend to foul things up in an effort to prove I'm lord of the manor. That being said ... I do have a few improvements to suggest regarding the tenant housing.'

'Oh?'

'A few inexpensive alterations in design would make the cottages more comfortable and attractive. And if the idea is to eventually establish a hamlet of sorts on the estate, it might behoove us to come up with a set of plans for a model village.'

'You want to work on plans and elevations?' Merripen asked, surprised at the show of interest from the usually indolent lord.

'If you have no objections.'

'Of course not. It's your estate.' Merripen

regarded him speculatively. 'Are you considering a return to your former profession?'

'Yes, actually. I might start as a jobbing architect. We'll see where some earnest dabbling might lead. And it makes sense to cut my teeth on my own tenants' houses.' He grinned. 'My reasoning is they'll be less likely than outsiders to sue me.'

★ ★ ★

On an estate with a crowded wood like the Ramsey lands, a thinning of the forest was necessary every ten years. By Merripen's calculation, the estate had missed at least two previous cycles, which meant there was a good thirty years' worth of dead, sickly, or suppressed-growth trees to be cleared from the Ramsay forests.

To Leo's dismay, Merripen insisted on dragging him through the entire process, until Leo knew far more than he had ever wanted to know about trees.

'Correct thinning helps nature,' Merripen said in response to Leo's grumbling. 'The estate wood will have healthier timber and far more value if the right trees are removed to help the others grow.'

'I'd rather leave the trees to settle it amongst themselves,' Leo said, which Merripen ignored.

To educate himself, and Leo, further, Merripen arranged a meeting with the small staff of estate woodmen. They went out to examine some targeted standing trees, while the woodmen explained how to measure the length and mean transverse area of a tree to determine its cubic contents. Using a girthing tape, a twenty-foot rod, and a ladder, they made some preliminary assessments.

Before Leo quite knew how it had happened, he had found himself atop a ladder, helping in the measurements.

'May I ask why,' he called down to Merripen, 'you happen to be standing down there while I'm up here risking my neck?'

'Your tree,' Merripen pointed out succinctly.

'Also my neck!'

Leo gathered that Merripen wanted him to take an active interest in the estate and all its affairs, great and small. It seemed these days that an aristocratic landowner could not simply relax in the library and drink port, no matter how appealing that scenario was. One could delegate estate responsibilities to managers and servants, but that meant one ran the risk of being fleeced.

As they went over other items on a daily list that only seemed to get longer as the week progressed, Leo began to comprehend just how overwhelming a job Merripen had undertaken for the past three years. Most estate managers had undergone apprenticeships, and most sons of the peerage had been educated from a young age in the various concerns of the estates they would someday inherit.

Merripen, on the other hand, had learned all of this — livestock management, farming, forestry, construction, land improvement, wages, profits, and rents — with no preparation and no time. But the man was ideally suited for it. He had an acute memory, an appetite for hard work, and a tireless interest in details.

'Admit something,' Leo had said after a particularly stultifying conversation on farming. 'You do find this tedious on occasion, don't you? You must be bored out of your skull after an hour of discussion on how intensive the crop rotation should be, and how much arable land should be allocated to corn and beans.'

Merripen had considered the question carefully, as if it had never occurred to him that he should find anything about the estate work tedious. 'Not if it needs to be done.'

That was when Leo had finally understood. If Merripen had decided on a goal, no detail was too small, no task beneath him. No amount of adversity would deter him. The workmanlike quality that Leo had derided in the past had found its perfect outlet. God or the devil help anyone who got in Merripen's way.

But Merripen had a weakness.

By now everyone in the family had become aware of the fierce and impossible attachment between Merripen and Win. And they all knew that to mention it would earn them nothing but trouble. Leo had never seen two people battle their mutual attraction so desperately.

Not long ago Leo would have chosen Dr. Harrow for Win without a moment's hesitation. To marry a Gypsy was a sure comedown in the world. And in London society it was perfectly reasonable to marry for advantage and find love elsewhere. That wasn't possible for Win, however. Her heart was too pure, her feelings too strong. And after having watched his sister's struggle to get well, and the grace of character that had never faltered, Leo thought it a damned shame that she couldn't have the husband she wanted.

★ ★ ★

On the third morning after their arrival in Hampshire, Amelia and Win went for a walk on a circular route that eventually led back to Ramsay House. It was a fresh, clear day, the path a bit muddy in places, the meadows covered with such a wealth of white oxeye daisies that at first glance it looked like new-fallen snow.

Amelia, who had always loved walking, matched Win's brisk pace easily.

'I love Stony Cross,' Win said, relishing the sweet, cool air. 'It feels like home even more than Primrose Place, even though I've never lived here for long.'

'Yes. There is something special about Hampshire. Whenever we return from London, I find it an indescribable relief.' Removing her bonnet, Amelia held it by the ribbons and swung it lightly as they walked. She seemed absorbed in the scenery, the tumbles of flowers everywhere, the clicks and drones of insects busy among the trees, the scents released by sun-warmed grasses and peppery watercress. 'Win,' she said eventually, her voice pensive, 'you don't have to leave Hampshire, you know.'

'Yes, I do.'

'Our family can weather any scandal. Look at

237

Leo. We survived all of his — '

'In terms of scandal,' Win interrupted wryly, 'I think I've actually managed to do something worse than Leo.'

'I don't think that's possible, dear.'

'You know as well as I that the loss of a woman's virtue can ruin a family far more effectively than the loss of a man's honor. It's not fair, but there you have it.'

'You didn't lose your virtue,' Amelia said indignantly.

'Not for lack of trying. Believe me, I wanted to.' Glancing at her older sister, Win saw that she had shocked her. She smiled faintly. 'Did you think I was above feeling that way, Amelia?'

'Well . . . yes, I suppose I did. You were never one to moon over handsome boys, or talk about balls and parties, or dream about your future husband.'

'That was because of Merripen,' Win admitted. 'He was all I ever wanted.'

'Oh, Win,' Amelia whispered. 'I'm so sorry.'

Win stepped up onto a stile leading through a narrow gap in a stone fence, and Amelia followed. They walked along a grassy footpath that led to a forest trail, and continued to a footbridge that crossed a stream.

Amelia linked her arm with Win's. 'In light of what you just said, I feel even more strongly that you should not marry Harrow. What I mean is, you should marry Harrow if you wish, but not because of any fear over a scandal.'

'I want to. I like him. I believe he is a good man. And if I stay here, it would result in endless misery for me and Merripen. One of us has to leave.'

'Why does it have to be you?'

'Merripen is needed here. He belongs here. And it truly doesn't matter to me where I am. In fact, I think it would be better for me to make a new beginning elsewhere.'

'Cam's going to talk to him,' Amelia said.

'Oh no, he mustn't! Not on my behalf.' Win's pride bristled, and she turned to face Amelia. 'Don't let him. *Please.*'

'I couldn't stop Cam no matter how I tried. He's not talking to Merripen for your sake, Win. It's for Merripen's own sake. We very much fear what will become of him once he's lost you for good.'

'He's already lost me,' Win said flatly. 'He lost me the moment he refused to stand up for me. And after I leave, he'll be no different than he has always been. He will never allow softness in himself. In fact, I think he despises the things that give him pleasure, because enjoyment of anything might make him soft.' All the tiny muscles of her face felt frozen. Win reached up to massage her tense, pinching forehead. 'The more he cares for me, the more determined it makes him to push me away.'

'Men,' Amelia grumbled, crossing the foot-bridge.

'Merripen is convinced he has nothing to give me. There's a kind of arrogance in that, don't you think? Deciding what I need. Disregarding my feelings. Setting me so high on the pedestal that it absolves him of any responsibility.'

'Not arrogance,' Amelia said softly. 'Fear.'

'Well, I won't live that way. I won't be bound by my fears, or his.' Win felt herself relaxing slightly, calmness stealing over her as she admitted the truth. 'I love him, but I don't want him if he has to be dragged or trapped into marriage. I want a willing partner.'

'Certainly no one could blame you for that. It has always irked me, really, the way people say a woman has 'caught' herself a man. As if they're trout we've managed to hook and jerk out of the water.'

Despite her moroseness, Win couldn't help smiling.

They pushed on through the damp, warm landscape. As they eventually approached Ramsay House, they saw a carriage coming to a stop before the entrance. 'It's Julian,' Win said. 'So early! He must have left London well before first light.' She quickened her pace and reached him just as he stepped from the carriage.

Julian's cool handsomeness had not been mussed one bit by the long journey from London. He took Win's hands and gripped them firmly, and smiled down at her.

'Welcome to Hampshire,' she said.

'Thank you, my dear. Have you been out walking?'

'Briskly,' she assured him, smiling.

'Very good. Here, I have something for you.' He reached in his pocket and withdrew a small object. Win felt him slide a ring onto her finger. She looked down at a ruby, the shade of red known as 'pigeon's blood,' set in gold and diamonds. 'It is said,' Julian told her, 'that to own a ruby is to have contentment and peace.'

'Thank you, it's lovely,' she murmured, leaning forward. Her eyes closed as she felt his lips press gently against her forehead. Contentment and peace ... God willing, perhaps someday she would have those things.

*   *   *

Cam doubted his own sanity, approaching Merripen when he was working in the timber yard. He watched for a moment as Merripen helped a trio of woodmen to unload massive logs from the wagon. It was a dangerous job, with one mistake resulting in the possibility of severe injury or death.

With the use of sloping planks and long levers, the men rolled the logs inch by inch to the ground. Grunting with effort, muscles straining, they fought to control the descending weight. Merripen, as the largest and strongest of the group, had taken the center position, making him the least likely to escape if anything went wrong.

Concerned, Cam started forward to help.

'*Get back*,' Merripen barked, seeing Cam out of the corner of his eye.

Cam stopped at once. The woodmen had worked out a method, he realized. Anyone who didn't know their procedures might inadvertently cause harm to them all.

He waited and watched as the logs were eased safely to the ground. The woodmen breathed heavily, leaning over and bracing their hands on their knees as they sought to recover from the dizzying effort. All except Merripen, who sank the tip of a deadly sharp hand hook into one of the logs. He turned to face Cam while still holding a pair of tongs.

Merripen looked demonic, his face dark and sweat-streaked, his eyes bright with hellfire. Although Cam had come to know him well over the past three years, he had never seen Merripen like this. He looked like a damned soul with no hope or desire for redemption.

God help me, Cam thought. Once Win was married to Dr. Harrow, Merripen might careen out of control. Remembering all the trouble they'd had with Leo, Cam groaned inwardly.

He was tempted to wash his hands of the entire damned mess, reasoning that he had far better things to do than fight for his brother's sanity. Let Merripen deal with the consequences of his own choices.

But then Cam considered how he himself would behave if anyone or anything threatened to take Amelia away from him. Not any better, surely. Reluctant compassion stirred inside him.

'What do you want?' Merripen asked curtly, setting the tongs aside.

Cam approached slowly. 'Harrow's here.'

'I saw.'

'Are you going inside to welcome him?'

Merripen gave Cam a contemptuous glance. 'Leo's the master of the household. He can welcome the bastard.'

'While you hide out here in the timber yard?'

242

The coffee-black eyes narrowed. 'I'm not hiding. I'm working. And you're in the way.'

'I want to talk to you, *phral*.'

'Don't call me that. And I don't need your interference.'

'Someone has to try and talk some sense into you,' Cam said softly. 'Look at you, Kev. You're behaving exactly like the brute the *rom baro* tried to make you into.'

'Shut up,' Merripen said hoarsely.

'You're letting him decide the rest of your life for you,' Cam insisted. 'You're clutching those damned chains around you with all your strength.'

'If you don't close your mouth — '

'If you were only hurting yourself, I wouldn't say a word. But you're hurting her as well, and you don't seem to give a d — '

Cam was interrupted as Merripen launched toward him, attacking him with a bloodthirsty force that sent them both to the ground. The impact was hard, even on the muddy ground. They rolled twice, thrice, each striving to gain the dominant position. Merripen was as heavy as hell.

Realizing that being pinned was going to result in some serious damage to himself, Cam twisted free and sprang to his feet. Raising his guard, he blocked and sidestepped as Merripen leaped upward like a striking tiger.

The woodmen all rushed forward, two of them grabbing Merripen and hauling him back, the other one pouncing on Cam.

'You're such an idiot,' Cam snapped, glaring at Merripen. He shook free of the man who was trying to restrain him. 'You're determined to foul things up for yourself no matter what, aren't you?'

Merripen lunged, his face murderous, while the woodmen fought to hold him back.

Cam shook his head in disgust. 'I'd hoped for a minute or two of rational conversation, but apparently that's beyond you.' He glanced at the woodmen. 'Let him go! I can handle him. It's easy to win against a man who lets his emotions get the best of him.'

At that, Merripen made a visible effort to control his rage, going still, the wildness in his eyes diminishing to a glint of cold hatred. Gradually, with the same care they had used to manage the heavy crushing logs, the woodmen released his arms.

'You've made your point,' Cam told Merripen. 'And it seems you'll keep on making it until you've proven it to everyone. So let me spare you the effort: I agree with you. You aren't fit for her.'

And he left the timber yard, while Merripen glared after him.

★ ★ ★

Merripen's absence cast a shadow over dinner that night, no matter how they all tried to behave naturally. The odd thing was, Merripen had never been one to dominate a conversation or take the central role of the gathering, and yet removing his unobtrusive presence was the same as taking off the leg of a chair. Everything was off-balance when he was gone.

244

Julian filled the gap with charm and lightness, relaying amusing stories about his acquaintances in London, discussing his clinic, revealing the origins of the therapies that served his patients to such good effect.

Win listened and smiled. She pretended interest in the scene around her, the table laden with china and crystal, platters of well-seasoned food, and a few pieces of good, serviceable silver. She was calm on the surface. But underneath she was nothing but writhing emotion, anger and desire and grief mixed so thoroughly that she couldn't divine their proportions.

Midway through the dinner, between the fish and carvery courses, a footman went to the head of the table with a tiny silver tray. He gave a note to Leo. 'My lord,' the footman murmured.

The entire table fell silent as everyone watched Leo read the note. Casually he tucked the slip of paper into his coat and murmured something to the footman about readying his horse.

A smile touched Leo's lips as he saw their gazes fastened on him. 'My apologies, all,' he said calmly. 'I'm needed for a bit of business that can't wait.' His light blue eyes held a sardonic glint as he glanced at Amelia. 'Perhaps you could have the kitchen save a plate of dessert for me? You know how I love trifle.'

'As a dessert or verb?' Amelia rejoined, and he grinned.

'Both, of course.' He stood from the table. 'Excuse me, please.'

Win was gripped with worry. She knew this had something to do with Merripen; she felt it in her bones. 'My lord,' she said in a suffocated voice. 'Is it — '

'All is well,' he said at once.

'Shall I go?' Cam asked, staring hard at Leo. It was a novel situation for all of them, Leo as a problem-solver. Novel especially to Leo.

'Not a chance,' Leo replied. 'I wouldn't be deprived of this for the world.'

★ ★ ★

The Stony Cross gaol was located on Fishmonger Lane. Locals referred to the two-room lockup as 'the pinfold.' The antique word referred to a pen where stray animals were kept, hearkening back to medieval times when the open field system had still been practiced. The owner of a lost cow, sheep, or goat had usually been able to find it at the pinfold, where he could claim it for a fee. Nowadays, drunkards and minor lawbreakers were claimed by their relatives in much the same way.

Leo had spent more than a few nights in the pinfold himself. But to his knowledge, Merripen had never run afoul of the law and had certainly never been guilty of drunkenness, public or private. Until now.

It was rather bemusing, this reversal of their situations. Merripen had always been the one to collect Leo from whatever gaol or strong room he had managed to land himself in.

Leo met briefly with the parish constable, who seemed similarly struck by the arse-about of it all.

'May I ask the nature of the crime?' Leo inquired diffidently.

'Got himself good and pickled at the tavern,' the constable replied, 'and went into a real Tom-'n'-Jerry with a local.'

'What were they fighting over?'

'The local made some remark about Gypsies and drink, and that set Mr. Merripen off like a Roman candle.' Scratching his head through his wiry hair, the constable said reflectively, 'Merripen had plenty of men jumping to defend him — he's well liked among the farmers here — but he fought them, too. And even then they tried to pay his bail. They said it wasn't like him, getting foxed and brawling. From what I know of Merripen, he's a quiet sort. Not like the others of his kind. But I said no, I wasn't taking bail money until he'd cooled his heels for a bit. Those fists are the size of Hampshire hams. I'm not releasing him until he's more than half-sober.'

'May I speak to him?'

'Yes, my lord. He's in the first room. I'll take you there.'

'You needn't trouble yourself,' Leo said pleasantly. 'I know the way.'

The constable grinned at that. 'I suppose you do, my lord.'

The cell was unfurnished except for a short-legged stool, an empty bucket, and a straw pallet. Merripen was sitting on the pallet, leaning his back against a timbered wall. One knee was propped up, his arm half-curled around it. The black head was lowered in a posture of utter defeat.

Merripen looked up as Leo approached the row of iron bars that separated them. His face was drawn and saturnine. He looked as if he hated the world and all its inhabitants.

Leo was certainly familiar with that feeling. 'Well, this is a change,' he remarked cheerfully. 'Usually you're on this side and I'm on that side.'

'Sod off,' Merripen growled.

'And that's what *I* usually say,' Leo marveled.

'I'm going to kill you,' Merripen said with guttural sincerity.

'That doesn't provide much incentive for me to get you out, does it?' Leo folded his arms across his chest and regarded the other man with expert assessment. Merripen was no longer drunk. Only mean as the devil. And suffering. Leo supposed in light of his own past misdeeds, he should have more patience with the man. 'Nevertheless,' Leo said, 'I will have you set free, since you've done the same for me on so many occasions.'

'Then do it.'

'Soon. But I have a few things to say. And it's obvious that if I let you out first, you'll bolt like a hare at a coursing, and then I won't have the chance.'

'Say what you like. I'm not listening.'

'Look at you. You're a filthy mess and you're locked up in the pinfold. And you're about to receive a lecture on behavior from me, which is obviously as low as a man can sink.'

From all appearances, the words fell on deaf ears. Leo continued undaunted. 'You're not suited for this, Merripen. You can't hold your drink worth a damn. And unlike people such as me, who become quite amicable when they drink, you turn into a vile-tempered troll.' Leo paused, considering how best to provoke him. 'Liquor brings out one's true inner nature, they say.'

That got him. Merripen flashed Leo a dark glance that contained both fury and anguish. Surprised by the strength of the reaction, he hesitated before continuing.

He understood the situation more than the bastard would have believed or wanted to believe. Perhaps Leo didn't know the whole mysterious tangle of Merripen's past, or the complex twists and turns of character that made him unable to have the woman he loved. But Leo knew one simple truth that superseded all others.

Life was too bloody short.

'Damn you,' Leo muttered, pacing back and forth. He would have preferred to take a knife and lay open a portion of his own flesh rather than say what needed to be said. But he had the sense that he was somehow standing between Merripen and annihilation, that some brace of essential words, a crucial argument, had to be set forth.

'If you weren't such a stubborn ass,' Leo said, 'I wouldn't have to do this.'

No response from Merripen. Not even a glance.

Leo turned to the side and rubbed the back of his neck, and dug his fingers into his own rigid muscles. 'You know I never speak of Laura Dillard. In fact, that may be the first time I've said her full name since she died. But I am going to say something about her, because not only do I owe you for what you've done for the Ramsay estate, but — '

'Don't, Leo.' The words were hard and cold. 'You're embarrassing yourself.'

'Well, I'm good at that. And you've left me no bloody choice. Do you understand what you are in, Merripen? A prison of your making. And even after you're out of here, you'll still be trapped. Your entire life will be a prison.' Leo thought of Laura, the physical details of her no longer precise in his mind. But she lingered inside him like the memory of sunlight, in a world that had been bitterly cold since her death.

Hell was not a pit of fire and brimstone. Hell was waking up alone, the sheets wet with your tears and your seed, knowing the woman you had dreamed of would never come back to you.

'Since I lost Laura,' Leo said, 'everything I do is merely a way of passing the time. It's hard to give a damn about much of anything. But at least I can live with the knowledge that I fought for her. At least I took every bloody minute with her that was possible to have. She died knowing I loved her.' He stopped pacing and stared at Merripen contemptuously. 'But you're throwing everything away — and breaking my sister's heart — because you're a damned coward. Either that or a fool. How can you — ' He broke off as Merripen hurled himself at the bars, shaking them like a lunatic.

'*Shut up, damn it.*'

'What will either of you have, once Win has gone with Harrow?' Leo persisted. 'You'll stay in your self-made prison, that's obvious. But Win will be worse off. She'll be alone. Away from her family. Married to a man who regards her as nothing more than a decorative object to keep on a bloody shelf. And what happens when her beauty fades and she loses her value to him? How will he treat her then?'

Merripen went motionless, his expression contorted, murder in his eyes.

'She's a strong girl,' Leo said. 'I spent two years with Win, watching as she met one challenge after another. After all the struggles she's faced, she's bloody well entitled to make her own decisions. If she wants to risk having a child — if she feels strong enough — that's her right. And if you're the man she wants, don't be a sodding idiot by turning her away.' Leo rubbed his forehead wearily. 'Neither you nor I are worth a damn,' he muttered. 'Oh, you can work the estate and show me how to balance account books and manage the tenants and inventory the stinking larder. I suppose we'll keep it running well enough. But neither of us will ever be more than half-alive, like most men, and the only difference is, we know it.'

Leo paused, vaguely surprised by the tightening sensation all around his neck, as if a noose had been cinched around it. 'Amelia told me once about a suspicion she'd had for a while. It bothered her quite a bit. She said that when Win and I had fallen ill with scarlet fever, and you

251

made the deadly nightshade syrup, you'd concocted far more than was necessary. And you kept a cup of it on Win's nightstand, like some sort of macabre nightcap. Amelia said that if Win had died, she thought you would have taken the rest of that poison. And I've always hated you for that. Because you forced me to stay alive without the woman I loved, while you had no bloody intention of doing the same.'

Merripen didn't answer, gave no sign that he registered Leo's words.

'Christ, man,' Leo said huskily. 'If you had the bollocks to die with her, don't you think you could work up the courage to *live* with her?'

There was nothing but silence as Leo walked away from the cell. He wondered what the hell he had done, what effect it would have.

Leo went to the parish constable's office and told him to let Merripen out. 'Wait another five minutes, however,' he added dryly. 'I need a running start.'

★   ★   ★

After Leo had left, the talk at the dinner table had taken on a tone of determined cheerfulness. No one wanted to speculate aloud on the reason for Merripen's absence, or why Leo had gone on a mysterious errand . . . but it seemed likely the two were connected.

Win had worried silently, and told herself sternly that it was not her place, nor her right, to worry about Merripen. And then she had worried some more. As she had forced a few bites of dinner down, she felt the food stick in her clenched throat.

She had gone to bed early, pleading a headache, and had left the others playing games in the parlor. After Julian had escorted her to the main staircase, she had let him kiss her. It was a lingering kiss, turning damp as he had searched just inside her lips. The patient sweetness of his mouth on hers had been — if not earth-shattering — very pleasant.

Win thought that Julian would be a skilled and sensitive partner when she finally did manage to coax him into making love to her. But he didn't seem terribly driven in that regard, which was both a disappointment and a relief. Had he ever looked at her with a fraction of the hunger, the need, that Merripen did, perhaps it might have awakened a response in her.

But Win knew that while Julian desired her, his feelings didn't begin to approach the all-encompassing primality of Merripen's. And she found it difficult to imagine Julian losing his composure even during that most intimate of acts. She couldn't picture him sweating and groaning and holding her tightly. She knew intuitively that Julian would never allow himself to descend to that level of abandonment.

She also knew that at some time in the future there was a possibility that Julian might sleep with another woman. The thought dejected her. But such a concern was not enough to deter her from marriage. After all, adultery was hardly an uncommon circumstance. While it was held as a social ideal that a man should keep his vows of fidelity, most people were quick to excuse a husband who had strayed. In society's view, a wife should be forgiving.

Win bathed and donned a white nightgown, and sat in bed reading for a while. The novel, loaned to her by Poppy, had such a confusingly large cast of characters and such extended flowery prose that one could only assume the author had been paid by the word. After finishing two chapters, Win closed the book and turned out the lamp. She lay down to stare despondently through the darkness.

Sleep claimed her eventually. She slept heavily, welcoming the escape. But some time later, while it was still very dark, she found herself struggling upward through layers of dreams. Someone or something was in the room. Her first thought was that it might be Beatrix's ferret, who sometimes slipped past the door to collect objects that intrigued him.

Rubbing her eyes, Win began to sit up, when there was a movement beside the bed. A large shadow crossed over her. Before bewilderment could give way to fear, she heard a familiar murmur, and felt a man's warm fingers press across her lips.

'It's me.'

Her lips moved soundlessly against his hand.

Kev.

Win's stomach constricted with an ache of pleasure, and her heartbeat hammered in her throat. But she was still angry with him, she was *done* with him, and if he had come here for a midnight talk, he was sadly mistaken. She started to tell him so, but to her astonishment, she felt a thick piece of cloth descend over her mouth, and then he was tying it deftly behind her head. In a few more seconds, he had bound her wrists in front of her.

Win was rigid with shock. Merripen would never do something like this. And yet it was him; she would know him if only by the touch of his hands. What did he want? What was going through his mind? His breath was faster than usual as it brushed against her hair. Now that her vision had adjusted to the darkness, she saw that his face was hard and austere.

Merripen drew the ruby ring off her finger and set it on the bedside table. Taking her head in his hands, he stared into her wide eyes. He said only two words. But they explained everything he was doing, and everything he intended to do.

'You're mine.'

He picked her up easily, draping her over one powerful shoulder, and he carried her from the room.

Win closed her eyes, yielding, trembling. She pressed a few sobs against the gag covering her mouth, not of unhappiness or fear, but of wild relief. This was not an impulsive act. This was ritual. This was an ancient Romany courtship rite, and there would be nothing half-hearted about it. She was going to be kidnapped and ravished.

Finally.

17

As far as abductions went, it was skillfully executed. One would have expected no less of Merripen. Although Win had assumed he would carry her to his room, he surprised her by taking her outside, where his horse was waiting. Wrapping her in his coat, he held her against his chest and rode off with her. Not to the gatehouse, but alongside the wood, through night mist and dense blackness that daylight would soon filter.

Win stayed relaxed against him, trusting him, and yet she shook with nerves. This was Merripen, and yet he wasn't at all familiar. The side of himself he had always kept under strict control had been set free.

Merripen guided the horse expertly through a copse of oak and ash. A small white cottage appeared, ghost-colored in the darkness. Win wondered whom it belonged to. It was tidy and new-looking, with smoke curling from the chimney stack. It was lit, welcoming, as if it had just been readied in anticipation of visitors.

Dismounting, Merripen tugged Win down into his arms, and he carried her to the front step. 'Don't move,' he said. She stayed obediently still while he tethered the horse.

Merripen closed his hand over her bound wrists and led her inside. Win followed easily, a willing captive. The cottage was sparely furnished, and it smelled of fresh wood and paint.

Not only was it empty of current residents, but it seemed that no one had ever lived there.

Taking Win into the bedroom, Merripen lifted her onto a bed covered with quilts and white linen. Her bare feet dangled over the edge of the mattress as she sat upright.

Merripen stood before her, the light from the hearth gilding one side of his face. His gaze was locked on her. Slowly he removed his coat and dropped it to the floor, heedless of the fine fabric. As he pulled his open-necked shirt over his head, Win was startled by the powerful expanse of his torso, all ribbed muscle and swarthy brawn. His chest was hairless, the skin gleaming like satin, and Win's fingers twitched with the urge to touch it. She felt herself flush with anticipation, her face rouged with heat.

Merripen's dark eyes took in her reaction. She sensed that he understood what she wanted, needed, even more than she did. He removed his half boots, kicked them aside, and came closer until she caught the scent of salty maleness. He touched the lace-edged collar of her nightgown, fingered it lightly. His hand slid over her chest and molded the weight of her breast. The warm squeeze drew a shiver from her, sensation gathering at the hardening tip. She wanted him to kiss her there. She wanted it so badly that she fidgeted, her toes curling, her lips parting with a gasp beneath the binding cloth.

To her relief, Merripen reached around to the back of her head and untied the gag.

Red and trembling, Win managed an unsteady whisper. 'You . . . you needn't have used that. I

257

would have kept quiet.'

Merripen's tone was grave, but there was a pagan gleam in the depths of his eyes. 'If I decide to do something, I do it properly.'

'Yes.' Her throat cinched around a sob of pleasure as his fingers slid into her hair and touched her scalp. 'I know that.'

Cradling her head in his hands, he bent to kiss her gently, with hot, shallow laps into her mouth, and as she responded he went deeper, demanding more. The kiss went on and on, making her gasp and strain, her own small tongue darting greedily past the edges of his teeth. She was so absorbed in tasting him, so dazed by the current of arousal humming through her, that it took her a little while to realize she was lying back on the bed with him, her bound hands flung over her head.

His lips slid to her throat, savoring her with slow, open kisses.

'Wh-where are we?' she managed to ask, shivering as his mouth found a particularly sensitive place.

'Gamekeeper's cottage.' He lingered on that vulnerable spot until she writhed.

'Where is the gamekeeper?'

Kev's voice was passion-thickened. 'We don't have one yet.'

Win rubbed her cheek and chin against the heavy locks of his hair, relishing the feel of him. 'How is it that I've never seen this place?'

His head lifted. 'It's far in the woods,' he whispered, 'away from noise.' He toyed with her breast, softly thumbing the tip. 'A gamekeeper needs peace and quiet to care for the birds.'

Win was feeling anything but peace and quiet inside, her nerves strung tight, her wrists pulling at the silk bonds. She was dying to touch him, to hold him. 'Kev, untie my arms.'

He shook his head. The leisurely pass of his hand along her front caused her to arch.

'Oh, please,' she gasped. 'Kev — '

'Hush,' he murmured. 'Not yet.' His mouth passed hungrily over hers. 'I've wanted you for too long. I need you too much.' His teeth caught at her lower lip with arousing delicacy. 'One touch of your hands and I wouldn't last a second.'

'But I want to hold you,' she said plaintively.

The look on his face sent a thrill through her. 'Before we're through, love, you're going to hold me with every part of your body.' He covered her wild heartbeat with a gentle palm. Lowering his head, he kissed her hot cheek and whispered, 'Do you understand what I'm going to do, Win?'

She took a fitful breath. 'I think so. Amelia told me a few things in the past. And of course, everyone sees the sheep and cattle in spring.'

That drew a rare grin from him. 'If that's the standard I'm being held to, we'll have no trouble at all.'

She captured him with her looped arms and struggled upward to reach his mouth. He kissed her, pushing her back down, sliding one of his knees carefully between her thighs. Gently farther, and farther, until she felt an intimate pressure against the part of her that had begun to ache. The subtle rhythmic friction made her writhe, a sort of squirmy, shivery delight surging from every slow prod. Dazed, Win wondered if doing this with a man she had known so well for so long wasn't somehow far more embarrassing than doing it with a complete stranger.

Night was dissolving into day, the silvery morning slanting into the room, the wood awakening with chirps and rustlings . . . red-starts, swallows. She thought briefly of everyone back at Ramsay House . . . Soon they would discover that she was gone. A chill went through her as she wondered if they would look for her. If she returned as a virgin, any future with Merripen would be very much in peril.

'Kev,' she whispered in agitation, 'perhaps you should hurry.'

'Why?' he asked against her throat.

'I'm afraid someone will stop us.'

His head lifted. 'No one will stop us. An entire army could surround the cottage. Explosions. Lightning strikes. It's still going to happen.'

'I still think you should go a bit faster.'

'Do you?' Merripen smiled in a way that made her heart stop. When he was relaxed and happy, she thought, he was the handsomest man who had ever lived.

He courted her mouth skillfully, distracting her with deep, fervid kisses. At the same time, he took the front of her nightgown in his hands and pulled, tearing the garment in half as if it were no more substantial than paper lace. Win gave a discomfited gasp but held still.

Merripen levered himself upward. Grasping her wrists, he pulled them over her head once more, exposing her body completely and causing her breasts to lift. He stared at her pale pink nipples. The soft growl that came from his throat caused her to quiver. He bent and opened his mouth over the tip of her right breast, and held it against his tongue . . . so hot . . . she flinched as if the contact had scalded her. When he lifted his head, the nipple was redder and tighter than it had ever been before.

His eyes were passion-drowsed as he kissed her other breast. His tongue provoked the soft peak into a stinging bud, soothing it with warm strokes. She pressed upward into the wetness, her breath mixed with low sobs. He drew her nipple between his teeth, clamped it carefully, flicked it. Win moaned as his strong hands traced over her body, lingering in places of unbearable sensation.

Reaching her thighs, he tried to part them, but Win held them bashfully closed. Her eagerness to proceed had been obliterated by the dawning awareness of lavish moisture, *there*, which she had never expected or been told about.

'I thought you said to hurry?' Merripen whispered near her ear. His lips wandered over her crimson face.

'Undo my hands,' she begged, perturbed. 'I need to . . . well, to tidy up.'

'Tidy up?' Giving her a quizzical glance, Merripen unwound the length of silk from around her wrists. 'You mean the room?'

'No, my . . . myself.'

Perplexity worked a notch between his dark brows. He stroked the seam of her clamped-together thighs, and she tightened them reflexively. Perceiving the problem, he smiled slightly, while utter tenderness rushed through him. 'Is this what worries you?' He pried her legs apart, finding the slick of moisture with gentle fingers. 'That you're wet here?'

She closed her eyes and nodded with a choked sound.

'No,' he soothed, 'this is good; this is how it's supposed to be. It helps me to go inside you, and . . . ' His breathing roughened. 'Oh, Win, you're so lovely, let me touch you; let me have you . . . '

In an agony of modesty, Win let him push her thighs open farther. She tried to stay quiet and still, but her hips jerked as he stroked the place that had become almost painfully sensitive. He murmured softly, passionately absorbed in the soft female flesh. More wetness, more heat, his touch skimming around and over her, tenderly nudging until one finger slid inside. She stiffened and gasped, and the touch was immediately withdrawn.

'Did I hurt you?'

Her lashes lifted. 'No,' she said in wonder. 'In fact, I didn't feel any pain.' She strained to look between them. 'Is there blood? Perhaps I should — '

'No. Win . . . ' There was a near-comical expression of dismay on his face. 'What I just did isn't going to cause pain or blood.' A brief pause. 'When I do it with my cock, however, it's probably going to hurt like hell.'

'Oh.' She pondered that for a moment. 'Is that the word men use for their private parts?'

'One of the words *gadjos* use.'

'What do Romas say?'

'They call it a *kori*.'

'What does that mean?'

' "Thorn." '

Win slid a bashful glance at the heavy protrusion straining behind his trousers. 'Rather too substantial for a thorn. I should have thought they would use a more fitting word. But I suppose — ' She inhaled sharply as his hand moved downward. 'I suppose if one wants roses, one must' — his finger had slipped inside her again — 'bear the occasional thorn.'

'Very philosophical.' He gently stroked and teased the clenching interior of her body.

Her toes curled into the quilt as wicked tension coiled low in her belly. 'Kev, what should I do?'

'Nothing. Only let me please you.'

All her life, she had hungered for this without quite knowing what it was, this slow, astonishing merging with him, this sweet dissolution of self. This mutual surrender. There was no doubt that he was in control, and yet he browsed over her with absolute wonder. She felt herself soaking up sensation, her body infused with color and heat.

Merripen wouldn't let her hide any part of herself from him . . . He took what he wanted, turning and lifting her body, rolling her this way and that, always with care, and yet with passionate insistence. He kissed beneath her arms and along her sides and all over her, running his tongue along every curve and humid crease. Gradually the accumulating pleasure shaped into something dark and raw, and she moaned from the pain of acute need.

The drive of her heartbeat reverberated everywhere, in her breasts and limbs and stomach, even at the tips of her fingers and toes. It was too much, this wildness he had aroused. She begged him for a moment's respite.

'Not yet,' he told her between ragged breaths, his tone rough with a triumph she didn't yet understand.

'*Please*, Kev — '

'You're so close, I can feel it. Oh God — ' He took her head in his hands, kissed her ravenously, and said against her lips, 'You don't want me to stop yet. Let me show you why.'

A whimper escaped her as he slid low between her thighs, his head bending to the swollen place he had been tormenting with his fingers. He put his mouth on her, licking along the delicate salty strait, spreading her with his thumbs. She tried to sit bolt-upright, but fell back against the pillows as he found what he wanted, his tongue strong and wet.

She was spread beneath him like a pagan sacrifice, illuminated by the daylight that now flooded the room. Merripen worshipped her with hot, glassy licks, savoring the taste of her pleasured flesh. Moaning, she closed her legs around his head, and he turned deliberately to nibble and lick at one pale inner thigh, then the other. Feasting on her. Wanting everything.

Win curled her fingers desperately in his hair, lost to shame as she guided him back, her body

264

arching wordlessly . . . *here, please, more, more, now* . . . and she groaned as he fastened his mouth over her with a fast, flicking rhythm. Pleasure seized her, wrenching an astonished cry from her, holding her stiff and paralyzed for excruciating seconds. Every movement and measure and pulse of the universe had distilled to the compelling, slippery heat, riveted there on that crucial place, and then it all released, the feeling and tension shattering exquisitely, and she was racked with hard, blissful shudders.

Win relaxed helplessly as the spasms faded. She was filled with glowing weariness, a sense of peace too pervasive to allow movement. Merripen let go of her just long enough to undress completely. Naked and aroused, he came back to her. He gathered her up with brute masculine need, settling over her.

She lifted her arms to him with a drowsy murmur. His back was tough and sleek beneath her fingers, the muscles twitching eagerly at her touch. His head descended, his shaven cheek rasping against hers. She met his power with utter surrender, flexing her knees and tilting her hips to cradle him.

He pushed gently at first. The innocent flesh resisted, smarting at the intrusion. He thrust more strongly, and Win caught her breath at the burning pain of his entrance. Too much of him, too hard, too deep. She writhed in reaction, and he buried himself heavily and pinned her down, gasping for her to be still, telling her to wait, he wouldn't move, it would be better. They both stilled, breathing hard.

'Should I stop?' Merripen whispered raggedly, his face taut.

Even now in this flash point of need, he was concerned for her. Understanding what it had cost him to ask, how much he needed her, Win was overwhelmed with love. 'Don't even think of stopping now,' she whispered back. Reaching down to his lean flanks, she stroked him in shy encouragement. He groaned and began to move, his entire body trembling as he pressed within her.

Although every thrust caused a sharp burn where they were joined, Win tried to pull him even deeper. The feeling of having him inside her went far beyond pain or pleasure. It was *necessary*.

Merripen stared down at her, his eyes brilliant in his flushed face. He looked fierce and ravenous and even a bit disoriented, as if he were experiencing something beyond the scope of ordinary men. Only now did Win grasp the enormity of his passion for her, the years it had accumulated despite all his efforts to smother it. How hard he had fought against their fate, for reasons she still didn't fully understand. But now he possessed her body with a reverence and intensity that eclipsed all other feeling.

And yet he loved her as a woman, not some ethereal creature. His feelings for her were full-blooded, lusty, elemental. Exactly as she had wanted.

She took him, and took him, wrapping him in her slender legs, burying her face in his throat and shoulder. She loved the sounds he made, the soft grunts and growls, the harsh flow of his breath. And the power of him around her and inside her. Tenderly she stroked his back and sides and pressed kisses on his neck. He seemed electrified by her attentions, his movements quickening, his eyes closing tightly. And then he thrust upward and held, and shook all over as if he were dying.

'Win,' he groaned, burying his face against her. 'Win.' The single syllable contained the faith and passion of a thousand prayers.

Minutes passed before either of them spoke. They stayed wrapped together, fused and damp and unwilling to part.

Win smiled as she felt Merripen's lips drift over her face. When he reached her chin, he gave it a little nip. 'Not a pedestal,' he said gruffly.

'Hmmn?' She stirred, raising her hand to the shaven bristle of his cheek. 'What do you mean?'

'You said I put you on a pedestal . . . remember?'

'Yes.'

'It was never that. I've always carried you in my heart. Always. I thought that would have to be enough.'

Moved, Win kissed him gently. 'What happened, Kev? Why did you change your mind?'

18

Kev didn't intend to answer that until he had taken care of her. He left the bed and went to the small kitchen, which had been fitted with a cookstove with a brass water reservoir and pipes leading through the firebox to provide hot water instantly. Filling a hot-water can, he brought it to the bedroom along with a clean tea towel.

He paused at the sight of Win lying on her side, the flowing curves draped in white linen, her hair spilling over her shoulders in rivers of silvery gold. And best of all, the sated softness of her face and the swollen rosiness of lips he had kissed and kissed. It was an image from his deepest dreams, seeing her in bed like that. Waiting for him.

He dampened the toweling with hot water and peeled back the sheet, enchanted by her beauty. He would have wanted her no matter what, virgin or no . . . but he privately acknowledged his satisfaction in having been her first lover. No one but he would touch her, pleasure her, see her . . . except . . .

'Win,' he said, frowning as he washed her, pressing the steaming cloth between her thighs. 'At the clinic, did you ever wear *less* than your exercise costume? That is, did Harrow ever look at you?'

Her face was composed, but there was a glitter

of amusement in her rich blue eyes. 'Are you asking if Julian ever saw me naked in a professional capacity?'

Kev was jealous, and they both knew it, but he couldn't stop from scowling. 'Yes.'

'No, he didn't,' she said primly. 'He was interested in my respiratory system, which, as you clearly know, is in a far different location than the reproductive organs.'

'He's interested in more than your lungs,' Kev said darkly.

She smiled. 'If you're hoping to divert me from the question I asked earlier, it's not working. What happened to you last night, Kev?'

He rinsed the bloodstains from the towel, wrung it out, and pressed another warm pad between her thighs. 'I was in the pinfold.'

Her eyes widened. 'The gaol? Is that where Leo went? To get you out?'

'Yes.'

'Why in heaven's name were you behind bars?'

'I was in a fight at the tavern.'

She clicked her tongue a few times. 'That's not like you.'

The statement was loaded with such unintended irony that Kev nearly laughed. In fact, a few huffs came from deep in his chest, and he was so amused and miserable that he couldn't speak. His expression must have been odd indeed, because Win stared at him intently and sat up. She removed the compress and set it aside, and pulled the sheet up over her breasts. She ran a light, graceful hand across his bare shoulder, her touch soothing. And she continued

269

to caress him, stroking his chest, his neck, his midriff, and each loving pass of her hand seemed to erode his self-restraint further.

'Until I came to your family,' he said hoarsely, 'it was the only reason I existed. To fight. To hurt people. I was . . . monstrous.' Looking into Win's eyes, he saw nothing but concern.

'Tell me,' she whispered.

He shook his head. A shiver chased across his back.

Her hand slipped around the nape of his neck. Slowly she drew his head down to her shoulder so that his face was half-hidden. 'Tell me,' she urged again.

Kev was lost, unable to withhold anything from her now. And he knew what he was about to confess would disgust and revolt her, but he found himself doing it anyway.

He revealed it all mercilessly, trying to make her understand the vicious bastard he had been, and still was. He told her about the boys he had beaten to a pulp, the ones he feared might have died later, but he'd never been certain. He told her how he had lived like an animal, eating scraps, stealing, and about the rage that had consumed him always. He had been a bully, a thief, a beggar. He revealed cruelties and humiliations that he should have had the pride and good sense to keep to himself.

Kev had kept the confessions inside forever, but now they were spilling out like garbage. And he was appalled to realize that he had lost all control, that whenever he tried to stop, all it took was a gentle touch and a murmur from Win and he was babbling like a criminal with a gallows priest.

'How could I touch you with these hands?' he asked, his tone shredded with anguish. 'How could you stand to let me? God, if you knew all the things I've done — '

'I love your hands,' she murmured.

'I'm not good enough for you. But no one is. And most men, good or bad, have limits to what they would do, even for someone they love. I have none. No God, no moral code, no faith in anything. Except you. You're my religion. I would do anything you asked. I would fight, steal, kill for you. I would — '

'Shhh. Hush. My goodness.' She sounded breathless. 'There's no need to break all the commandments, Kev.'

'You don't understand,' he said, drawing back to look at her. 'If you believed anything I've told you — '

'I do understand.' Her face was like an angel's, soft and compassionate. 'And I believe what you've said . . . but I don't agree at all with the conclusions you seem to have drawn.' Her hands lifted, molding against his lean cheeks. 'You are a good man, a loving one. The *rom baro* tried to kill all that inside you, but he couldn't succeed. Because of your strength. Because of your heart.'

She eased back onto the bed and drew him down to her. 'Be at ease, Kev,' she whispered. 'Your uncle was an evil man, but what he did must be buried with him. 'Let the dead bury the dead' — do you know what that means?'

He shook his head.

'To leave the past behind and look only to the journey ahead. Only then can you find a new way. A new life. It's a Christian saying . . . but it would make sense to a Rom, I think.'

It made more sense than Win perhaps even realized. The Rom were infinitely superstitious regarding death and the dead, destroying all the possessions of those who had passed, mentioning the name of the deceased as seldom as possible. It was for the benefit of the dead as well as the living, to keep them from returning to the living world as wretched ghosts. Let the dead bury the dead . . . but he wasn't certain he could.

'Hard to let go,' he said thickly. 'Hard to forget.'

'Yes.' Her arms tightened around him. 'But we'll fill your mind with much better things to think about.'

Kev was quiet for a long time, pressing his ear to Win's heart, listening to the even beat, and the flow of her breathing.

'I knew when I first saw you, what you would mean to me,' Win murmured eventually. 'Wild, angry boy that you were. I loved you at once. You felt it, too, didn't you?'

He nodded slightly, luxuriating in the feel of her. Her skin smelled sweet like plums, with an arousing hint of feminine musk.

'I wanted to tame you,' she said. 'Not all the way. Just enough that I could be close to you.' She threaded her fingers through his hair. 'Outrageous man. What possessed you to kidnap me, when you knew I would have come willingly?'

'I was making a point,' he said in a muffled voice.

She chuckled and stroked his scalp, the scrape of her oval fingernails nearly causing him to purr. 'Your point was well-taken. Must we go back now?'

'Do you want to?'

Win shook her head. 'Although . . . I wouldn't mind having something to eat.'

'I brought food to the cottage before I went to get you.'

She ran a flirtatious fingertip around the rim of his ear. 'What an efficient villain you are. May we stay all day, then?'

'Yes.'

Win wriggled with delight. 'Will anyone come for us?'

'I doubt it.' Kev drew the bed linens lower and nuzzled into the lush valley between her breasts. 'And I would kill the first person who approached the threshold.'

A quiet laugh caught in her throat.

'What is it?' he asked without moving.

'Oh, I was just thinking of all the years I spent trying to get out of bed, to be with you. And when I came home, all I wanted was to get back into bed. With you.'

★ ★ ★

For breakfast they had strong tea and rarebit, cheese melted on thick slices of buttered toasted bread. Wrapped in Merripen's shirt, Win perched on a low stool in the kitchen. She took pleasure in watching the play of muscles on his back as he poured steaming water into a portable hip bath. Smiling, she popped the last morsel of rarebit into her mouth. 'Being abducted and ravished,' she commented, 'gives one an appetite.'

'The ravisher as well.'

There seemed a near-magical aura about this ordinary place, this small and quiet cottage. Win felt as if she had been caught in some enchanted spell. She was almost afraid she was dreaming, that she would wake alone in her chaste bed. But Merripen's presence was too vital and real for it to be a dream. And the small aches and twinges in her body offered further proof that she had been taken. Possessed.

'They all know by now,' Win said absently, thinking of everyone at Ramsay House. 'Poor Julian. He must be furious.'

'What about heartbroken?' Merripen set the water can aside and came to her dressed only in trousers.

Win frowned thoughtfully. 'He'll be disappointed, I think. And I believe he cares for me. But no, he won't be heartbroken.' She leaned against Merripen as he stroked her hair, and her cheek brushed the taut smoothness of his stomach. 'He never wanted me the way you do.'

'Any man who didn't would have to be a eunuch.' There was a hitch in his breath as Win kissed the rim of his navel. 'Did you tell him what the London doctor said? That you were healthy enough to bear children?'

Win nodded.

'What did Harrow say?'

'Julian told me that I could visit a legion of doctors, and get any number of differing opinions to support the conclusion I wanted. But in Julian's view, I should remain childless.'

Merripen brought her to a standing position and looked down at her, his expression unfathomable. 'I don't want to put you at risk. But neither do I trust Harrow, or his opinions.'

'Because you think of him as a rival?'

'That's part of it,' he admitted. 'But it's also instinct. There's something . . . lacking in him. There's something false.'

'Perhaps it's because he's a doctor,' Win suggested, shivering as Merripen drew his shirt away from her. 'Men of his profession often seem aloof. Superior, even. But that's necessary, because — '

'It's not that.' Merripen guided her to the hip bath and helped to lower her in. Win gasped not only from the heat of the water, but also from being naked in front of him. The hip bath obliged one to straddle the tub and relax into the water with the legs held apart, which was wonderfully comfortable in private, but rather mortifying with someone else present. Her modesty was further violated as Merripen knelt beside the tub and washed her. But his manner was not at all lascivious, only caring, and she couldn't help but relax under the ministrations of those strong, soothing hands.

'You still suspect Julian of having harmed his first wife, I know,' Win said while Merripen bathed her. 'But he is a healer. He would never hurt anyone, least of all his own wife.' She paused as she read Merripen's expression. 'You don't believe me. You're determined to think the worst of him.'

'I think he feels entitled to play with life and death. Like the gods of those mythology stories you and your sisters are so fond of.'

'You don't know Julian as I do.'

Merripen didn't reply, only continued to wash her.

She watched his dark face through the veil of steam, as beautiful and implacable as an ancient carving of a Babylonian warrior. 'I shouldn't even bother to defend him,' she said ruefully. 'You'll never be disposed to think well of him, will you?'

'No,' he admitted.

'And if you believed Julian was the better man?' she asked. 'Would you have allowed him to marry me?'

She saw the muscles in his throat tense before he answered, 'No.' There was a touch of self-hatred in his response. 'I'm too selfish for that. I could never have let it happen. If it came down to it, I would have carried you off on your wedding day.'

Win wanted to tell him that she had no desire for him to be noble. She was happy — thrilled — to be loved in just this way, with a passion that left no room for anything else. But before she could say a word, Merripen had taken up more soap, and his hand glided over the soreness between her thighs.

He touched her with love. And ownership. Her

eyes half-closed. His finger eased inside her, and his free arm slid behind her back, and she leaned weakly into the cradle of his hard chest and shoulder. Even this small invasion hurt. Her flesh was still too newly broached, unused to being entered. But the hot water soothed her, and Merripen was so gentle that her thighs relaxed, supported in the buoyant warmth.

She breathed in the morning air, luminous with steam, scented of soap and wood and hot copper. And the intoxicating fragrance of her lover. She brushed her lips against his shoulder, savoring the rich taste of skin salt.

His warm tickling fingers stroked against her like the idle sway of river reeds . . . cunning fingertips that quickly discovered where she most wanted them. He toyed with her, parting her, slowly investigating the cambered softness and the sensitive places within. Blindly she reached down to grip his strong wrist, feeling the intricate movements of bone and tendon. He slid two fingers inside her, his thumb gliding over her sex in tender circles.

The water sloshed in the tub as she began to push up rhythmically, urging herself into his hand. A third finger worked inside, and she tightened and gasped out a protest — it was too much, she couldn't — but he whispered that she could, she must, and he stretched her carefully and took her groans into his mouth.

Splayed and floating, Win felt herself loosening, opening to the sensuality of the fingers reaching inside her. She felt greedy and wild, undulating to capture more of the obliterating pleasure. She actually clawed him a little, her hands scrabbling against his hard, bare skin, and he growled as if it pleased him. An abbreviated cry left her lips at the first shock of release. She tried to stifle it, but another was torn from her, and another, and the bathwater rippled as she shuddered, the climax lengthened by the delicately emphatic thrusting that continued until she was limp and panting.

Settling her against the high-backed tub, Merripen left her for a few minutes. She soaked in the steaming water, too replete to ask or notice where he'd gone. He returned with a length of toweling and lifted her from the bath. She stood passively before him, letting him dry her as if she were a child. As she leaned against him, she saw that she had scored little red marks on his skin, not deep ones, but marks nonetheless. She should have been apologetic, horrified, but all she wanted was to do it again. To feast on him. It was so unlike her that she withdrew into herself to ponder it.

Merripen carried her back into the bedroom and tucked her into a freshly made bed. She slid deep beneath the quilts and waited for him, drowsing, while he went to wash himself and empty the tub. She was steeped in a feeling she hadn't experienced in years . . . the kind of incandescent joy she had felt as a child waking on Christmas morning. She had stayed quietly in her bed, relishing the knowledge of all the good things that would soon happen, her heart alight with anticipation.

Win's eyes half-opened as she felt him climb

into bed eventually. His weight depressed the mattress, his body startlingly warm against Win's coolness. Snuggling into the crook of his arm and shoulder, she sighed deeply. His hand made a slow, lovely pattern over her back.

'Will we have a cottage like this someday?' she murmured.

Being Merripen, he had already come up with a plan. 'We'll live at Ramsay House for a year, more likely two, until the restoration is complete and Leo is on his feet. Then I'll find a suitable property for a farm, and build a house for you. A bit larger than this, I expect.'

His hand slid to her bottom, rubbing in slow circles. 'It won't be an extravagant life, but it will be comfortable. You'll have a cookmaid and a footman and a driver. And we'll live near your family, so you can see them whenever you like.'

'That sounds lovely,' Win managed to say, so filled with happiness she could scarcely breathe. 'It will be heaven.' She had no doubt of his ability to take care of her, nor did she doubt that she could make him happy. They would create a good life together, though she was fairly certain it would not be an ordinary one.

His tone was sober. 'If you marry me, you'll never be a lady of position.'

'There is no better position for me than being your wife.'

One of his big hands clasped over her skull, pressing her head against his shoulder. 'I've always wanted more for you than this.'

'Liar,' she whispered. 'You always wanted me for yourself.'

Laughter stirred in his chest. 'Yes,' he admitted.

They were quiet then, relishing the sensation of lying together in the morning-filled room. They had been close in so many ways before this . . . They had known each other so well . . . and yet not at all. Physical intimacy had created a new dimension to Win's feelings, as if she had taken not only his body inside hers, but also a part of his soul. She wondered how it was that people could engage in this act without love, how empty and pointless it must be by comparison.

Her bare foot explored the hairy surface of his leg, toes nudging against hard-sculpted muscle. 'Did you think about me when you were with them?' she asked tentatively.

'Who?'

'The women you slept with.'

She knew from the way Merripen tensed that he didn't like the question. His reply was low and guilt-roughened. 'No. I didn't think about anything when I was with them.'

Win let her hand wander over his smooth chest, finding the small brown nipples, teasing them into points. Rising on her elbow, she said frankly, 'When I imagine you doing this with someone else, I can hardly bear it.'

His hand came over hers, securing it against his strong heartbeat. 'They meant nothing to me. It was always a transaction. Something to be done with as quickly as possible.'

'I think that makes it even worse. To use a woman in that way, with no feeling . . .'

'They were well compensated,' he said

sardonically. 'And always willing.'

'You should have found someone you cared for, someone who cared for *you*. That would have been infinitely better than a loveless transaction.'

'I couldn't.'

'Couldn't what?'

'Care about anyone else. You took up too much room in my heart.'

Win wondered what it said about her terrible selfishness that such an answer moved and pleased her.

'After you left,' Merripen said, 'I thought I would go mad. There was no place I could go to feel better. No person I wanted to be with. I wanted you to get well — I would have given my life for it. But at the same time I hated you for leaving. I hated everything. My own heart for beating. I had only one reason to live, and that was to see you again.'

Win was touched by the severe simplicity of his declaration. He was a force, she thought. One couldn't subdue him any more than one could settle a lightning storm. He would love her as intemperately as he pleased, and devil take the hindmost.

'Did the women help?' she asked softly. 'Did it ease you to lie with them?'

He shook his head. 'It made it worse,' came his soft reply. 'Because they weren't you.'

Win leaned farther over him, her hair falling in glinting light ribbons that went across his chest and throat and arms. She stared into eyes as black as sloe. 'I want us to be faithful to each other,' she said gravely. 'From this day forward.'

There was a brief silence, a hesitation born not of doubt, but awareness. As if their vows were being heard and witnessed by some unseen presence.

Merripen's chest rose and fell in a long, deep breath. 'I'll be faithful to you,' he said. 'Forever.'

'So will I.'

'Promise also that you'll never leave me again.'

Win lifted her hand from the center of his chest and pressed a kiss there. 'I promise.'

She was entirely willing, eager, to seal their vows then, but he wouldn't. He wanted her to rest, her body to have respite, and when she objected, he quieted her with gentle kisses. 'Sleep,' he whispered, and she obeyed, sinking into the sweetest, darkest oblivion she had ever known.

★ ★ ★

Daylight canted impatiently against the unlined curtains at the windows, turning them into bright butter-colored rectangles. Kev had held Win for hours. He had not slept at all in that time. The pleasure of staring at her eclipsed the need for rest. There had been other times in his life when he had watched over her like this, especially when she'd been ill. But it was different now that she belonged to him.

He had always been consumed with miserable longing, loving Win and knowing nothing would ever come of it. Now, holding her, he felt something unfamiliar, a bloom of euphoric heat. He let himself kiss her, unable to resist following the glinting arc of her eyebrow with his lips. He moved on to the rosy curve of her cheek. The tip of a nose so adorable that it seemed worthy of an entire sonnet. He loved every part of her. It occurred to him that he had not yet kissed the spaces between her toes, an omission that desperately needed to be corrected.

Win slept with one of her legs hitched over him, her knee tucked between his. Feeling the intimate brush of blond curls against his hip, he went erect, his flesh alive with a hard, precise throbbing he could feel against the linen sheet that covered him.

She stirred and moved her limbs in a trembling stretch, and her eyes half-opened. He sensed her surprise at waking in his arms this way, and the slow dawning of satisfaction as she remembered what had gone before. Her hands crept over him, exploring softly. He was taut everywhere, aroused and unmoving, letting her discover him as she wished.

Win reconnoitered his body with an innocent abandon that seduced him utterly. Her lips brushed the taut skin of his chest and side. Finding the edge of his lowest rib, she gnawed gently, like a fastidious little cannibal. One of her hands trailed over his thigh and wandered up to his groin.

He said her name between fragmented breaths, reaching down to those tormenting fingers. But she swatted his hand away with an audible crack of skin against skin. And that aroused him beyond reason.

Win cupped the mass of him below, the shifting weights heavy against her palm. She squeezed, gently rolled the roundness, while he set his teeth and endured her touch as if he were being drawn and quartered.

Moving upward, she gripped the shaft lightly — too lightly. Kev would have begged her to do it harder had he been able to spare the breath. But he could only wait, gasping. Her head bent over him, her golden hair trapping him in a glimmering net. Despite his will to remain still, he couldn't stop the vicious twitch of his cock, the length of it jutting upward. To his shock, he felt her lean down to kiss him. And she continued, working upward along the stiff shaft, while he groaned with pleasure and disbelief.

Her beautiful mouth on him . . . he was dying, losing his sanity. She was too inexperienced to know how to proceed. She didn't take him deep, only licked the tip as he had done to her before. But holy Christ, it was enough for now. Kev let out an anguished groan as he felt a sweet, wet tug and heard the sound of her suckling. Muttering a garbled mixture of Romany and English, he seized her hips and dragged them upward. He buried his face in her, his tongue working voraciously until she writhed like a captured mermaid.

Tasting her arousal, he sank his tongue deep, again and again. Her legs stiffened, as if she were about to come. But he had to be inside her when it happened, had to feel her grip and clench around him. So he toppled her carefully and eased her to her front, and pushed a pillow beneath her hips.

She moaned and parted her knees wider.

Needing no further invitation, he positioned himself, his cock slick with the moisture from her mouth. Reaching beneath her, he found the tiny swollen bud, and he massaged slowly while he fed his shaft into her, his fingers stroking faster with every hard inch that pushed forward, and when he had finally buried his full length, she climaxed with a sobbing cry.

Kev could have found his own release then, but he had to prolong it. If it were possible, he would have gone on forever. He drew one hand along the pale, elegant curve of her back. She arched into the caress, sighing his name. He lay over her, changing the angle between them, still cupping her sex as he thrust. She shuddered as a few more spasms were teased out, passion splotches rising on her shoulders and back. He put his mouth to the patches of color, kissing every blushing place as he rocked slowly, working deeper in her, tighter, until he finally went still and came with violent spurts.

Rolling off her, Kev gathered Win against his ribs and struggled to catch his breath. His heartbeat hammered in his ears for some minutes, which was why he was slow to notice a knock at the door.

Win reached up to his cheeks and guided his face to hers. Her eyes were round. 'Someone's here,' she said.

19

Cursing beneath his breath, Kev dragged on his trousers and shirt and went barefoot to the door. Opening it, he saw Cam Rohan standing there nonchalantly, a valise in one hand and a covered basket in the other.

'Hello.' Cam's hazel eyes danced with mischief. 'I've brought you a few things.'

'How did you find us?' Kev asked without heat.

'I knew you hadn't gone far. None of your clothes were missing, nor any bags or trunks. And since the front gatehouse was too obvious, this was the next place I thought of. Aren't you going to invite me in?'

'No,' Kev said shortly, and Cam grinned.

'If our positions were reversed, *phral*, I suppose I'd be just as inhospitable. There's food in the basket, and clothes for both of you in the valise.'

'Thank you.' Kev took the items and set them just inside the door. Straightening, he looked at his brother, searching for any sign of censure. There was none.

'*Ov yilo isi?*' Cam asked.

It was an old Romany phrase, meaning 'Is all well here?' But it was literally translated as 'Is there heart here?' which seemed rather appropriate.

'Yes,' Kev said softly.

286

'There is nothing you need?'

'For the first time in my life,' Kev admitted, 'there is nothing I need.'

Cam smiled. 'Good.' Nonchalantly tucking his hands in his coat pockets, he braced a shoulder against the door frame.

'What is the situation at Ramsay House?' Kev asked, half-dreading the answer.

'There were a few moments of chaos this morning, when it was discovered that you were both gone.' A diplomatic pause. 'Harrow's been insisting that Win was taken against her will. At one point he threatened to go to the parish constable. Harrow says if you don't return with Win by nightfall, he'll take drastic action.'

'What would that be?' Kev inquired darkly.

'I don't know. But you might give a thought to the rest of us having to stay at Ramsay House with him while you're out here with his fiancée.'

'She's my fiancée now. And I'll bring her back when I damn well please.'

'Understood.' Cam's lips twitched. 'You intend to marry her soon, I hope?'

'Not soon,' Kev said. 'Immediately.'

'Thank God. Even for the Hathaways, this is all a bit untoward.' Cam glanced over Merripen's disheveled form and smiled. 'It's good to see you at ease finally, Merripen. If it were anyone but you, I'd say you actually looked happy.'

It was not easy to shed the habit of privacy. But Kev was actually tempted to confide in his brother, things he wasn't even certain he had words for. Such as the discovery that the love of a woman could make the entire world seem new.

Or his wonder that Win, who had always seemed so fragile and in need of protection, had emerged as an even stronger presence than he.

'Rohan,' he asked quietly, to keep Win from overhearing, 'I have a question . . . '

'Yes?'

'Do you conduct your marriage the way of the *gadje* or the Rom?'

'Mostly the way of the *gadje*,' Rohan said without hesitation. 'It wouldn't work otherwise. Amelia is hardly the kind of woman who could be treated as a subordinate. But as a Rom, I will always reserve the right to protect and look after her as I see fit.' He smiled slightly. 'You will find a middle way, just as we have.'

Kev scrubbed his hand through his hair and asked guardedly, 'Are the Hathaways angry about what I've done?'

'You mean carrying Win off?'

'Yes.'

'The only complaint I heard was that you took far too long.'

'Do any of them know where we are?'

'Not that I'm aware of.' Cam's smile turned wry. 'I can buy you a few more hours, *phral*. But have her back by nightfall, if for no other reason than to shut Harrow up.' He frowned slightly. 'He's an odd one, that *gadjo*.'

Kev gave him an alert glance. 'Why do you say that?'

Cam shrugged. 'Most men in his position would have done something, *anything*, by now. Destroyed some furniture. Gone for someone's throat. By this time, I would have turned all of

Hampshire upside down to find my woman. But Harrow only talks. And talks.'

'About what?'

'He's said quite a lot about what his rights are, what he's entitled to, his sense of betrayal . . . but so far it hasn't occurred to him to express any concern about Win's welfare, or consider what she wants. Overall, he acts like a child whose toy has been taken from him and who wants it to be given back.' Cam grimaced. 'Damned embarrassing, even for a *gadjo*.' He raised his voice and called to the unseen Win, 'I'm leaving now. Good day, little sister.'

'And to you, Mr. Rohan!' her cheerful voice floated back.

★   ★   ★

They unpacked a feast from the basket: cold roast fowl, a variety of salads, fruit, and thick slices of seed-cake. After devouring the lot, they sat before the hearth on a quilt. Dressed only in Kev's shirt, Win sat between his thighs while he brushed the tangles from her hair. He ran his fingers repeatedly through the length of silk, which gleamed like moonlight in his hands.

'Shall we go for a walk, now that I have my clothes?' Win asked.

'If you like.' Kev held her hair aside and kissed the nape of her neck. 'And afterward, back to bed.'

She shivered and made a sound of amusement. 'I've never known you to spend so much time abed.'

'Until now I've never had a good reason.' Setting the brush aside, he pulled her into his lap and cradled her. He kissed her lazily. She pushed upward with increasing demand, making him smile and pull back. 'Easy,' he said, stroking her jaw. 'We're not going to start that again.'

'But you just said you wanted to go back to bed.'

'I meant to rest.'

'We aren't going to make love anymore?'

'Not today,' he said gently. 'You've had enough.' He brushed his thumb over her kiss-swollen lips. 'If I made love to you again, you wouldn't be able to walk tomorrow.'

But as he was discovering, any challenge to Win's physical stamina was met with immediate resistance. 'I'm quite well,' she said stubbornly, sitting up in his lap. She spread kisses over his face and throat, everywhere she could reach. 'Once more, before we go back. I need you, Kev; I need — '

He quieted her with his mouth, and received such an ardently impatient response that he couldn't help chuckling against her lips. She drew back and demanded, 'Are you laughing at me?'

'No. No. It's only . . . you're adorable, you please me so much. My eager little *gadji* . . . ' He kissed her again, trying to calm her. But she was insistent, stripping off his shirt, pulling his hands to her naked body.

'Why are you so anxious?' he whispered, lying back on the quilt with her. 'No . . . wait . . . Win, talk to me.'

She went still in his arms, her small frowning face close to his. 'I'm afraid to go back,' she admitted. 'I feel as if something bad will happen. It doesn't seem real that we can truly be together now.'

'We can't hide here forever,' Kev murmured, stroking her hair. 'Nothing will happen, love. We've gone too far to turn back. You're mine now, and no one can change that. Are you afraid of Harrow? Is that it?'

'Not afraid, exactly. But I'm not looking forward to facing him.'

'Of course not,' Kev said quietly. 'I'll help you through it. I'll talk to him first.'

'I don't think that would be wise,' she said uncertainly.

'I insist on it. I won't lose my temper. But I'm going to take responsibility for what I've done. I would hardly leave you to handle the consequences without me.'

Win lowered her cheek to his shoulder. 'Are you certain nothing will happen to change your mind about marrying me?'

'Nothing in the world could do that.' Feeling the tension in her body, he ran his hands over her, lingering on her chest, where every heartbeat was a hard, anxious collision. He rubbed a circle to soothe her. 'What can I do to make you feel better?' he asked tenderly.

'I already told you, and you wouldn't,' she said in a small, sullen voice, and that drew a smothered laugh from him.

'Then you'll have your way,' he whispered. 'But slowly, so I won't hurt you.' He kissed the spaces behind her earlobes and moved down to the smooth whiteness of her shoulders, the pulse at the base of her throat. More softly still he kissed the plump curves of her breasts. Her nipples were bright and stung-looking from all his previous attentions. He was careful with them, his mouth gentle as he covered a swollen peak.

Win made a little movement, gave a faint hiss, and he guessed the nipple was smarting. But her hands came to his head, holding him there. He used his tongue to make languid circles, sucking only enough to keep the tender flesh inside the clamp of his lips. He spent a long time at her breasts, keeping his mouth soft, until she moaned and stirred her hips, needing more than the faint, feathery stimulation.

Dragging his lips down between her thighs, Kev rooted in the hot silk of her, finding the delicate blunt point of her clitoris, using the velvet flat of his tongue to paint and caress. She clutched his head more tightly and sobbed his name, the throaty sound exciting him.

When the responsive movements of her hips took on a regular rhythm, he pulled his mouth from her and pushed her knees wide and apart. He took an eternity to ease into the lush clenching flesh. Fully seated, he wrapped his arms around her, securing her against his body.

She wriggled, urging him to thrust, but he held still and fast and pressed his mouth to her ear, and whispered that he would make her come just like this, he would stay hard inside her as long as it took. Her ear turned scarlet, and she tightened and throbbed around him. 'Please move,' she whispered, and he gently said no.

'Please move, please . . . '

No.

But after a while he began to flex his hips in a subtle rhythm. She whimpered and trembled as he drove her, nudging deeper, relentless in his restraint. The climax broke over her finally, tearing low cries from her lips, bringing wild shudders to the surface. Kev was quiet, experiencing a release so acute and paralyzing that it robbed him of all sound. Her slender body pulled at him, milked him, enclosed him in delicate heat.

The pleasure was so great it caused an unfamiliar stinging in his eyes and nose, and that shook him to his foundations. *Bloody hell*, Kev thought, realizing that something had changed in him, something that could never be put back. All his defenses had been reduced to the uncertain strength of one small woman.

*   *   *

The sun was descending into the basin of rich wooded valleys by the time they had both dressed. The fires were extinguished, leaving the cottage cold and dark.

Win clung to Merripen's hand anxiously as he led her to the horse. 'I wonder why happiness always seems so fragile,' she said. 'I think the things our family has experienced . . . losing our parents, Leo losing Laura, the fire, my illness . . . have made me aware of how easily the things

293

we value can be snatched away. Life can change from one moment to the next.'

'Not everything changes. Some things last forever.'

Win stopped and turned to face him, wrapping her arms around his neck. He responded immediately, holding her secure and close, locking her against his powerful body. Win buried her face in his chest. 'I hope so,' she said after a moment. 'Are you really mine now, Kev?'

'I've always been yours,' he said against her ear.

★   ★   ★

Braced for the usual clamor of her sisters, Win was relieved when she and Kev returned to Ramsay House and found it serene and quiet. So unusually serene that it was clear everyone had agreed to behave as if nothing unusual had transpired. She found Amelia, Poppy, Miss Marks, and Beatrix in the upstairs parlor, the first three doing needlework while Beatrix read aloud.

As Win entered the room cautiously, Beatrix paused, and the women looked up with bright, curious gazes.

'Hello, dear,' Amelia said warmly. 'Did you have a nice outing with Merripen?' As if it had been nothing more than a picnic or carriage drive.

'Yes, thank you.' Win smiled at Beatrix. 'Do go on, Bea. Whatever you're reading sounds lovely.'

'It's a sensation novel,' Beatrix said. 'Very

exciting. There's a dark and gloomy mansion, and servants who behave oddly, and a secret door behind a tapestry.' She lowered her voice dramatically. 'Someone's about to be murdered.'

While Beatrix continued, Win sat beside Amelia. Win felt her older sister's hand reach for hers. A small but capable hand. A comforting grip. So much was expressed in Amelia's loving clasp, and in the returning pressure of Win's fingers . . . concern, acceptance, reassurance.

'Where is he?' Amelia whispered.

Win felt a pang of worry, though she kept her expression serene. 'He's gone to talk to Dr. Harrow.'

Amelia's grip tightened. 'Well,' she returned wryly, 'it should be a lively conversation. I've gotten the impression that your Harrow has been saving up quite a few things to say.'

★   ★   ★

'You crude, stupid peasant.' Julian Harrow was white-faced but controlled as he and Kev met in the library. 'You have no idea what you've done. In your haste to reach out and grab what you want, you've given no heed to the consequences. And you won't until it's too late. Until you've killed her.'

Having a fairly good idea of what Harrow was going to say, Kev had already decided how he would deal with him. For Win's sake, Kev would tolerate any number of insults or accusations. The doctor would have his say . . . and Kev would let it all roll off his back. He had won. Win

295

was his now, and nothing else mattered.

It wasn't easy, however. Harrow was the perfect picture of an outraged romantic hero . . . slim, elegant, his face pale and indignant. He made Kev feel like a swarthy oafish villain by contrast. And those last words, *until you've killed her*, chilled him to the marrow.

So many vulnerable creatures had suffered at his hands. No one with Kev's past could ever deserve Win. And even though she had forgiven his history of brutality, he could never forget.

'No one is going to harm her,' Kev said. 'It's obvious that as your wife, she would have been well cared for, but it wasn't what she wanted. She's made her choice.'

'Under duress!'

'I didn't force her.'

'Of course you did,' Harrow said with contempt. 'You carried her off in a display of brute strength. And being a woman, of course she thought it thrilling and romantic. Women can be dominated and persuaded into accepting nearly anything. And in the future, as she's dying in childbirth, in grotesque pain, she won't blame you for it. But you'll know that you're responsible.' A harsh laugh escaped him as he saw Kev's expression. 'Are you really so simple that you don't understand what I'm saying?'

'You believe she's too fragile to bear children,' Kev said. 'But she consulted another doctor in London, who — '

'Yes. Did Winnifred tell you the name of this doctor?'

Harrow's eyes were frosty gray, his tone brittle

with condescension.

Kev shook his head.

'I persisted in asking,' Harrow said, 'until she told me. And I knew at once it was an invented name. A sham. But just to make certain, I checked the registers of every legitimate physician in London. The doctor she named doesn't exist. She was lying, Merripen.' Harrow raked his hands through his hair and paced back and forth. 'Women are as devious as children when it comes to getting their way. My God, you're easily manipulated, aren't you?'

Kev couldn't answer. He had believed Win, for the simple reason that she never lied. As far as he knew, there was only one time in her life she had ever deceived him, and that had been to trick him into taking morphine when he'd been suffering from a burn wound. Later he'd understood why she'd done it, and he had forgiven her at once. But if she had lied about this . . . Anguish burned like acid in his blood.

Now he understood why Win had been so nervous about returning.

Harrow paused at the library table and went to half-sit, half-lean on it. 'I still want her,' he said quietly. 'I'm still willing to have her. On condition that she hasn't conceived.' He broke off as Kev fastened a lethal glare on him. 'Oh, you may glower, but you can't deny the truth. Look at you — how can you justify what you've done? You're a filthy Gypsy, attracted to pretty baubles like the rest of your ilk.'

Harrow watched Kev closely as he continued. 'I'm sure you love her, in your fashion. Not in a refined way, not in the way she truly needs, but as much as someone of your kind is capable. I find that somewhat touching. And pitiable. No doubt Winnifred feels that the bonds of childhood kinship give you more of a claim on her than any other man could possibly have. But she has been too long sheltered from the world. She has neither the wisdom nor the experience to know her own needs. If she does marry you, it will only be a matter of time before she tires of you, and wants more than you could ever offer. Go find a sturdy peasant girl, Merripen. Better yet, a Gypsy woman who would be happy with the simple life you could give her. You want a nightingale, when you would be so much better served with a nice, robust pigeon. Do the right thing, Merripen. Give her to me. It's not too late. She'll be safe with me.'

Kev could barely hear his own rasping voice, his pulse hammering with confusion and despair and fury. 'Maybe I should ask the Lanhams. Would they agree that she'd be safer with you?'

And without glancing to judge the effect of his words, Kev strode from the library.

★   ★   ★

Win's sense of unease grew as evening settled over the house. She stayed in the parlor with her sisters and Miss Marks until Beatrix had tired of reading. The only relief from Win's growing tension was in watching the antics of Beatrix's ferret, Dodger, who seemed enamored of Miss

Marks, despite — or perhaps because of — her obvious antipathy. He kept creeping up to the governess and trying to steal one of her knitting needles, while she watched him with narrowed eyes.

'Don't even consider it,' Miss Marks told the hopeful ferret with chilling calm. 'Or I'll cut off your tail with a carving knife.'

Beatrix grinned. 'I thought that only happened to blind mice, Miss Marks.'

'It works on any offending rodent,' Miss Marks returned darkly.

'Ferrets are not rodents, actually,' Beatrix said. 'They're classified as *mustelidae*. Weasels. So one might say the ferret is a distant cousin of the mouse.'

'It's not a family I'd care to become closely acquainted with,' Poppy said.

Dodger draped himself across the arm of the settee and pinned a love-struck gaze on Miss Marks, who ignored him.

Win smiled and stretched. 'I'm fatigued. I'll bid everyone good night now.'

'I'm fatigued as well,' Amelia said, covering a deep yawn.

'Perhaps we should all retire,' Miss Marks suggested, deftly packing away her knitting in a little basket.

They all went to their rooms, while Win's nerves bristled in the ominous silence of the hallway. Where was Merripen? What had been said between him and Julian?

A lamp burned low in her room, its glow pushing feebly against the encroaching shadows.

299

She blinked as she saw a motionless form in the corner . . . Merripen, occupying a chair.

'Oh,' she breathed in surprise.

His gaze tracked her as she came closer to him.

'Kev?' she asked hesitantly, while a chill slithered down her spine. The talk had not gone well. Something was wrong. 'What is it?' she asked huskily.

Merripen stood and towered over her, his expression unfathomable. 'Who was the doctor you saw in London, Win? How did you find him?'

Then she understood. Her stomach dropped, and she took a few steadying breaths. 'There was no doctor,' she said. 'I didn't see the need for it.'

'You didn't see the need,' he repeated slowly.

'No. Because — as Julian said later — I could go from doctor to doctor until I found one who would give me the answer I wanted.'

Merripen let out a breath that sounded like a scrape in his throat. He shook his head. 'Jesus.'

Win had never seen him look so devastated, beyond shouting or anger. She moved toward him with her hand outstretched. 'Kev, please, let me — '

'Don't. Please.' He was struggling visibly to control himself.

'I'm sorry,' she said earnestly. 'I wanted you so much, and I was going to have to marry Julian, and I thought if I told you about having seen another doctor, it would . . . well, push you a bit.'

He turned away from her, his hands clenched.

'It makes no difference,' Win said, trying to sound calm, trying to think above the desperate pounding of her heart. 'It changes nothing, especially after today.'

'It makes a difference if you lie to me,' he said in a guttural tone.

Romany males could not countenance being manipulated by their women. And she had broken Merripen's trust at a time when he had been particularly vulnerable. He had let down his guard, had let her inside. But how else could she have had him?

'I didn't feel I had a choice,' she said. 'You're impossibly stubborn when your mind is made up. I didn't know how to change it.'

'Then you've just lied again. Because you're not sorry.'

'I'm sorry that you're hurt and angry, and I understand how much you — '

She broke off as Merripen moved with astonishing swiftness, seizing her by the upper arms, bringing her up against the wall. His snarling face descended close to hers. 'If you understood anything, you wouldn't expect me to give you a baby that will kill you.'

Rigid and trembling, she stared into his eyes until she was drowning in darkness. She gulped a deep breath before managing to say stubbornly, 'I'll see as many doctors as you like. We'll gather a full variety of opinions, and you can calculate the odds. But no one can predict of a certainty what will happen. And none of it will change how I intend to spend the rest of my life. I will live it on my terms. And you . . . you can have all of me or nothing. I won't be an invalid any longer. Not even if it means losing you.'

'I don't take ultimatums,' he said, giving her a little shake. 'Least of all from a woman.'

Win's eyes went blurry, and she damned the rising tears. She wondered in furious despair why fate seemed determined to withhold from her the ordinary life that other people took for granted. 'You arrogant Rom,' she said hoarsely. 'It's not your choice; it's mine. My body. My risk. And it may already be too late. I may have already conceived — '

'No.' He gripped her head and pressed his forehead to hers, his breath striking her lips in bursts of heat. 'I can't do this,' he said raggedly. 'I won't be forced into hurting you.'

'Just love me.' Win wasn't aware that she was crying until she felt his mouth on her face, his throat vibrating with low growls as he licked at her tears. He kissed her desperately, savaging her mouth with a wildness that made her quiver from head to toe. As he crushed his body against hers, she felt the prodding of his arousal even through the bunched layers of their clothes. It sent a shock of response through all her veins, and she felt her intimate flesh prickling, turning wet. She wanted him inside her, to pull him deep and close, to pleasure him until his ferocity was soothed. She reached down to the stiff length of him, kneading and gripping until he groaned into her mouth.

She pulled her lips free long enough to gasp, 'Take me to bed, Kev. Take me . . .'

But he shoved away from her with a vicious curse.

'Kev — '

A scalding glance, and he left the room, the door trembling on its hinges from the abrupt slam.

20

The early-morning air was fresh and heavy with the promise of rain, a cool breeze sweeping through the half-open window of Cam and Amelia's room. Cam awakened slowly as he felt his wife's voluptuous body snuggling close to his. She always slept in a nightgown made of modest white cambric, with infinite numbers of tucks and tiny ruffles. It never failed to stir him, knowing what splendid curves were concealed beneath the demure garment.

The nightgown had ridden up to her knees during the night. One of her bare legs was hooked over his, her knee resting near his groin. The slight roundness of her stomach pressed against his side. Pregnancy had made her feminine form more ample and delicious. There was a glow about her these days, a burgeoning vulnerability that filled him with an overwhelming urge to protect her. And knowing that the changes in her were caused by his seed, a part of him growing inside her . . . that was undeniably arousing.

He wouldn't have expected to be this enthralled by Amelia's condition. In the eyes of the Rom, childbirth and all related issues were considered *mahrime*, polluting events. And since the Irish were notoriously suspicious and prudish when it came to matters of reproduction, there wasn't much on either side of his lineage to justify his delight in his wife's pregnancy. But he couldn't help it. She was the most beautiful and fascinating creature he had ever encountered.

As he patted her hip drowsily, the urge to make love to her was too much to resist. He inched her gown upward and caressed her bare bottom. He kissed her lips, her chin, savoring the fine texture of her skin.

Amelia stirred. 'Cam,' she murmured sleepily. Her legs parted, inviting more of the gentle exploration.

Cam smiled against her cheek. 'What a good little wife you are,' he whispered in Romany. She stretched and gave a pleasured sigh as his hands slipped over her warm body. He arranged her limbs carefully, stroking and praising her, kissing her breasts. His fingers played between her thighs, teasing wickedly until she began to breathe in quiet moans. Her hands clutched at his back as he mounted her, his body hungry for the warm, wet welcome of her —

A tap at the door. A muffled voice. 'Amelia?'

They both froze.

The soft feminine voice tried again. 'Amelia?'

'One of my sisters,' Amelia whispered.

Cam muttered a curse that explicitly described what he had been about to do, and was apparently not going to be able to finish. 'Your family — ,' he began in a dark tone.

'I know.' She flipped back the bedclothes. 'I'm sorry. I — ' She broke off as she saw the extent of his arousal and said weakly, 'Oh dear.'

Although he was usually tolerant when it came

to the Hathaways' multitude of quirks and issues, Cam was currently in no mood to be understanding.

'Get rid of whoever it is,' he said, 'and come back here.'

'Yes. I'll try.' She pulled a dressing robe over her nightgown and hastily fastened the top three buttons. As she hurried into the adjoining sitting room, the thin white dressing robe flapped behind her like the mainsail of a schooner.

Cam remained on his side, listening intently. There was the sound of the door to the hallway opening, and someone coming into the little sitting room. There was also the calm lilt of Amelia's questioning voice, and the anxious response of one of her sisters. Win, he guessed, since Poppy and Beatrix would only awaken this early in the event of some major catastrophe.

One of the things Cam adored about Amelia was her tender and unflagging interest in all the concerns, large and small, of her siblings. She was a little mother hen, valuing family as much as any Romany wife. That felt good to him. It hearkened back to his early childhood, when he'd still been allowed to live with the tribe. Family was equally important to them. But it also meant having to share Amelia, which, at times like this, was damned annoying.

After a few minutes, the feminine chatter still hadn't stopped. Gathering that Amelia wasn't going to return to bed any time soon, Cam sighed and left the bed.

He dragged on some clothes, went into the sitting room, and saw Amelia on a small settee with Win. Who looked wretched.

They were so intent on their conversation that Cam's appearance was barely heeded. Sitting in a nearby chair, Cam listened until he comprehended that Win had lied to Merripen about having seen a doctor, that Merripen had been furious, and that the relationship between the two was in a shambles.

Amelia turned to Cam, her forehead puckered with concern. 'Perhaps Win shouldn't have deceived him, but it is her right to make this decision for herself.' Amelia retained Win's hand in hers as she spoke. 'You know that I would love nothing better than to keep Win safe from harm, always . . . but even I have to acknowledge that it isn't possible. Merripen must accept that Win wants to have a normal married life with him.'

Cam rubbed his face and stifled a yawn. 'Yes. But the way to get him to accept that is *not* to manipulate him.' He looked at Win directly. 'Little sister, you should know that ultimatums never work with Romany men. It goes completely against a Rom's grain, being told what to do by his woman.'

'I didn't tell him what to do,' Win protested miserably. 'I just told him — '

'That it didn't matter what he thought or felt,' Cam murmured. 'That you intend to live your life on your own terms, no matter what.'

'Yes,' she said faintly. 'But I didn't mean to imply that I didn't care about his feelings.'

Cam smiled ruefully. 'I admire your fortitude, little sister. I even happen to agree with your position. But that's not the way to manage a

Rom. Even your sister, who is not generally known for her diplomacy, knows better than to approach me in such an uncompromising fashion.'

'I am *quite* diplomatic when I wish to be,' Amelia protested, frowning, and he gave her a brief grin. Turning to Win, Amelia admitted reluctantly, 'Cam is correct, however.'

Win was quiet for a moment, absorbing that. 'What should I do now? How can things be made right?'

Both women looked at Cam.

The last thing he wanted was to involve himself in Win and Merripen's problems. And God knew Merripen would probably be as charming as a baited bear this morning. All Cam wanted was to go back to bed and plow his wife. And perhaps sleep a bit longer. But as the sisters stared at him with entreating blue eyes, he sighed. 'I'll talk to him,' he muttered.

'He's most likely awake now,' Amelia said hopefully. 'Merripen always rises early.'

Cam gave her a glum nod, hardly relishing the prospect of talking to his surly brother about womanish matters. 'He's going to beat me like a dusty parlor rug,' Cam said. 'And I won't blame him a bit.'

★ ★ ★

After dressing and washing, Cam went downstairs to the morning room, where Merripen invariably took breakfast. Passing the sideboard, Cam saw toad-in-the-hole, a casserole of

308

sausages covered in batter and roasted, platters of bacon and eggs, sole fillets, fried bread, and a bowl of baked beans.

A chair had been pushed back from one of the round tables. There was an empty cup and saucer, and a small steaming silver pot next to it. The scent of strong black coffee lingered in the air.

Cam glanced at the glass doors that led to a back terrace, and saw Merripen's lean, dark form. Merripen appeared to be staring at the fruit orchard beyond the structured formal garden. The set of his shoulders and head conveyed both irritability and moroseness.

Hell. Cam had no idea what he was going to say to his brother. They had far to go before they approached a basic level of trust. Any advice Cam tried to give Merripen would probably be tossed summarily back into his face.

Picking up a slice of fried bread, Cam ladled a spoonful of orange marmalade on it, and wandered out to the terrace.

Merripen gave Cam a cursory glance and returned his attention to the landscape: the flourishing fields beyond the manor grounds, the heavy forests nourished by the thick artery of the river.

A few gentle streams of smoke arose from the distant riverbank, one of the places where Gypsies were wont to camp as they traveled through Hampshire. Cam had personally carved identifying marks on the trees to indicate that this was a friendly place to the Rom. And every time a new tribe came, Cam went to visit them on the off-chance that someone from his long-ago family might be there.

'Another *kumpania* passing through,' he remarked casually, joining Merripen at the balcony. 'Why don't you come with me to visit them this morning?'

Merripen's tone was distant and unfriendly. 'The workmen are casting new plasterwork moldings for the east wing. And after the way they fouled it up last time, I have to be there.'

'Last time, the screeds they nailed up weren't properly aligned,' Cam said.

'I know that,' Merripen snapped.

'Fine.' Feeling sleepy and annoyed, Cam rubbed his face. 'Look, I have no desire to stick my nose in your affairs, but — '

'Then don't.'

'It's not going to hurt you to hear an outside perspective.'

'I don't give a damn about your perspective.'

'If you weren't so bloody self-absorbed,' Cam said acidly, 'it might occur to you that you're not the only one who's got something to worry about. Do you think I haven't given a thought to what might happen to Amelia now that she's conceived?'

'Nothing will happen to Amelia,' Merripen said dismissively.

Cam scowled. 'Everyone in this family chooses to think of Amelia as indestructible. Amelia herself thinks it. But she's subject to all the usual problems and frailties of any other woman in her condition. The truth is that it's always a risk.'

Merripen's dark eyes simmered with hostility. 'More so for Win.'

'Probably. But if she wants to assume that risk, it's her decision.'

'That's where we differ, Rohan. Because I — '

'Because you don't take risks on anyone, do you? It's too bad you've fallen in love with a woman who won't be kept on a shelf, *phral*.'

'If you call me that again,' Merripen growled, 'I'll take your bloody head off.'

'Go ahead and try.'

Merripen would probably have launched at Cam then, if not for the glass doors opening and another figure stepping out on the terrace. Glancing in the direction of the intruder, Cam groaned inwardly.

It was Harrow, looking controlled and capable. He approached Cam and ignored Merripen. 'Good morning, Rohan. I've just come to tell you that I will be leaving Hampshire later in the day. If I can't persuade Miss Hathaway to come to her senses, that is.'

'Of course,' Cam said, schooling his expression into pleasant blankness. 'Please let me know if there is anything we can do to facilitate your departure.'

'I only want what is best for her,' the doctor murmured, still not looking at Merripen. 'I will continue to believe that going to France with me is the wisest choice for all concerned. But it is Miss Hathaway's decision.' He paused, his gray eyes somber. 'I hope you will exert any influence you have to make certain *all* parties concerned understand what is at stake.'

'I think we all have a reasonably good grasp of the situation,' Cam said with a gentleness that masked the sting of sarcasm.

Harrow stared at him suspiciously and gave a short nod. 'I'll leave the two of you to your *discussion*, then.' He placed a subtle, skeptical emphasis on the word 'discussion,' as if he was aware that they'd been on the verge of an outright brawl. He left the terrace, closing the glass door behind him.

'I hate that bastard,' Merripen said beneath his breath.

'He's not my favorite, either,' Cam admitted. Wearily he gripped the back of his own neck, trying to ease the stiffness of the pinching muscles. 'I'm going down to the Romany campsite. And if you don't mind, I'll take a cup of that evil brew you drink. I despise the stuff, but I need something to help me stay awake.'

'Have whatever's left in the pot,' Merripen muttered. 'I'm more awake than I care to be.'

Cam nodded and went to the French doors. But he paused at the threshold, and smoothed the hair at the back of his neck, and spoke quietly. 'The worst part about loving someone, Merripen, is that there will always be things you can't protect her from. Things beyond your control. You finally realize there is something worse than dying . . . and that is having something happen to her. You have to live with that fear always. But you have to take the bad part, if you want the good part.'

Kev looked at him bleakly. 'What's the good part?'

A smile touched Cam's lips. 'All the rest of it is the good part,' he said, and went inside.

*   *   *

'I've been warned on pain of death not to say anything,' was Leo's first comment as he joined Merripen in one of the east wing rooms. There were two plasterers in the corner, measuring and marking on the walls, and another was repairing scaffolding that would support a man close to the ceiling.

'Good advice,' Kev said. 'You should take it.'

'I never take advice, good or bad. That would only encourage more of it.'

Despite Kev's brooding thoughts, he felt an unwilling smile tug at his lips. He gestured to a nearby bucket filled with light gray ooze. 'Why don't you pick up a stick and stir the lumps out of that?'

'What is it?'

'A lime plaster and hairy clay mix.'

'Hairy clay. Lovely.' But Leo obediently picked up a discarded stick and began to poke around in the bucket of plaster. 'The women are gone for the morning,' he remarked. 'They went to Stony Cross Manor to visit Lady Westcliff. Beatrix warned me to be on the lookout for her ferret, which seems to be missing. And Miss Marks stayed here.' A reflective pause. 'An odd little creature, wouldn't you say?'

'The ferret or Miss Marks?' Kev carefully positioned a strip of wood on the wall and nailed it in place.

'Marks. I've been wondering . . . Is she a misandrist, or does she hate everyone in general?'

'What is a misandrist?'

'A man-hater.'

'She doesn't hate men. She's always been pleasant to me and Rohan.'

Leo looked genuinely puzzled. 'Then . . . she merely hates *me*?'

'It would seem so.'

'But she has no reason!'

'What about your being arrogant and dismissive?'

'That's part of my aristocratic charm,' Leo protested.

'It would appear your aristocratic charm is lost on Miss Marks.' Kev arched a brow as he saw Leo's scowl. 'Why should it matter? You have no personal interest in her, do you?'

'Of course not,' Leo said indignantly. 'I'd sooner climb into bed with Bea's pet hedgehog. Imagine those pointy little elbows and knees. All those sharp angles. A man could do fatal harm to himself, tangling with Marks . . . ' He stirred the plaster with new vigor, evidently preoccupied with the myriad dangers in bedding the governess.

A bit too preoccupied, Kev thought.

★   ★   ★

It was a shame, Cam mused as he walked through a green meadow with his hands tucked in his pockets, that being part of a close-knit family meant one could never enjoy his own good fortune when someone else was having problems.

There was much for Cam to take pleasure in

314

at the moment . . . the benediction of sunshine on the spring-roughened landscape, and all the waking, droning, vibrant activity of plants pushing from the damp earth. The promising tang of smoke from a Romany campfire floated on a breeze. Perhaps today he might finally find someone from his old tribe. On a day like this, anything seemed possible.

He had a beautiful wife who was carrying his child. He loved Amelia more than life. And he had so much to lose. But Cam wouldn't let fear cripple him, or prevent him from loving her with all his soul. Fear . . . He slowed his pace, perplexed by the sudden rapid escalation of his heartbeat. As if he'd been running for miles without stopping. Glancing across the field, he saw that the grass was unnaturally green.

The thump of his heart became painful, as if someone were kicking him repeatedly. Bewildered, Cam tensed like a man held at knifepoint, putting a hand to his chest. Jesus, the sun was bright, boring through his eyes until they watered. He blotted the moisture with his sleeve, and was abruptly surprised to find himself on the ground, on his knees.

He waited for the pain to subside, for his heart to slow as it surely must, but it only got worse. He struggled to breathe, tried to stand. His body would not obey. A slow boneless collapse, the green grass stabbing harshly into his cheek. More pain, and more, his heart threatening to explode from the extraordinary force of its beats.

Cam realized with a kind of wonder that he was dying. He couldn't think why it was happening, or how, only that no one would take care of Amelia and she needed him, he couldn't leave her. Someone had to watch over her; she needed someone to rub her feet when she was tired. So tired. He couldn't lift his head or arm, or move his legs, but muscles in his body were jumping independently, tremors jerking him like a puppet on strings. *Amelia. I don't want to go away from you. God, don't let me die; it's too soon.* And yet the pain kept pouring over him, drowning him, smothering every breath and heartbeat.

Amelia. He wanted to say her name, and he couldn't. It was an unfathomable cruelty that he couldn't leave the world with those last precious syllables on his lips.

★   ★   ★

After an hour of nailing up screeds and testing various mixtures of lime, gypsum, and hairy clay, Kev and Leo and the workmen had settled on the right proportions.

Leo had taken an unexpected interest in the process, even devising an improvement on the three-coat plasterwork by improving the base layer, or scratch coat. 'Put more hair in this layer,' he had suggested, 'and rough it up with a darby tool, and that will give more of a clinch to the next coat.'

It was clear to Kev that although Leo had little interest in the financial aspects of running the estate, his love of architecture and all related matters of construction was more keenly developed than ever.

As Leo was climbing down from the scaffolding, the housekeeper, Mrs. Barnstable, came to the doorway with a boy in tow. Kev regarded him with sharp interest. The boy appeared to be about eleven or twelve years of age. Even if he hadn't been dressed in colorful clothes, his bold features and coppery complexion would have identified him as a Rom.

'Sir,' the housekeeper said to Kev apologetically, 'I beg your pardon for interrupting your work. But this lad came to the doorstep speaking gibberish, and he refuses to be chased away. We thought you might be able to understand him.'

The gibberish turned out to be perfectly articulate Romany.

'*Droboy tume Romale,*' the boy said politely.

Kev acknowledged the greeting with a nod. '*Mishto avilan.*' He continued the conversation in Romany. 'Are you from the *vitsa* by the river?'

'Yes, *kako*. I was sent by the *rom phuro* to tell you that we found a Rom lying in the field. He's dressed like a *gadjo*. We thought he might belong to someone here.'

'Lying in the field,' Kev repeated, while a cold, biting urgency rose inside him. He knew at once that something very bad had happened. With an effort, he kept his tone patient. 'Was he resting?'

The boy shook his head. 'He is ill and out of his head. And he shakes like this — ' He mimicked a tremor with his hands.

'Did he tell you his name?' Kev asked. 'Did he say anything?' Although they were still speaking in Romany, Leo and Mrs. Barnstable stared at

Kev intently, gathering that some emergency was taking place.

'What is it?' Leo asked, frowning.

The boy answered Kev, 'No, *kako*, he can't say much of anything. And his heart — ' The boy hit his own chest with a small fist, in a few emphatic thumps.

'Take me to him.' There was no doubt in Kev's mind that the situation was dire. Cam Rohan was never ill, and he was in superb physical condition. Whatever had befallen him, it was outside the category of ordinary maladies.

Switching to English, Kev spoke to Leo and the housekeeper. 'Rohan has been taken ill . . . He's at the Romany campsite. My lord, I would suggest that you dispense a footman and driver to Stony Cross Manor to collect Amelia at once. Mrs. Barnstable, send for the doctor. I'll bring Rohan here as soon as I can.'

'Sir,' the housekeeper asked in bewilderment, 'are you referring to Dr. Harrow?'

'No,' Kev said instantly. All his instincts warned him to keep Harrow out of this. 'In fact, don't let him know what's going on. For the time being, keep this as quiet as possible.'

'Yes, sir.' Although the housekeeper didn't understand Kev's reasons, she was too well trained to question his authority. 'Mr. Rohan seemed perfectly well earlier this morning,' she said. 'What could have happened to him?'

'We'll find out.' Without waiting for further questions or reactions, Kev gripped the boy's shoulder and steered him toward the doorway. 'Let's go.'

The *vitsa* appeared to be a small and prosperous family tribe. They had set up a well-organized camp, with two *vardos* and some healthy-looking horses and donkeys. The leader of the tribe, whom the boy identified as the *rom phuro*, was an attractive man with long black hair and warm, dark eyes. Although he was not tall, he was fit and lean, with an air of steady authority. Kev was surprised by the leader's relative youth. The word *phuro* usually referred to a man of advanced age and wisdom. For a man who appeared to be in his late thirties, it signified that he was an unusually respected leader.

They exchanged cursory greetings, and the *rom phuro* led Kev to his own *vardo*. 'Is he your friend?' the leader asked with obvious concern.

'My brother.' For some reason Kev's comment earned an arrested glance.

'It is good that you're here. It may be your last chance to see him this side of the veil.'

Kev was astonished by his own visceral reaction to the comment, the rush of outrage and grief. 'He's not going to die,' Kev said harshly, quickening his stride and fairly leaping into the *vardo*.

The interior of the Gypsy caravan was approximately twelve feet long and six feet broad, with the typical stove and metal chimney pipe located to the side of the door. A pair of transverse berths was located at the other end of the *vardo*, one upper and one lower. Cam Rohan's long body was stretched out on the lower berth, his booted feet dangling over the end. He was twitching and juddering, his head rolling ceaselessly on the pillow.

'Holy hell,' Kev said thickly, unable to believe such a change had been wrought in the man in such a short amount of time. The healthy color had been leeched out of Rohan's face until it was as white as paper, and his lips were cracked and gray. He moaned in pain, panting like a dog.

Kev sat on the edge of the berth and put his hand on Rohan's icy forehead. 'Cam,' he said urgently. 'Cam, it's Merripen. Open your eyes. Tell me what happened.'

Rohan struggled to control the tremors, to focus his gaze, but it was clearly impossible. He tried to form a word, but all he could produce was an incoherent sound.

Flattening a hand on Rohan's chest, Kev felt a ferocious and irregular heartbeat. He swore, recognizing that no man's heart, no matter how strong, could go on at that manic pace for long.

'He must have eaten some herb without knowing it was harmful,' the *rom phuro* commented, looking troubled.

Kev shook his head. 'My brother is very familiar with medicinal plants. He would never make that kind of mistake.' Staring down at Rohan's drawn face, Kev felt a mixture of fury and compassion. He wished his own heart could take over the work for his brother's. 'Someone poisoned him.'

'Tell me what I can do,' the tribe leader said quietly.

'First, we need to get rid of as much of the poison as possible.'

'His stomach emptied before we brought him into the *vardo*.'

That was good. But for the reaction to be this bad, even after expelling the poison, meant it was a highly toxic substance. The heart beneath Kev's hand seemed ready to burst from Rohan's chest. He would go into convulsions soon. 'Something must be done to slow his pulse and ease the tremors,' Kev said curtly. 'Do you have laudanum?'

'No, but we have raw opium.'

'Even better. Bring it quickly.'

The *rom phuro* gave orders to a pair of women who had come to the entrance of the *vardo*. In less than a minute, they had produced a tiny jar of thick brown paste. It was the dried fluid of the unripened poppy pod. Scraping up some of the paste with the tip of a spoon, Kev tried to feed it to Rohan.

Rohan's teeth clattered violently against the metal, his head jerking until the spoon was dislodged. Doggedly Kev slid his arm beneath Rohan's neck and lifted him upward. 'Cam. It's me. I've come to help you. Take this for me. Take it now.' He shoved the spoon back into Rohan's mouth and held it there while he choked and shook in Kev's grip. 'That's it,' Kev murmured, withdrawing the spoon after a moment. He laid a warm hand on his brother's throat, rubbing gently. 'Swallow. Yes, *phral*, that's it.'

The opium worked with miraculous speed. Soon the tremors began to subside, and the frantic gasping eased. Kev wasn't aware of holding his breath until he let it out in a relieved sigh. He put his palm over Rohan's heart, feeling the jerking rhythm slow.

'Try giving him some water,' the tribe leader suggested, handing a carved wooden cup to Kev. He pressed the edge of the cup against Rohan's lips, and coaxed him to take a sip.

The heavy lashes lifted, and Rohan focused on him with effort. 'Kev . . . '

'I'm here, little brother.'

Rohan stared and blinked. He reached up and clutched the placket of Kev's open-necked shirt like a drowning man. 'Blue,' he whispered raggedly. 'Everything . . . blue.'

Kev slid his arm around Rohan's back and gripped him firmly. He glanced at the *rom phuro*, and tried desperately to think. He'd heard of such a symptom before, a blue haze over the vision. It was caused by taking too much of a potent heart medicine. 'It could be digitalis,' he murmured. 'But I don't know what that derives from.'

'Foxglove,' the *rom phuro* said. His tone was matter-of-fact, but his face was taut with anxiety. 'Quite lethal. Kills livestock.'

'What's the antidote?' Kev asked sharply.

The leader's reply was soft. 'I don't know. I don't even know if there is one.'

21

After dispatching a footman for the village doctor, Leo decided to go to the Gypsy camp and see how Rohan was faring. Leo couldn't stand the inactivity or suspense of waiting. And he was deeply troubled by the thought of anything happening to Rohan, who seemed to have become the linchpin of the entire family.

Rapidly navigating his way down the grand staircase, Leo had just reached the entrance hall when he was approached by Miss Marks. She had a housemaid in tow and was holding the hapless girl by the wrist. The maid was pale and red-eyed.

'My lord,' Miss Marks said tersely, 'I bid you to come with us to the parlor immediately. There is something you should — '

'In your supposed knowledge of etiquette, Marks, you should know that no one *bids* the master of the house to do anything.'

The governess's stern mouth twisted impatiently. 'Devil take etiquette. This is important.'

'Very well. Apparently you must be humored. But tell me here and now, as I've no time for parlor chitchat.'

'The parlor,' she insisted.

After a brief glance heavenward, Leo followed the governess and housemaid through the entrance hall. 'I warn you, if this is about some trivial household matter, I'll have your head. I've got a pressing issue to deal with right now, and — '

'Yes,' Marks cut him off as they walked swiftly to the parlor. 'I know about that.'

'You do? Hang it all, Mrs. Barnstable wasn't supposed to tell anyone.'

'Secrets are rarely kept belowstairs, my lord.'

As they went into the parlor, Leo stared at the governess's straight spine, and experienced the same sting of irritation he always felt in her presence. She was like one of those unreachable itches on one's back. It had something to do with the coil of light brown hair pinned so tightly at her nape. And the narrow torso and tiny corseted waist, and the dry, pristine paleness of her skin. He couldn't help thinking about what it would be like to unlace, unpin, and unloosen her. Remove her spectacles. Do things that would make her all pink and steamy and profoundly bothered.

Yes, that was it. He wanted to bother her. Repeatedly.

Good God, what the bloody hell was wrong with him?

Once they were in the parlor, Miss Marks closed the door and patted the housemaid's arm with a slender white hand. 'This is Sylvia,' she told Leo. 'She saw something untoward this morning and was afraid to tell anyone. But after learning of Mr. Rohan's illness, she came to me with this information.'

'Why wait until now?' Leo asked impatiently. 'Surely anything untoward should be reported at once.'

Miss Marks answered with annoying calmness, 'There are no protections for a servant who inadvertently sees something she shouldn't. And being a sensible girl, Sylvia doesn't want to be made a scapegoat. Do we have your assurance that Sylvia will suffer no ill consequences from what she is about to divulge?'

'You have my word,' Leo said. 'No matter what it is. Tell me, Sylvia.'

The housemaid nodded and leaned against Miss Marks for support. Sylvia was so much heavier than the frail governess, it was a wonder they didn't both topple over. 'My lord,' the maid faltered, 'I polished the fish forks this morning and brought them to the breakfast sideboard, for the sole fillets. But as I came into the morning room, I saw Mr. Merripen and Mr. Rohan out on the terrace, talking. And Dr. Harrow was in the room, watching them . . . '

'And?' Leo prompted as the girl's lips trembled.

'And I thought I saw Dr. Harrow put something into Mr. Merripen's coffeepot. He reached for something in his pocket — it looked like one of those queer little glass tubes at the apothecary's. But it was so fast, I couldn't be sure what he'd done. And then he turned around and looked at me as I came into the room. I pretended not to see anything, my lord. I didn't want to make trouble.'

'We think that perhaps Mr. Rohan drank the adulterated beverage,' the governess said.

Leo shook his head. 'Mr. Rohan doesn't take coffee.'

'Isn't it possible that he might have made an exception this morning?'

The edge of sarcasm in her voice was unbearably annoying.

'It's possible. But it wouldn't be in character.' Leo let out a harsh sigh. 'Damn it all. I'll try to find out what, if anything, Harrow did. Thank you, Sylvia.'

'Yes, my lord.' The housemaid looked relieved.

As Leo strode from the room, he was exasperated to discover that Miss Marks was at his heels. 'Do *not* come with me, Marks.'

'You need me.'

'Go somewhere and knit something. Conjugate a verb. Whatever it is governesses do.'

'I would,' she said acerbically, 'had I any confidence in your ability to handle the situation. But from what I've seen of your skills, I highly doubt you'll accomplish anything without my help.'

Leo wondered if other governesses dared to talk to the master this way. He didn't think so. Why the devil couldn't his sisters have chosen a quiet, pleasant woman instead of this little wasp? 'I have skills you'll never be fortunate enough to see or experience, Marks.'

She made a scornful *humph* and continued to follow him.

Reaching Harrow's room, Leo gave a perfunctory knock and went inside. The wardrobe was empty, and there was an open trunk by the bed. 'Do excuse the intrusion, Harrow,' Leo said with only the shallowest pretense of politeness. 'But a situation has arisen.'

'Oh?' The doctor looked remarkably incurious. 'Someone has been taken ill.'

'That is unfortunate. I wish I could be of assistance, but if I am to reach London before midnight, I must leave shortly. You'll have to find another doctor.'

'Surely you have an ethical obligation to help someone who needs it,' Miss Marks said incredulously. 'What about the oath of Hippocrates?'

'The oath is not obligatory. And in light of recent events, I have every right to decline. You will have to find another doctor to treat him.'

Him.

Leo didn't have to look at Miss Marks to know that she, too, had caught the slip. He decided to keep Harrow talking. 'Merripen won my sister fairly, old fellow. And what brought them together was set in motion long before you entered the scene. It's not sporting to blame them.'

'I do not blame them,' Harrow said curtly. 'I blame you.'

'*Me?*' Leo was indignant. 'What for? I had nothing to do with this.'

'You have so little regard for your sisters that you would allow not one but *two* Gypsies to be brought into your family.'

Out of the corner of his eye, Leo saw Dodger the ferret creeping across the carpeted floor. The inquisitive creature reached a chair over which a dark coat had been draped. Standing on his hind legs, he rummaged in the coat pockets.

Miss Marks was speaking crisply. 'Mr.

Merripen and Mr. Rohan are men of excellent character, Dr. Harrow. One may fault Lord Ramsay for many other things, but not for that.'

'They're *Gypsies*,' Harrow said scornfully.

Leo began to speak, but he was cut off as Miss Marks continued her lecture. 'A man must be judged by what he makes of himself, Dr. Harrow. By what he does when no one else is looking. And having lived in proximity to Mr. Merripen and Mr. Rohan, I can state with certainty that they are both fine, honorable men.'

Dodger extracted an object from the coat pocket and wriggled in triumph. He began to lope slowly around the edge of the room, watching Harrow warily.

'Forgive me if I don't accept assurances of character from a woman such as you,' Harrow said to Miss Marks. 'But according to rumor, you've been in rather *too much* proximity with certain gentlemen in your past.'

The governess turned white with outrage. 'How dare you?'

'I find that remark entirely inappropriate,' Leo said to Harrow. 'It's obvious that no sane man would ever attempt something scandalous with Marks.' Seeing that Dodger had made it to the doorway, Leo reached for the governess's rigid arm. 'Come, Marks. Let's leave the doctor to his packing.'

At the same moment, Harrow caught sight of the ferret, who was carrying a slim glass vial in his mouth. Harrow's eyes bulged, and he went pale. 'Give that to me!' he cried, and launched toward the ferret. 'That's mine!'

Leo leaped on the doctor and brought him to the floor. Harrow surprised him with a sharp right hook, but Leo's jaw had been hardened from many a tavern fight. He traded blow for blow, rolling across the floor with the doctor as they struggled for supremacy.

'What the devil' — Leo grunted — 'did you put into that coffee?'

'Nothing.' The doctor's strong hands clamped on his throat. 'Don't know what you're talking about —'

Leo bashed him in the side with a closed fist until the doctor's grip weakened. 'The hell you don't,' Leo gasped, and kneed him in the groin. It was a dirty trick Leo had picked up from one of his more colorful escapades in London.

Harrow collapsed to his side, groaning. 'Gentleman . . . wouldn't . . . do that . . . '

'Gentlemen don't poison people, either.' Leo seized him. 'Tell me what it was, damn you!'

Despite his pain, Harrow's lips curved in an evil grin. 'Merripen will get no help from me.'

'Merripen didn't drink the filthy stuff, you idiot! Rohan did. Now tell me what you put in that coffee or I'll rip your throat out.'

The doctor looked stunned. He clamped his mouth shut and refused to speak. Leo struck him with a right and then a left, but the bastard remained silent.

Miss Marks's voice broke through the boiling fury. 'My lord, stop it. *This instant.* I need your assistance in retrieving the vial.'

Hauling Harrow upward, Leo dragged him to the empty wardrobe and closed him inside. Leo locked the door and turned to face Miss Marks, his face sweating and his chest heaving.

Their gazes locked for a split second. Her eyes turned as round as her spectacle lenses. But the peculiar awareness between them was immediately punctured by Dodger's triumphant chatter.

The blasted ferret waited at the threshold, doing a happy war dance that consisted of a series of sideways hops. Clearly he was delighted by his new acquisition, and even more by the fact that Miss Marks seemed to want it.

'Let me out!' Harrow cried in a smothered voice, and there was a violent pounding from inside the wardrobe.

'That blasted weasel,' Miss Marks muttered. 'This is a game to him. He'll spend hours teasing us with that vial and keeping it just out of reach.'

Staring at the ferret, Leo sat on the carpet and relaxed his voice. 'Come here, you flea-ridden hair wad. You'll have all the sugar biscuits you want, if you'll give your new toy to me.' He whistled softly and clicked.

But the blandishments did not work. Dodger merely regarded him with bright eyes and stayed at the threshold, clutching the vial in his tiny paws.

'Give him one of your garters,' Leo said, still staring at the ferret.

'I beg your pardon?' Miss Marks asked frostily.

'You heard me. Take off a garter and offer it to him as a trade. Otherwise we'll be chasing this damned animal all through the house. And I doubt Rohan will appreciate the delay.'

The governess gave Leo a long-suffering

glance. 'Only for Mr. Rohan's sake would I consent to this. Turn your back.'

'For God's sake, Marks, do you think anyone really wants a glance at those dried-up matchsticks you call legs?' But Leo complied, facing the opposite direction.

He heard a great deal of rustling as Miss Marks sat on a bedroom chair and lifted her skirts.

It just so happened that Leo was positioned near a full-length looking glass, the oval cheval style that tilted up or down to adjust one's reflection. And he had an excellent view of Miss Marks in the chair. And the oddest thing happened — he got a flash of an astonishingly pretty leg. He blinked in bemusement, and then the skirts were dropped.

'Here,' Miss Marks said gruffly, and tossed it in Leo's direction. Turning, he managed to catch it in midair.

Dodger surveyed them both with beady-eyed interest.

Leo twirled the garter enticingly on his finger. 'Have a look, Dodger. Blue silk with lace trim. Do all governesses anchor their stockings in such a delightful fashion? Perhaps those rumors about your unseemly past are true, Marks.'

'I'll thank you to keep a civil tongue in your head, my lord.'

Dodger's little head bobbed as it followed every movement of the garter. Fitting the vial in his mouth, the ferret carried it like a miniature dog, loping up to Leo with maddening slowness.

'This is a trade, old fellow,' Leo told him. 'You

can't have something for nothing.'

Carefully Dodger set down the vial and reached for the garter. Leo simultaneously gave him the frilly circlet and snatched the vial. It was half-filled with a fine dull green powder. He stared down at it intently, rolling it in his fingers.

Miss Marks was at his side in an instant, crouching on her hands and knees. 'Is it labeled?' she asked breathlessly.

'No. Damn it all.' Leo was gripped with volcanic fury.

'Let me have it,' Miss Marks said, prying the vial from him.

Leo jumped to his feet immediately, hurling himself at the wardrobe. He slammed it with both his fists. 'Damn you, Harrow, what is it? What is this stuff? Tell me, or you'll stay in there until you rot.'

There was nothing but silence from the wardrobe.

'By God, I'm going to — ,' Leo began, but Miss Marks interrupted.

'It's digitalin powder.'

Leo threw her a distracted glance. She had opened the vial and was sniffing it cautiously. 'How do you know?'

'My grandmother used to take it for her heart. The scent is like tea, and the color is unmistakable.'

'What's the antidote?'

'I have no idea,' Miss Marks said, looking more distressed by the moment. 'But it's a powerful substance. A large dose could very well stop a man's heart.'

Leo turned back to the wardrobe. 'Harrow,' he bit out, 'if you want to live, you'll tell me the antidote now.'

'Let me out first,' came the muffled reply.

'No negotiating! Tell me what counteracts the poison, damn you!'

'*Never.*'

'Leo?' A new voice entered the fray. He turned swiftly to see Amelia, Win, and Beatrix at the threshold. They were staring at him as if he'd gone mad.

Amelia spoke with admirable composure. 'I have two questions, Leo: Why did you send for me, and why are you having an argument with the wardrobe?'

'Harrow's in there,' he told her.

Her expression changed. 'Why?'

'I'm trying to make him tell me how to counteract an overdose of digitalin powder.' He glared vengefully at the wardrobe. 'And I'll *kill* him if he doesn't.'

'Who's taken an overdose?' Amelia demanded, her face draining of color. 'Is someone ill? Who is it?'

'It was meant for Merripen,' Leo said in a low voice, reaching out to steady her before he continued. 'But Cam took it by mistake.'

A strangled cry escaped her. 'Oh God. Where is he?'

'The Gypsy campsite. Merripen's with him.'

Tears sprang to Amelia's eyes. 'I must go to him.'

'You won't do him any good without the antidote.'

333

Win brushed by them, striding to the bedside table. Moving with swift deliberation, she picked up an oil lamp and a tin matchbox, and brought them to the wardrobe.

'What are you doing?' Leo demanded, wondering if she had lost her wits entirely. 'He doesn't need a lamp, Win.'

Ignoring him, Win removed the glass fount and tossed it to the bed. She did the same with the brass wick burner, exposing the oil reservoir. Without hesitation, she poured the lamp oil over the front of the wardrobe. The pungent odor of highly flammable paraffin spread through the room.

'Have you lost your mind?' Leo demanded, astonished not only by her actions, but also by her calm demeanor.

'I have a matchbox, Julian,' she said. 'Tell me what to give Mr. Rohan, or I'll set the wardrobe on fire.'

'You wouldn't dare,' Harrow cried.

'Win,' Leo said, 'you'll burn the entire damned house down, just after it's been rebuilt. Give me the bloody matchbox.'

She shook her head resolutely.

'Are we starting a new springtime ritual?' Leo demanded. 'The annual burning-of-the-manse? Come to your senses, Win.'

Win turned from him and glared at the wardrobe door. 'I was told, Julian, that you killed your first wife. Possibly by poison. And now knowing what you have done to my brother-in-law, I believe it. And if you don't help us, I'm going to roast you like a piece of Welsh rarebit.'

She opened the matchbox.

Realizing she couldn't possibly be serious, Leo decided to back her bluff. 'I'm begging you, Win,' he said theatrically, 'don't do this. There's no need to — *Christ*!'

This last as Win struck a match and set the wardrobe on fire.

It wasn't a bluff, Leo thought dazedly. She actually intended to broil the bastard.

At the first bright, curling blossom of flame, there was a terrified cry from inside the wardrobe. 'All right! Let me out! *Let me out!* It's tannic acid. *Tannic acid.* It's in my medical case; let me *out!*'

'Very well, Leo,' Win said, a bit breathless. 'You may extinguish the fire.'

In spite of the panic that raced through his veins, Leo couldn't suppress a choked laugh. She spoke as if she'd asked him to snuff a candle, not put out a large flaming piece of furniture. Tearing off his coat, he rushed forward and beat wildly at the wardrobe door. 'You're a madwoman,' he told Win as he passed her.

'He wouldn't have told us otherwise,' Win said.

Alerted by all the commotion, a few servants appeared, one of them a footman who removed his own coat and hastened to assist Leo. Meanwhile, the women were rummaging for Harrow's black leather medical case.

'Isn't tannic acid the same as tea?' Amelia asked, her hands shaking as she fumbled with the latch.

'No, Mrs. Rohan,' the governess said. 'I believe

the doctor was referring to tannic acid from oak leaves, not the tannins from tea.' She reached out quickly as Amelia nearly overturned the case. 'Careful, don't knock it over. He doesn't label his vials.' Opening the hard-sided case, they found rows of neatly arranged glass tubes containing powders and liquids. Although the vials themselves were not marked, the slots they fit in had been identified with inked letters. Poring over the vials, Miss Marks extracted one filled with pale yellow-brown powder. 'This one.'

Win took it from her. 'Let me take it to them,' she said. 'I know where the campsite is. And Leo's busy putting out the wardrobe.'

'I'll take the vial to Cam,' Amelia said vehemently. 'He's my husband.'

'Yes. And you're carrying his child. If you fell while riding at a breakneck pace, he would never forgive you for risking the baby.'

Amelia gave her an anguished glance, her mouth trembling. She nodded and croaked, '*Hurry*, Win.'

★ ★ ★

'Can you fashion a sling with canvas and poles?' Merripen asked the *rom phuro*. 'I must get him back to Ramsay House.'

The tribe leader nodded at once. He called out to a small group waiting near the entrance of the *vardo*, gave a few instructions, and they disappeared instantly. Turning back to Merripen, he murmured, 'We'll have something put together in a few minutes.'

Kev nodded, staring down at Cam's ashen face. He wasn't well by any means, but at least the threat of convulsions and heart failure had been temporarily staved off. Robbed of his usual expressiveness, Cam looked young and defense-less.

It was peculiar to think that they were brothers and yet had spent their lives never knowing about each other. Kev had occupied his self-imposed solitude for so long, but lately it seemed to be wearing away, like a threadbare suit of clothes that was falling apart at the seams. He wanted to know more about Cam, to exchange memories with him. He wanted a brother. *I always knew I wasn't supposed to be alone*, Cam had told him on the day they discovered their blood ties. Kev had felt the same. He just hadn't been able to say it.

Taking up a cloth, he blotted the film of sweat from Cam's face. A quiet whimper escaped Cam's lips, as if he were a child having a nightmare.

'It's all right, *phral*,' Kev murmured, putting a hand on Cam's chest, testing the slow and lurching heartbeat. 'You'll be well soon. I won't leave you.'

'You are close to your brother,' the *rom phuro* said softly. 'That is good. Do you have other family?'

'We live with *gadje*,' Kev said, his gaze daring the man to disapprove. The tribe leader's expression remained friendly and interested. 'One of them is his wife.'

'I hope she's not pretty,' the *rom phuro* commented.

337

'She is,' Kev said. 'Why shouldn't she be?'

'Because one should choose a wife using the ears, not the eyes.'

Kev smiled slightly. 'Very wise.' He glanced down at Cam again, thinking he was starting to look worse. 'If they need help making the sling to carry him — '

'No, my men are fast. They'll be finished soon. But it must be made well, and strong, to carry a man of his size.'

Cam's hands were twitching, his long fingers plucking fitfully at the blanket they had put over him. Kev took the cold hand and gripped it firmly, trying to warm and reassure him.

The *rom phuro* stared at the visible tattoo on Cam's forearm, the striking lines of the winged black horse.

'When did you meet Rohan?' he asked quietly.

Kev gave him a startled glance, his protective grasp tightening on Cam's hand. 'How do you know his name?'

The tribe leader smiled, his eyes warm. 'I know other things as well. You and your brother were separated for a long time.' He touched the tattoo with his forefinger. 'And this mark . . . you have one, too.'

Kev stared at him without blinking.

The sounds of a minor to-do filtered in from outside, and someone came pushing through the doorway. A woman. With surprise and concern, Kev saw the gleam of white-blond hair. 'Win!' he exclaimed, carefully setting Cam's hand down and coming to his feet. Unfortunately, he couldn't stand fully upright in the low-ceilinged vehicle. 'Tell me you didn't come here alone. It's not safe. Why are you — '

'I'm trying to help.' The skirts of Win's riding habit rustled stiffly as she hurried into the *vardo*. One of her hands was ungloved, and she was holding something in it. She didn't spare a glance for the *rom phuro*, she was so intent on reaching Kev. 'Here. *Here.*' She was breathing hard from riding to the camp at a breakneck pace, her cheeks flushed.

'What is it?' Kev murmured, gently taking the object from her, his free hand coming to rub her back. He looked down at a small vial filled with powder.

'The antidote,' she said. 'Give it to him quickly.'

'How do you know it's the right medicine?'

'I made Dr. Harrow tell me.'

'He might have been lying.'

'No. I'm sure he wasn't, because at that moment he was nearly on f — I mean, he was under duress.'

Kev's fingers closed around the vial. There wasn't much choice. They could wait until they consulted a trustworthy doctor, but from the look of it, Cam didn't have much time to spare. And doing nothing was not an option, either.

Kev proceeded to dissolve ten grains in a small quantity of water, reasoning that it was better to start with a weak solution rather than overdose Cam with yet another poison. He eased Cam to a sitting position, supporting him against his chest. Delirious and unsteady, Cam made a protesting noise as the movement sent new pain through his cramping muscles.

Although Kev couldn't see Cam's face, he saw Win's compassionate expression as she reached out to grip Cam's jaw. She rubbed the frozen muscles and pried his mouth open. After tilting the liquid from a spoon into his mouth, she massaged his cheeks and throat, coaxing him to swallow. Cam downed the medicine and shuddered, and rested heavily against Kev.

'Thank you,' Win whispered, stroking back Cam's damp hair, flattening her palm against the side of his cold face. 'You'll be better now. Lie easy, and let it take effect.' Kev thought she had never looked as lovely as she did at that moment, her face soft with tender gravity. After a few minutes Win said quietly, 'His color is improving.'

And so was his breathing, the jagged rhythm lengthening and slowing. Kev felt Cam's body relax, the clenched muscles softening as the active principles of the digitalis were neutralized.

Cam stirred as if he were waking from a long sleep. 'Amelia,' he said in an opium-slurred voice.

Win took one of his hands in hers. 'She's quite well, and waiting for you at home, dear.'

'Home,' he repeated with an exhausted nod.

Kev lowered Cam carefully to the berth and looked over him in sharp assessment. The masklike pallor was vanishing second by second, healthy color returning to his face. The rapidity of the transformation was no less than astonishing.

The amber eyes cracked open, and Cam

focused on Kev. 'Merripen,' Cam said in a tone so lucid that Kev was overcome with relief.

'Yes, *phral*?'

'Am I dead?'

'No.'

'I must be.'

'Why?' Kev asked, amused.

'Because . . . ' Cam paused to moisten his dry lips. 'Because you're *smiling* . . . and I just saw my cousin Noah over there.'

22

The *rom phuro* came forward and knelt beside the berth. 'Hello, Camlo,' he murmured.

Cam regarded him with puzzled wonder. 'Noah. You're older.'

His cousin chuckled. 'Indeed. The last time I saw you, you barely came up to my chest. And now you look as if you could be nearly a head taller than me.'

'You never came back for me.'

Kev broke in tautly. 'And you never told him he had a brother.'

Noah's smile turned regretful as he regarded them both. 'I couldn't do either of those things. For your own protection.' His gaze swerved in Kev's direction. 'We were told you were dead, Kev. I'm glad to find out we were wrong. How did you survive? Where have you been living?'

Kev scowled at him. 'Never mind about that. Rohan has spent *years* looking for you. Looking for answers. You tell him the truth now, about why he was sent away from the tribe, and what that cursed tattoo means. And don't leave anything out.'

Noah looked mildly taken aback by Kev's autocratic manner. As the leader of the *vitsa*, Noah wasn't used to taking orders from anyone.

'He's always like this,' Cam told Noah. 'You get used to it.'

Reaching beneath the berth, Noah pulled out

342

a wooden box and began to rummage through its contents.

'What do you know about our Irish blood?' Kev demanded. 'What was our father's name?'

'There is much I don't know,' Noah admitted. Finding what he had evidently been looking for, he pulled it from the box and looked at Cam. 'But our grandmother told me as much as she could on her deathbed. And she gave me this — '

He raised a tarnished silver knife.

In a lightning-swift reflex, Kev seized his cousin's wrist in a crushing grip. Win gave a startled cry, while Cam tried unsuccessfully to lift up on his elbows.

Noah stared hard into Kev's eyes. 'Peace, Cousin. I would never harm Camlo.' He let his hand open. 'Take it from me. It belongs to you; it was your father's. His name was Brian Cole.'

Kev took the knife and slowly released Noah's wrist. He stared at the object, a boot knife with a double-edged fixed blade approximately four inches long. The handle was silver, with engraving on the bolsters. It looked old and costly. But what amazed Kev was the engraving on the flat of the handle . . . a perfect stylized symbol of the Irish *pooka*.

He showed it to Cam, who stopped breathing for a moment.

'You are Cameron and Kevin Cole,' Noah said. 'That horse symbol was the mark of your family . . . It was in their crest. When we separated the two of you, it was decided to put the mark on both of you. Not only to identify you, but also as an appeal to the second son of

Moshto, to preserve and protect you.'

'Who is Moshto?' Win asked softly.

'A Romany deity,' Kev said, hearing his own dazed voice as if it belonged to someone else. 'The god of all things good.'

'I looked . . . ,' Cam began, still staring at the knife, and shook his head as if the effort to explain was too much.

Kev spoke for him. 'My brother hired heraldic experts and researchers to go through books of Irish family crests, and they never found this symbol.'

'I believe the Coles removed the *pooka* from the crest about three hundred years ago, when the English king declared himself the head of the Church of Ireland. The *pooka* was a pagan symbol. No doubt they thought it might threaten their standing in the reformed Church. But the Coles still had a fondness for it. I remember your father wore a big silver ring engraved with the *pooka*.'

Glancing at his brother, Kev sensed that Cam felt just as he did, that it was like having been in a closed room all his life and suddenly having a door opened.

'Your father, Brian,' Noah continued, 'was the son of Lord Cavan, an Irish representative peer in the British House of Lords. Brian was his only heir. But your father made a mistake — he fell in love with a Romany girl named Sonya. Quite beautiful. He married her in defiance of his family, and hers. They lived away from everyone long enough for Sonya to have two sons. She died in her childbed when Cam was born.'

'I always thought my mother died having me,' Kev said softly. 'I never knew about a younger brother.'

'It was after the second son that she went to God.' Noah looked pensive. 'I was old enough to remember the day Cole brought the two of you to our grandmother. He told *Mami* it had been a misery trying to live in both worlds, and he wanted to go back where he belonged. So he left his children with the tribe and never returned.'

'Why did you separate us?' Cam asked, still looking exhausted but far more like his usual self.

Noah stood in an easy movement and went to the corner near the stove. As he replied, he made tea with deft assurance, measuring out dried leaves into a little pot of steaming water. 'After a few years, your father remarried. And then other *vitsas* told us that some *gadjos* had come looking for the boys, offering money for information and doing violence when the Rom wouldn't tell them anything. We realized your father wanted to get rid of his half-breed sons, who were the legitimate heirs to the title. He had a new wife, who would bear him white children.'

'And we were in the way,' Kev said grimly.

'It would seem so.' Noah strained the tea into a pot. He poured a cup, added sugar, and brought it to Cam. 'Have some, Camlo. You need to wash the poison out.'

Cam sat up and leaned his back against the wall. He took the cup in a wobbling grip and sipped the hot brew carefully. 'So to reduce the chances of both of us being found,' he said, 'you

345

kept me and gave Kev to our uncle.'

'Yes, to Uncle Pov.' Noah frowned and averted his gaze from Kev. 'Sonya was his favorite sister. We thought he would be a good protector. No one expected that he would blame her children for her death.'

'He hated the *gadje*,' Kev said in a low voice. 'That was something else he held against me.'

Noah made an effort to look at him. 'After we heard that you had died, we thought it too dangerous to keep Cam. So I brought him to London, and helped him find work.'

'In a gaming club?' Cam said, a note of questioning skepticism in his voice.

'Sometimes the best hiding places are in plain sight,' came Noah's prosaic reply.

Cam was shaking his head ruefully. 'I'll bet half of London has seen my tattoo. It's a wonder Lord Cavan never caught wind of it.'

Noah frowned. 'I told you to keep it covered.'

'No, you didn't.'

'I did,' Noah insisted, and put his hand on his forehead. 'Ah, Moshto, you were never good at listening.'

*   *   *

Win sat quietly beside Merripen. She listened as the men talked, but she was also busy taking in her surroundings. The *vardo* was old but scrupulously maintained, the interior clean and tidy. A faint, crisp scent of smoke seemed to emanate from the walls, the boards seasoned by thousands of meals that had been prepared in the vehicle. Children played outside, laughing and quarreling. It was odd to think that this caravan was a family's only refuge from the outside world. The lack of sheltered space compelled the tribe to live mostly out-of-doors. As foreign as that idea was, there was a kind of freedom in it.

It was possible to imagine Cam taking to this way of life, adapting to it, but not Kev. There would always be something in him that would drive him to control and master his surroundings. To build, to organize. Having lived with her kind for so long, he had come to understand them. And in understanding them, he had become more like them.

She wondered how he felt at having his Romany past finally uncovered, the mysteries explained. He seemed perfectly calm and controlled, but it would be unsettling for anyone to experience this.

' . . . with all the time that has passed,' Cam was saying, 'I wonder if there's still danger to us? And is our father still alive?'

'It would be easy enough to find out,' Merripen replied, and added darkly, 'He probably wouldn't be happy to find out that *we* were still alive.'

'You're more or less safe as long as you remain Roma,' Noah said. 'But if Kev reveals himself as the Cavan heir and tries to claim the title, there could be trouble.'

Merripen looked scornful. 'Why would I do that?'

Noah shrugged. 'No Rom would. But you are half *gadjo*.'

'I don't want the title or what comes with it,' Merripen said firmly. 'And I want nothing to do with the Coles, Lord Cavan, or anything Irish.'

'And ignore half of yourself?' Cam asked.

'I've spent most of life not knowing about my Irish half. It will be no problem to ignore it now.'

A Romany boy came to the *vardo* to let them know that the sling had been finished.

'Good,' Merripen said decisively. 'I'll help him outside, and he — '

'Oh no,' Cam said, scowling. 'There is no possible way I'm going to let myself be carried in a sling to Ramsay House.'

Merripen gave him a sardonic glance. 'How are you planning to get there?'

'I'll ride.'

Merripen's brows lowered. 'You're in no condition to ride. You'll fall and break your neck.'

'I can do it,' Cam insisted stubbornly. 'It's not far.'

'You'll fall off the horse!'

'I'm not going in the bloody sling. It would frighten Amelia.'

'You're not worried about Amelia nearly so much as your own pride. You'll be carried, and that's final.'

'Bugger you,' Cam snapped.

Win and Noah exchanged a worried glance. The brothers seemed ready to come to blows.

'As the tribe leader, I may be able to help settle the dispute — ,' Noah began diplomatically.

Merripen and Cam answered at the same time, 'No.'

348

'Kev,' Win murmured, 'could he ride with me? He could sit behind me and hold on to me for balance.'

'All right,' Cam said immediately. 'We'll do that.'

Merripen scowled at them both.

'I'll go as well,' Noah said with a slight smile. 'On my own horse. I'll tell my son to saddle him.' He paused. 'Can you stay a few minutes more? You have many Romany cousins to meet. And I have a wife and children I want to show to you, and — '

'Later,' Merripen said. 'I need to take my brother to his wife without delay.'

'Very well.'

After Noah had gone outside, Cam stared absently into the dregs of his tea.

'What are you thinking?' Merripen asked.

'I'm wondering if our father had children by his second wife. And if so, how many? Are there half brothers and half sisters we don't know about?'

Merripen's eyes narrowed. 'What does it matter?'

'They're our family.'

Merripen smacked his forehead with his hand in an uncharacteristically dramatic gesture. 'We've got the Hathaways, and we've got more than a dozen Roma running around outside, who are all apparently cousins. How much more damned family do you want?'

Cam only smiled.

★   ★   ★

Not surprisingly, Ramsay House was in an uproar. The Hathaways, Miss Marks, the servants, the parish constable, and a doctor were crowded in the entrance hall. Since the short ride had depleted Cam's strength, he was forced to lean on Merripen as they went inside.

They were immediately surrounded by the family, with Amelia pushing her way to Cam. She gave a sob of relief as she reached him, fighting tears as she ran frantic hands over his chest and face. Letting go of Merripen, Cam wrapped his arms around Amelia, his head lowering nearly to her shoulder. They were quiet amid the tumult, breathing in measured sighs. One of her hands crept up to his hair, fingers closing in the dark layers. Cam murmured something against her ear, some soft and private reassurance. And he swayed, causing Amelia to grip him more tightly, while Kev took his shoulders to steady him.

Cam lifted his head and looked down at his wife. 'I drank some coffee this morning,' he told her. 'It didn't sit well.'

'So I heard,' Amelia said, smoothing her hand across his chest. She threw a worried glance at Kev. 'His gaze isn't focused.'

'He's higher than a jackdaw,' Kev said. 'We gave him raw opium to calm his heart before Win brought the antidote.'

'Let's take him upstairs,' Amelia said, using the edge of her sleeve to scrub her wet eyes. Raising her voice, she spoke to the elderly bearded man who stood outside the group. 'Dr. Martin, please accompany us upstairs and you will be able to evaluate my husband's condition in private.'

'I don't need a doctor,' Cam protested.

'I wouldn't complain, if I were you,' Amelia told him. 'I'm tempted to send for at least a half-dozen doctors, not to mention specialists from London.' She paused long enough to glance at Noah. 'Are you the gentleman who helped Mr. Rohan? We are indebted to you, sir.'

'Anything for my cousin,' Noah replied.

'Cousin?' Amelia repeated, her eyes widening.

'I'll explain upstairs,' Cam said, lurching forward. Immediately Noah took one side and Merripen the other, and they half-dragged, half-carried Cam up the grand staircase. The family followed, exclaiming and talking excitedly.

'These are the noisiest *gadje* I've ever met,' Noah remarked.

'This is nothing,' Cam said, panting with effort as they ascended. 'They're usually much worse.'

'Moshto!' Noah exclaimed, shaking his head.

Cam's privacy was marginal at best as he was deposited on the bed and Dr. Martin began to examine him. Amelia made a few attempts to shoo family and relatives from the room, but they kept pushing back in to see what was happening. After Martin tested Cam's pulse, pupil size, lung sounds, skin moisture and color, and reflexes, he pronounced that in his opinion, the patient would make a full recovery. If there were any troublesome symptoms during the night, such as heart palpitations, they could be soothed by imbibing a drop of laudanum in a glass of water.

The doctor also said that Cam should be given clear liquids and bland foods and he should rest for the next two or three days. He would probably experience a loss of appetite, and almost certainly some headaches, but when he was fully rid of the last traces of digitalis, everything would be back to normal.

Satisfied that his brother was in good condition, Kev went to Leo in the corner of the room and asked softly, 'Where is Harrow?'

'Out of your reach,' Leo said. 'They took him off to the gaol just before you returned. And don't bother trying to get to him. I've already told the constable not to let you within a hundred yards of the pinfold.'

'I should think you'd like to reach him first,' Merripen said. 'You despise him as much as I do.'

'True. But I believe in letting due process take its course. And I don't want Beatrix to be disappointed. She's hoping for a trial.'

'Why?'

'She wants to present Dodger as a witness.'

Lifting his gaze heavenward, Kev went to the corner of the room and leaned his back against the wall. He listened as the Hathaways exchanged their versions of the day's events and the constable asked questions and even Noah became involved, which then led to the revelation of Kev's and Cam's pasts, and so forth. Information flew in animated volleys. It was never going to end.

Cam, in the meantime, seemed more than content to lie on the bed while Amelia fussed over him. She smoothed his hair, gave him water, straightened the covers, and caressed him repeatedly. He yawned and struggled to keep his eyes open, and turned his cheek into the pillow.

Kev turned his attention to Win, who was sitting in a chair near the bed, her back straight as always. She looked serene and proper, except for the loose strands of hair that had slipped from their pins. One would never guess that she was capable of setting a wardrobe on fire. With Dr. Harrow in it. As Leo had put it, the deed may not have reflected well on her intelligence, but one had to give her points for ruthlessness. And it had gotten the job done.

Kev had been rather sorry to hear that Leo had pulled Harrow out, smoky but unharmed.

Eventually Amelia announced that the visit must soon come to an end, as Cam needed to rest. The constable departed, as did Noah and the servants, until the only ones left were immediate family.

'I think Dodger's under the bed.' Beatrix dropped to the floor and peered under it.

'I want my garter back,' Miss Marks said darkly, lowering to the carpet beside Beatrix. Leo regarded Miss Marks with covert interest.

Meanwhile, Kev wondered what to do about Win.

It seemed that love was working through him inexorably, more exotic and sweet and disorienting than raw opium. More pervasive than oxygen from air. He was so damn tired of trying to resist it.

Cam had been right. You could never predict

what would happen. All you could do was love her.

Very well.

He would give in to it, to her, without trying to qualify or control anything. He would surrender. He would come out of the shadows for good. He took a long, slow breath and let it out.

I love you, he thought, looking at Win. *I love every part of you, every thought and word . . . the entire complex, fascinating bundle of all the things you are. I want you with ten different kinds of need at once. I love all the seasons of you, the way you are now, the thought of how much more beautiful you'll be in the decades to come. I love you for being the answer to every question my heart could ask.*

And it seemed so easy, once he capitulated. It seemed natural and right.

Kev wasn't certain if he was surrendering to Win or to his own passion for her. Only that there was no more holding back. He would take her. And he would give her everything he had, every part of his soul, even the broken pieces.

He stared at her without blinking, half-fearing that the slightest movement on his part might precipitate actions he wouldn't be able to control. He might simply launch toward her and drag her from the room. The anticipation was delicious, knowing he was going to have her soon.

Drawn by his gaze, Win glanced at him. Whatever she saw in his face caused her to blink and color. Her fingers fluttered to her throat as if to soothe her own racing pulse. That made it worse, his desperate need to hold her. He wanted to taste the blush on her skin, absorb the heat with his lips and tongue. His most primitive impulses began firing, and he stared intently at her, willing her to move.

'Excuse me,' Win murmured, standing in a graceful motion that impassioned him beyond sanity. Her fingers made that little flutter again, this time near her hip, as if her nerves were jumping, and he wanted to seize her hand and bring it to his mouth. 'I will leave you to rest, dear Mr. Rohan,' she said unsteadily.

'Thank you,' Cam mumbled from the bed. 'Little sister . . . thank you for . . . '

As he hesitated, Win said with a quick little grin, 'I understand. Sleep well.'

The grin faded as she risked a glance at Kev. Seeming inspired by a healthy sense of self-preservation, she left the room hastily.

Before another second had passed, Kev was at her heels.

'Where are they going in such a hurry?' Beatrix asked from beneath the bed.

'Backgammon,' Miss Marks said hastily. 'I'm sure I heard them planning to play a round or two of backgammon.'

'So did I,' Leo commented.

'It must be fun to play backgammon in bed,' Beatrix said innocently, and snickered.

★   ★   ★

It immediately became clear that it would not be an arbitration of words, but of something far more primal. Win went swiftly and silently toward her room, not daring to look back, though she had to be aware that he was following closely. The carpeted floor absorbed the sound of their footsteps, one set hurried, the other predatory.

Still without looking at him, Win stopped at her closed door, her fingers curling around the handle. 'My terms,' she said softly. 'As I told them to you before.'

Kev understood. Nothing would happen between them now unless Win had her way implicitly. And he loved her for her stubborn strength, while at the same time his Romany half bristled. She might have mastered him in some regards, but not all. He shouldered the door open, nudged her into the room, and closed them both inside. He turned the key in the lock.

Before she could take another breath, he had secured her head in his hands and he was kissing her, opening her mouth with his. The taste of her inflamed him, but he went slowly, letting the kiss become a deep, luscious gnawing, sucking to draw her tongue into his mouth. He felt her body mold against his, or at least as much as her heavy skirts would allow.

'Don't lie to me again,' he said gruffly.

'I won't. I promise.' Her blue eyes were brilliant with love.

He wanted to touch the soft flesh beneath the layers of cloth and lace. He began to pull at the back of her gown, unfastening the ornate buttons, tearing off the resistant ones, tugging his way down until the whole mass of it loosened and she was gasping. Crushing the billows with his feet, he stood with her in the deep pink folds of the ruined gown as if they were at the heart of some gigantic flower. He reached for her undergarments, untying the ribbon at the neckline of her chemise and the tapes of her drawers. She moved to help him, her slender arms and legs emerging from the crumpled linen.

Her pink-and-white nakedness was breathtaking. The slim, strong calves were sheathed in white stockings tied with plain garters. It was unbearably erotic, the contrast of luxurious warm flesh and prim white cotton. Intending to unfasten the garters, he knelt in the soft heaps of pink muslin. She crooked one of her knees to help him, the shy offering distracting him insanely. He bent to kiss her knees, the silken inner thighs, and when she murmured and tried to evade him, he gripped her hips and kept her still. He nuzzled gently into the pale curls, into the roseate fragrance and softness, using his tongue to separate her. Open her. Her moan was soft and pleading.

'My knees are shaking,' she whispered. 'I'll fall.'

Kev ignored her, searching deeper. He lapped and sucked and ate her, his hunger surging at the first taste of female elixir. She pulsed around him as he thrust his tongue deeply, and he felt the response resonating through her body. Breathing into the plush folds, he licked one side of her, then the other, then straight between to the place where her pleasure centered. Entranced, he stroked her over and over, until her hands were gripped in his hair and her hips urged forward in tight undulations.

He took his mouth from her and came to his feet. Her face was dazed, her gaze distant, as if she didn't quite see him. She was trembling from head to toe. His arms slid around her, gathering her naked body against his clothed one. Lowering his mouth to the tender crook of her neck and shoulder, he kissed her skin and touched his tongue to it. At the same time, he reached for the fastenings of his trousers and undid them.

She clung to him as he lifted her and pressed her against the wall, one of his arms protecting her back from abrasion. Her body was supple and surprisingly light, her spine tensing as he eased her weight down and she realized what he meant to do. He settled her fully, watching her mouth draw into a soft *O* of surprise as she was impaled in a slow, sure glide.

The stockinged legs clamped around his waist, and she held on to him desperately, as if they were on the tossing deck of a storm-ravaged ship. But Kev kept her pinned and secure, letting his hips do the work. The band of his trousers slipped free of the anchoring clips of his braces, and the garment slid to his knees. He averted his face to hide a brief grin, momentarily considering the idea of stopping to take his clothes off . . . but it felt too good, the lust rising until it eclipsed every trace of amusement.

Win let out a little breath with each wet, rolling drive, feeling herself being filled, ransacked. He paused to kiss her hungrily, while he reached down with gentle fingers and teased the swollen lips apart. When the rhythm resumed,

358

his thrusts grazed the little peak with each firm inward plunge. Her eyes closed as if in sleep, her intimate flesh working on him in frantic pulses.

In, and in, rooting deeper, driving her further to the edge. Her legs went tight around his waist. She stiffened and cried out against his mouth, and he sealed the kiss to keep her quiet. But little moans slipped through, her pleasure shuddering and overrunning. As Kev buried himself in the lovely milking softness, ecstasy shot through him, spilling hotly, gradually easing into helpless throbs.

Gasping, Kev lowered her legs to the floor. They stood, their bodies moistly locked, their mouths rubbing in soothing kisses and sighs. Win's hands slipped beneath his shirt and moved over his sides and back in gentle benediction. He withdrew from her carefully and stripped the clothes from his steaming body.

Somehow they made it to the bed. Kev dragged them both into the cocoon of wool and linen and nestled Win against him. The scents of her, of both of them, rose in a light saline perfume to his nose. He breathed it in, stirred by the mingled fragrance.

'*Me voliv tu*,' he whispered, and brushed her smiling lips with his. 'When a Rom tells his woman, 'I love you,' the meaning of the word is never chaste. It expresses desire. Lust.'

That pleased Win. '*Me voliv tu*,' she whispered back. 'Kev . . . '

'Yes, love?'

'How does one marry the Romany way?'

'Join hands in front of witnesses, and make a

vow. But we'll do it the way of the *gadje*, too. And every other way I can think of.' He took off her garters and unrolled her stockings one by one, and wiggled her toes individually until she made a little purring sound.

Reaching for him, she guided his head to her breasts, arching upward invitingly. He obliged her, taking a pink tip into his mouth and circling it with his tongue until it contracted into a tender-hard bud.

'I don't know what to do now,' Win said, her voice languid.

'Just lie there. I'll take care of the rest.'

She chuckled. 'No, what I meant was, what do people do when they finally reach their happy-ever-after?'

'They make it a long one.' He fondled her other breast, gently shaping the roundness with his fingers.

'Do you believe in happy-ever-after?' she persisted, gasping a little as he gave her a playful nip.

'As in the children's tales? No.'

'You don't?'

He shook his head. 'I believe in two people loving each other.' A smile curved his lips. 'Finding pleasure in ordinary moments. Walking together. Arguing over things like the timing of an egg, or how to manage the servants, or the size of the butcher's bill. Going to bed each night, and waking up together each morning.' Lifting his head, he cradled the side of her face in his hand. 'I've always started every day by going to the window for a glimpse of the sky. But now I won't have to.'

'Why not?' she asked softly.

'Because I'll see the blue of your eyes instead.'

'How romantic you are,' she murmured with a grin, kissing him gently. 'But don't worry. I won't tell anyone.'

Merripen began to make love to her again, so engrossed that he didn't seem to notice the slight rattle of the door lock.

Peeking over his shoulder, Win saw the long, skinny body of Beatrix's ferret stretching upward to pluck the key from the lock. Her lips parted to say something, but then Merripen kissed her and spread her thighs. *Later*, she thought giddily, ignoring the sight of Dodger squeezing beneath the door with the key in his mouth. Perhaps later would be a better time to mention it . . .

And soon she forgot all about the key.

23

Although the *pliashka*, or betrothal ceremony, traditionally went on for several days, Kev had decided it would last for only one night.

'Have we locked away the silver?' he had asked Cam earlier, when the Gypsies from the river campsite had begun pouring into the house, dressed in colorful clothes and jingling finery.

'*Phral*,' Cam had said cheerfully, 'there's no need for that. They're family.'

'It's because they're our family that I want the silver locked away.'

In Kev's opinion, Cam was enjoying the betrothal process a bit too much. A few days earlier he had made a show of presenting himself as Kev's representative, to negotiate a bride-price with Leo. The two of them had mock-debated the respective merits of groom and bride, and how much the groom's family should pay for the privilege of acquiring a treasure such as Win. Both sides had concluded, with great hilarity, that it was worth a fortune to find a woman who would tolerate Merripen. All this while Kev sat and scowled at them, which seemed to amuse the addlepates even more.

With that formality concluded, the *pliashka* had been quickly planned and enthusiastically undertaken. A huge feast would be served after the betrothal ceremony, featuring roast pig and beef joints, all manner of fowl, and platters of potatoes fried with herbs and copious amounts of garlic. In deference to Beatrix, hedgehog was not on the menu.

Music from guitars and violins filled the ballroom, while the guests gathered in a circle. Dressed in a loose white shirt, leather breeches and boots, and a red sash knotted at the side of his waist, Cam went to the center of the circle. He held a bottle wrapped in bright silk, the neck of it wrapped with a string of gold coins. He gestured for everyone to be quiet, and the music obligingly settled into a vibrant lull.

Enjoying the colorful tumult of the gathering, Win stood beside Merripen and listened as Cam made several remarks in Romany. Unlike his brother, Merripen wore *gadjo* attire, except that he had left off a cravat and collar. The glimpses of his smooth brown throat beguiled Win. She wanted to put her lips to the spot where a steady pulse lurked. Instead, she contented herself with the discreet brush of his fingers against hers. Merripen was rarely given to public demonstrations. In private, however . . .

She felt his hand wrap slowly around hers, his thumb stroking the tender flesh just above her palm.

Finishing the short speech, Cam came to Win. Deftly he removed the coins from the bottle and placed them around her neck. They were heavy and cool against her skin, settling in a jubilant clatter. The necklace advertised that she was now betrothed, and any man other than Merripen would now approach her at his own peril.

Smiling, Cam embraced Win firmly, murmured

something affectionate in her ear, and gave her the bottle to drink from. She took a cautious sip of strong red wine, and gave the bottle to Merripen, who drank after her. Meanwhile, wine in liberally filled goblets was given to all the guests. There were various cries of 'Sastimos,' or good health, as they drank in honor of the betrothed couple.

The celebration began in earnest. Music flared into life and the goblets were quickly drained.

'Dance with me,' Merripen surprised her by murmuring.

Win shook her head with a little laugh, watching the couples twirl and move sinuously around each other. Women used their hands in shimmering motions around their bodies, while men stomped with their heels and clapped their hands, and all the while they circled each other while holding each other's gaze as long as possible.

'I don't know how,' Win said.

Merripen stood behind her and crossed his arm around her front, drawing her back against him. Another surprise. She had never known him to touch her so openly. But amid the goings-on, it seemed no one noticed or cared.

His voice was hot and soft in her ear. 'Watch for a moment. You see how little space is needed? How they circle each other? When Roma dance they lift their hands to the sky, but they stomp their feet to express connection to the earth. And to earthly passions.' He smiled against her cheek and gently turned her to face him. 'Come,' he murmured, and hooked his hand around her waist to urge her forward.

Win followed him shyly, fascinated by a side of him she hadn't seen before. She wouldn't have expected him to be this self-assured, drawing her into the dance with animal grace, watching her with a wicked gleam in his eyes. He coaxed her to raise her arms upward, to snap her fingers, even to swish her skirts at him as he moved around her. She couldn't seem to stop giggling. They were dancing, and he was so good at it, turning it into a cat-and-mouse game.

She twirled in a circle, and he caught her around the waist, pulling her close for one scalding moment. The scent of his skin, the movement of his chest against hers, filled her with intense desire. Leaning his forehead against hers, Merripen stared at her until she was drowning in the depths of his eyes, as dark and bright as hellfire.

'Kiss me,' she whispered unevenly, not caring where they were or who might see them.

A smile touched his lips. 'If I start now, I won't be able to stop.'

The spell was broken by an apologetic throat clearing from nearby.

Merripen glanced to the side, where Cam was standing.

Cam's face was carefully blank. 'My apologies for interrupting. But Mrs. Barnstable just came to me with the news that an unexpected guest has arrived.'

'More family?'

'Yes. But not from the Romany side.'

Merripen shook his head, perplexed. 'Who is it?'

Cam swallowed visibly. 'Lord Cavan. Our grandfather.'

★ ★ ★

It was decided that Cam and Kev would meet Cavan with no other family members present. While the *pliashka* continued in full vigor, the brothers withdrew to the library and waited. Two footmen dashed back and forth, bringing in objects from a carriage outside: cushions, a velvet-covered footstool, a lap blanket, a foot warmer, a silver tray bearing a cup. After a multitude of preparations was made, Cavan was announced by one of the footmen, and he entered the room.

The old Irish earl was physically unimposing, old and small and slight. But Cavan had the presence of a deposed monarch, a faded grandeur textured with weary pride. A frill of white hair had been cut to lie against his ruddy scalp, and a goatee framed his chin like a lion's whiskers. His shrewd brown eyes assessed the young men dispassionately.

'You are Kevin and Cameron Cole,' he said rather than asked in a flowing Anglo-Irish accent, the syllables graceful and lightly arid.

Neither of them replied.

'Who is the elder?' Cavan asked, seating himself in an upholstered chair. A footman immediately arranged a footstool beneath his heels.

'He is,' Cam said, helpfully pointing at Kev, while Kev gave him a sideways glare. Ignoring the look, Cam spoke casually. 'How did you find us, my lord?'

'A heraldic master recently approached me in London with the information that you had hired him to research a particular design. He had identified it as the Coles' ancient mark. When he showed me the sketch he'd made of the tattoo on your arm, I knew at once who you were, and why you wanted the design researched.'

'And why is that?' Cam asked softly.

'You want social and financial gain. You wish to be recognized as a Cole.'

Cam smiled without amusement. 'Believe me, my lord, I wish for neither gain nor recognition. I merely wanted to know who I was.' His eyes flashed with annoyance. 'And I paid that bloody researcher to give the information to *me*, not to take it to you first. I'll take a strip out of his hide for that.'

'Why do you want to see us?' Kev asked brusquely. 'We want nothing from you, and you'll get nothing from us.'

'First, it may interest you to learn that your father is dead. He expired a matter of weeks ago, as a result of a riding accident. He was always inept with horses. It eventually proved the death of him.'

'Our condolences,' Cam said flatly.

Kev merely shrugged.

'*This* is how you receive the death of your sire?' Cavan demanded.

'I'm afraid we didn't know our sire well enough to display a more satisfying reaction,' Kev said sardonically. 'Pardon the lack of tears.'

'I want something other than tears from you.'

'Why am I alarmed?' Cam wondered aloud.

'My son left behind a wife and three daughters. No sons, except for you.' The earl made a temple of his pale, knotty fingers. 'The lands are entailed to male issue only, and there are none to be found in the Cole line, in any of its branches. As things stand at present, the Cavan title and all that is attached to it will become extinct upon my death.' His jaw hardened. 'I will not let the patrimony be lost forever merely because of your father's inability to reproduce.'

Kevin arched a brow. 'I'd hardly call two sons and three daughters an inability to reproduce.'

'Daughters are of no consequence. And the two of you are half-breeds. One can hardly claim that your father succeeded in furthering the family's interests. But no matter. The situation must be tolerated. You are, after all, legitimate issue.' An acrid pause. 'You are my only heirs.'

The vast cultural chasm between them was revealed in its entirety at that moment. Had Lord Cavan bestowed such bounty on any other kind of man, it would have been received with nothing short of ecstasy. But presenting a pair of Roma with the prospect of lofty social status and vast material riches did not get Cavan the reaction he had anticipated.

Instead, they both appeared singularly — rather maddeningly — unimpressed.

Cavan spoke irritably to Kev. 'You are Viscount Mornington, inheritor of the Mornington estate in County Meath. Upon my death you will also receive Knotford Castle in Hillsborough, the Fairwall estate in County Down, and Watford Park in Hertfordshire. Does that mean anything to you?'

'Not really.'

'You are the last in line,' Cavan persisted, his voice sharpening, 'to a family that traces its origins to a thane created by Athelstan in the year 936. Moreover, you are the heir to an earldom of more distinguished lineage than three-quarters of all the peerages of the Crown. Have you *nothing* to say? Do you even understand the remarkable good fortune that has befallen you?'

Kev understood all of that. He also understood that an imperious old bastard who had once wanted him dead now expected him to fall over himself because of an unasked-for inheritance. 'Weren't you once searching for us with the intention of dispatching us like a pair of unwanted pups?'

Cavan scowled. 'That question has no relevance to the matter at hand.'

'That means yes,' Cam told Kev.

'Circumstances have altered,' Cavan said. 'You have become more useful to me alive than dead. A fact for which you should be appreciative.'

Kev was about to tell Cavan where he could shove his estates and titles when Cam shouldered Kev roughly aside.

'Excuse us,' Cam said over his shoulder to Cavan, 'while we have a brotherly chat.'

'I don't want to chat,' Kev muttered.

'For once would you listen to me?' Cam

asked, his tone mild, his eyes narrowed. '*Just once?*'

Folding his arms over his chest, Kev inclined his head.

'Before you toss him out on his withered old arse,' Cam said softly, 'you may want to consider a few points. First, he's not going to live long. Second, the tenants on the Cavan lands are probably in desperate need of decent management and help. There is much you could do for them, even if you choose to reside in England and oversee the Irish portion of the entailment from afar. Third, think about Win. She would have wealth and position. No one would dare slight a countess. Fourth, we apparently have a stepmother and three half sisters with no one to care for them after the old man turns up his toes. Fifth — '

'There's no need for fifth,' Kev said. 'I'll do it.'

'What?' Cam raised his brows. 'You agree with me?'

'Yes.'

All the points had been well-taken, but the mere mention of Win would have been enough. She would live better and be treated with far more respect as a countess than a Gypsy's wife.

The old man regarded Kev with a sour expression. 'You seem to be under the misapprehension that I was giving you a choice. I wasn't *asking* you for anything. I was *informing* you of your good fortune and your duty. Furthermore — '

'Well, it's all settled,' Cam interrupted hastily. 'Lord Cavan, you now have an heir and a spare.

370

I propose that we all take leave of each other to contemplate our new circumstances. If it pleases you, my lord, we will meet again on the morrow to discuss the particulars.'

'Agreed.'

'May we offer you and your servants lodging for the night?'

'I have already arranged to bestow my company on Lord and Lady Westcliff. No doubt you have heard of the earl. A most distinguished gentleman. I was acquainted with his father.'

'Yes,' Cam said gravely. 'We've heard of Westcliff.'

Cavan's lips thinned. 'I suppose it will fall to me to introduce you to him someday.' He slid a disdainful glance over both of them. '*If* we can do something about your manner of dress and personal deportment. And your education. God help us all.' He snapped his fingers, and the two footmen swiftly collected the items they had brought in. Rising from the chair, Cavan allowed his coat to be draped over his narrow shoulders. With a morose shake of his head, he looked at Kev and muttered, 'As I frequently remind myself, you're better than nothing. Until tomorrow.'

The moment Cavan left the parlor, Cam went to the sideboard and poured two generous brandies. Looking bemused, he gave one to Kev. 'What are you thinking?' he asked.

'He seems like the kind of grandfather we'd have,' Kev said, and Cam nearly choked on his brandy as he laughed.

★ ★ ★

Much later that evening Win lay draped across Kev's chest, her hair streaming over him like trickles of moonlight. She was naked except for the coin necklace. Gently disentangling it from her hair, Kev pulled the necklace off and set it on the nightstand.

'Don't,' she protested.

'Why?'

'I like wearing it. It reminds me that I'm betrothed.'

'I'll remind you,' he murmured, rolling until she lay in the crook of his arm. 'As often as you need.'

She smiled up at him, touching the edges of his lips with exploring fingertips. 'Are you sorry that Lord Cavan found you, Kev?'

He kissed the delicate pads of her fingers as he pondered the question. 'No,' he said eventually. 'He's a bitter old cretin, and I wouldn't care to spend a great deal of time in his company. But now I have the answers to things I wondered about for my entire life. And . . . ' he hesitated before admitting sheepishly, ' . . . I wouldn't mind being the Earl of Cavan someday.'

'You wouldn't?' She regarded him with a quizzical grin.

Kev nodded. 'I think I might be good at it,' he confessed.

'So do I,' Win said in a conspiratorial whisper. 'In fact, I think a great many people will be surprised by your absolute brilliance at telling them what to do.'

Kev grinned and kissed her forehead. 'Did I tell you the last thing Cavan said before he left this evening? He said he frequently reminds himself that I'm better than nothing.'

'What a silly old windbag,' Win said, slipping her hand behind Kev's neck. 'And he's utterly wrong,' she added, just before their lips met. 'Because, my love, you're better than *everything*.'

For a long time afterward, there were no words.

Epilogue

According to the doctor, it had been the first delivery during which he had more concerns for the expectant father than the mother and infant.

Kev had conducted himself quite well during the majority of Win's confinement, though he had tended to overreact at times. The commonplace aches and twinges of pregnancy had caused nothing short of alarm, and there had been many a time that he had insisted on sending for the doctor for no good reason at all, despite Win's exasperated refusal.

But parts of it had been marvelous. The quiet evenings when Kev had rested beside her with his hands flattened on her stomach to feel the baby kicking. The summer afternoons when they had walked through Hampshire, feeling at one with nature and the life teeming everywhere. The unexpected discovery that marriage, rather than weighting their relationship with seriousness, had somehow given life a sense of lightness, of buoyancy.

Kev laughed often now. He was far more apt to tease, to play, to show his affection openly. He seemed to adore Cam and Amelia's son, Ronan, and readily joined in the family's general spoiling of the dark-haired infant.

However, during the last few weeks of Win's pregnancy, Kev hadn't been able to conceal his growing dread. And when Win's labor had begun in the middle of the night, he had gone into a state of subdued terror that nothing would soothe. Every birthing pain, every sharp gasp she took, had caused Kev to turn ashen, until Win had realized she was faring far better than he.

'Please,' Win had whispered to Amelia privately, 'do something with him.'

And so Cam and Leo had dragged Kev from the bedroom down to the library, plying him with good Irish whiskey for most of the day.

When the future Earl of Cavan was born, the doctor said he was perfectly healthy, and that he wished all births could go so well. Amelia and Poppy bathed Win and dressed her in a fresh nightgown, and cleaned and swaddled the baby in soft cotton. Only then was Kev allowed to come up to see them. After ascertaining for himself that his wife and child were both in good condition, Kev wept in unashamed relief and promptly fell asleep on the bed beside Win.

She glanced from her handsome, slumbering husband to the baby in her arms. Her son was small but perfectly formed, fair-skinned, with a remarkable quantity of black hair. His eye color was indeterminate at the moment, but Win thought his eyes would eventually turn out to be blue. She lifted him higher against her chest until her lips were close to his miniature ear. And in accordance with Romany tradition, she told him his secret name.

'You are Andrei,' she whispered. It was a name for a warrior. A son of Kev Merripen could be no less. 'Your *gadjo* name is Jason Cole. And your tribal name . . . ' She paused thoughtfully.

'Jàdo,' came her husband's drowsy voice from beside her.

Win looked down at Kev and reached out to stroke his thick, dark hair. The lines on his face were gone, and he looked relaxed and content. 'What does that mean?' she asked.

'One who lives outside the Rom.'

'That's perfect.' She let her hand linger in his hair. '*Ov yilo isi?*' she asked him gently.

'Yes,' Kev said, answering in English. 'There is heart here.'

And Win smiled as he sat up to kiss her.